REVOLUTION

Volume 12

GEORGES CUVIER

GEORGES CUVIER

Vocation, Science and Authority in Post-Revolutionary France

DORINDA OUTRAM

LONDON AND NEW YORK

First published in 1984 by Manchester University Press

This edition first published in 2022
by Routledge
4 Park Square, Milton Park, Abingdon, Oxon OX14 4RN

and by Routledge
605 Third Avenue, New York, NY 10158

Routledge is an imprint of the Taylor & Francis Group, an informa business

© 1984 Dorinda Outram

All rights reserved. No part of this book may be reprinted or reproduced or utilised in any form or by any electronic, mechanical, or other means, now known or hereafter invented, including photocopying and recording, or in any information storage or retrieval system, without permission in writing from the publishers.

Trademark notice: Product or corporate names may be trademarks or registered trademarks, and are used only for identification and explanation without intent to infringe.

British Library Cataloguing in Publication Data
A catalogue record for this book is available from the British Library

ISBN: 978-1-032-12623-4 (Set)
ISBN: 978-1-003-26095-0 (Set) (ebk)
ISBN: 978-1-032-12627-2 (Volume 12) (hbk)
ISBN: 978-1-032-12631-9 (Volume 12) (pbk)
ISBN: 978-1-003-22549-2 (Volume 12) (ebk)

DOI: 10.4324/9781003225492

Publisher's Note
The publisher has gone to great lengths to ensure the quality of this reprint but points out that some imperfections in the original copies may be apparent.

Disclaimer
The publisher has made every effort to trace copyright holders and would welcome correspondence from those they have been unable to trace.

Dorinda Outram

Georges Cuvier

Vocation, science and authority in post-revolutionary France

Manchester University Press

© Dorinda Outram 1984

Published by Manchester University Press
Oxford Road, Manchester M13 9PL
and 51 Washington Street,
Dover, New Hampshire 03820

British Library cataloguing in publication data

Outram, Dorinda
   Georges Cuvier.
   1. Cuvier, Georges   2. Zoologists — France —
   Biography
   I. Title
   508'.092'4   QL31.C9
   ISBN 0-7190-1077-2

Library of Congress cataloging in publication data

Outram, Dorinda.
   Georges Cuvier: vocation, science and authority
in post revolutionary France.
   Includes bibliographies.
   1. Cuvier, Georges, Baron, 1769-1832.   2. Natural
history – France – History.   3. Life sciences – France –
History.   4. Naturalists – France – Biography.   I. Title.
QH31. C89095 1984   508.32 [B]   84-861
ISBN 0-7190-1077-2

Phototypeset in Trump Medieval by
Harvest Printers Ltd, Park Street, Macclesfield

Printed in Great Britain by
Butler & Tanner Ltd, Frome and London

Contents

	Abbreviations	page	vi
	Acknowledgements		vii
	Genealogical table		ix
	Introduction		1
I	The cosmopolitan province		13
II	Youth, revolution and vocation		30
III	The conquest of the city		49
IV	Problems and opportunities of the Empire: science and the Imperial University		69
V	The Restoration and the crisis of patronage		93
VI	Controversy, authority and the market: Lamarck, Gall and *Naturphilosophie*		118
VII	Geology, history and the shaping of a self-image		141
VIII	Families, friends and institutions: the Paris Museum of Natural History		161
IX	Patronage and the post-revolutionary élite: enquiry and conclusion		189
	Notes		203
	Manuscript sources		252
	Publications by Cuvier		255
	Cuvier's works: bibliography and sources		260
	Reviews of Cuvier's works: bibliography and sources		260
	Iconography		260
	General Bibliography		260
	Appendix: positions held by Cuvier		292
	Index		293

Abbreviations

ANP	Archives nationales, Paris
APS	American Philosophical Society, Philadelphia
AST	Archivio di Stato, Turin
BIFC	Bibliothèque de l'Institut de France, Paris, Fonds Cuvier
BL	British Library, London
BMNH	British Museum (Natural History)
BNP	Bibliothèque nationale, Paris
BU	*Biographie universelle*
DBF	*Dictionnaire de biographie française*
LBS	Landesbibliothek, Stuttgart
ME	*Magasin Encyclopédique*
MNHN	Muséum national d'histoire naturelle, Paris
MSEM	*Mémoires de la Société d'Emulation de Montbéliard*
MU	*Moniteur universelle*
RSL	*Royal Society List of Scientific Papers*
SHPF	Société pour l'histoire du Protestantisme français
WHM	Wellcome Historical Medical Library, London

Unless otherwise stated, the text of Cuvier's biography quoted here is MS Flourens 2598/3 of BIFC.

Acknowledgements

It is almost impossible to enumerate or weigh the many acts of kindness which have made this book possible. Over the years devoted to its preparation this sense of indebtedness has constantly deepened and as constantly been renewed. It is doubtful if this book would ever have been written without the financial and moral support provided by the British Academy, the Wolfson Foundation, and the Department of History of Royal Holloway College. Over many years, Jack Morrell has provided a stream of friendly and astringent criticism which has sharpened style, clarified formulations and renewed enthusiasm for what often seemed an unending task. Roger Hahn shared with me his enormous knowledge of this period and his thoughtful, just and witty appreciation of its personalities. Robert Fox has enlivened my writing both with his own sense of the new areas waiting to be discovered in the history of science, and with detailed criticism both of this book and of articles written during its preparation. David Kohn has given constant moral support, and much advice on the importance of Cuvier's achievement in a Darwinian century. Toby Appel and Camille Limoges both allowed me to consult unpublished material, and in discussion clarified many of the ideas explored in chapters five and eight. Jonathan Mandelbaum enriched my knowledge of the Parisian scientific societies, and Jean Théodoridès made an essential contribution to the work of collecting and calendaring Cuvier's letters. William Coleman supplied important information in the tracing of Cuvier's contacts with German science. Charles Petitmengin made available to me information relating to Cuvier's library. Many of the ideas of Chapters VI and VII were developed in conversation of a positively Cuvierian blend of passion and precision with Pietro Corsi. Conversations with Michael Holroyd deepened my appreciation of the problems involved in the tracing of individual fates; but my first, last and greatest debt must always be to Peter Brown, whose constantly accessible friendship, insight and illumination have sustained me in the long task of delineating both the ideal of science, and the shifting worlds of power inhabited by Georges Cuvier.

I

```
                    David CUVIER = Catherine MÉQUILLET                                  Joseph CHATEL              Frédéric COULMANN
                            d. 1743
    ┌──────────────────────────┼──────────────────────────┐                    ┌─────────────┼─────────────┐
Jean Nicolas Pierre    Catherine =         Jean-Georges           Anne- =              Samuel         Catherine                = LOUISE-
d. 1787, Pastor of     J. C. WERNER        1716–96                Clémentine           b. 1754        = Georges-Henri            SALOMÉ
Roche-les-Bains        (municipal architect                       d. 1793                              WALTHER, pastor           COULMANN
                       of Montbéliard)                                                                 of Obenheim               d. 1822
                                                    ┌───────────┬─────────────┬───────────┐                          │
Marc-Antoine COQUET DE TRAYZAILLE                   Georges    Georges      Frédéric =   Christine                General
                                                    1769–1832  1765–69      1773–1838    MACLER                   WALTHER
Louise =       LOUIS- = Anne-Marie                                                       d. 1803                  d. 1813
Charles BRACQ  PHILLIPPE DUVAUCEL                                  Charles Frédéric 1803–1893                  ┌─────────┬─────────┐
               DUVAUCEL  1764–1849                                 = 1852 Constance FARINE (qv)            Henriette  Louise
               d. 1794                                             d. 1870. d. of Pierre-Joseph            d. 1886 =   d. 1875
                                                                   FARINE 1770–1833                        J. ANDRE
Fortuné    ┌───────┬────────┬────────┐        ┌──────────┬──────────┐                                                 │
1789–1850  Sophie  Martial  Alfred   Thélème, Son      Clémentine  Georges  Anne                                  BARONNE DE  Helene,
= Constance 1789–1867        d. 1824 d. 1809  d. 1804  d. 1827     d. 1813  d. 1812                               NEUFITZ     BARONNE
FARINE     = Admiral                                                                                                          MALLET
           Alexandre
           Ducrest   Louise = Eugène
           de Villeneuve  (son of Ducrest de
           d. 1852        Villeneuve from first
                          marriage)
Jacques-Christofle = Charlotte              Pierre-Nicolas = Suzanne BONSEN
d. 1821              MASON                  d. 1827
Pastor of Etupes                                   │
         │                              ┌──────────┴──────────┐                Louis-Christophe
    Charles  Rodolphe                Charles Nicolas =     Caroline =          Pastor of Bréviliers      Charles CUVIER
    d. 1839  d. 1867                 Amélie PEUGEOT        Pierre JAPY         m. Catherine WILDE        1796–1881
        │
   ┌────┴────┐
 Othon     Camille
 d. 1896   = Rodolphe CUCUEL
 = Adèle   Mayor of Montbéliard
 FILLON
```

Introduction

Avec J. J. Rousseau, la nature s'attache à nous par des liens tenaces. Elle devient une inspiratrice et une confidante; elle est celle qui nous console, et nous conseille sans lassitude. Sans doute, il n'y a pas contraste brusque entre cette nature qui s'anime de notre vie profonde, et les sentiments plus simples qui nous attache à elle, associant la nature aux plus profondes destinées de notre âme. (Mornet, 1907, p.465.)[1]

This is neither a new biography of Cuvier, nor an attempt to analyse exhaustively all aspects of his thinking. Rather than write a complete account of Cuvier's extraordinarily productive and varied life, I have chosen rather to focus my attention on specific problems which attended the formation of his career. Cuvier rose to occupy a commanding position in French science at a time when both scientific thought and the whole public realm of which the scientific life was a part, were undergoing great changes. For both contemporaries and for later biographers, Cuvier's career embodied all the problems encountered by science in the public arena. The biographical tradition which surrounds his life has focused on these issues to an extent granted to no other figure of the period, and to few afterwards. But in spite of its concern with such questions as the extent to which Cuvier's public career harmed his scientific achievement, the biographical tradition has in fact contributed curiously little to our historical understanding of the problems which Cuvier faced in the making and pursuit of his career, or of his own reactions to specific situations and issues. In spite of the vast mass of documentary material left by Cuvier, historians have often chosen not to investigate in detail the incidents of his career, but rather to rely upon a few stock incidents, sometimes of doubtful authenticity, for the substance of their narrative. All these reasons seemed to call for a new study of Cuvier.

Two specific areas of concern are the focus of these pages. The first is the study of how science and the social–political world interacted – whether in fact there was that division between them implied by the use of such terms as 'the world of science' and 'the political world'. The second is the process by which men of learning, among them scientists, became part of the new French governing class which emerged from the Revolutionary period. Behind these two concerns lurks a further one, of overwhelming importance for the general history of this period.

This is the problem of the description of the public realm of post-revolutionary France, and of the exchanges of power which took place within it. The problem of the definition of the public context occupied by men of science has never been satisfactorily solved by their historians. The world of power and the world of thought are habitually separated in many accounts of this period. Though scientists are often described as a part of an 'élite', we have little or no precise idea of how this 'élite' related to other parts of the dominant social classes, or what divisions of power, social status and income there were within this group. Even more importantly, the tactic of separating 'life' from 'work', 'power' from 'thought', has had the effect of completely begging the question of how far the political and intellectual worlds can in fact be separated at this time. Historians of science have faithfully reproduced the ideology of science in their insistence on its pure, progressive and value-free, hence non-political character. But they have also endorsed the very modern idea that it is possible to define and separate political events from non-political areas of life. This is far easier to do in modern societies, with their politics of mass-representation, their large and highly professionalised bureaucracies, and their highly formalised and localised political processes, than it is for the societies with which we have to deal. For the historian, post-revolutionary France fails to qualify as a modern state in this sense. Far closer to the realities of life as experienced by its élite would be a notion of power and the exchanges of power as mediated not by political

Introduction

systems and institutions, but as a far more fluid medium, dependent upon symbolic display, upon personal relationships of all kinds – friendship, family ties, patronage relations – in fact upon a continuous series of micronegotiations. If this is true, then it becomes less than plausible to separate science, or indeed any intellectual activity, from the world of power.

We are thus left with the very question whose posing in the right way will help us towards the reconciliation of enquiry relating to science, and enquiry relating to the public world, if we ask, as it is the intention of this book to ask, how ideas were affected in their presentation and structure by their involvement in the fluid world of power. How far was the ascent of men like Cuvier aided by their scientific interests and their social uses, and how did they manipulate the different sorts of authority implicit in the scientific pursuit? In attempting to answer these sorts of questions we also come some way to approaching the general problem of the exercise of symbolic power in the Napoleonic and Restoration states, a topic which lies at the heart of the problem of the rise of the intellectual bourgeoisie in this period. In this enquiry we will certainly find many striking parallels between the structures of power in general politics, and those in science. Both, for example, were characterised by the power of patrons rather than of institutions; both found it difficult to produce firm programmes commanding wide-spread support; in both, power and ideology were highly personalised.

For all these reasons, it will be argued, science contributed to those anxious debates on the nature of authority in which the period is so rich. The problems of self-determination and of personal autonomy were nowhere so acute as in the ideology of the vocation of science itself. One of the major themes of this book is accordingly, the process by which Cuvier arrived at a conscious knowledge of his own scientific vocation, and the difficulties he encountered when this vocational ideology was confronted with the real world of career making. Cuvier's career, with its combination of scientific eminence, and visibility in public office, is unique in the range of the opportunities it offers for the exploration of these problems. Analysis of Cuvier's scientific ideas *for themselves*, which have in any case already been the subject of many excellent studies, will be secondary in these pages to the location of his career in its public context.

It cannot be too strongly emphasised at this point that this book does not aim to provide any general account of Cuvier's scientific work. This has already been the subject of many excellent studies by *inter alia* William Coleman, Toby Appel and Jean Piveteau. However, one cannot escape the fact that Cuvier's work certainly contributed to his career an input which was specific to natural history. Secondly, his approach to specific topics in natural history was not only guided by appraisals of intellectual power-plays, but were also influenced by the internal state of the discipline. As stated before, these problems are approached in this book not through a full-scale examination of Cuvier's thought, but through case studies in Cuvier's management of ideas in certain key areas of his thought. The chapter on the structures of scientific controversy in this period (Chapter VI) establishes that the life sciences in Cuvier's day were in an extraordinary state of flux, so that there were few or no research programmes or methodologies approved by all workers in any given field. In other words, the internal state of natural history was not such as to place very strong restraints on the strategies for intellectual power and reputation which were performed upon them. In this situation of fluidity, disciplines, instead of providing limitations upon argumentation, were in fact *created through* argumentation in the public arena, and through acts of intellectual strategy formed by individuals. The setting of scientific norms to which Cuvier devoted so much time and energy (see Chapters IV–VII), especially in the case of geology and paleontology, was thus a controversial act crucial to the staking of intellectual claims, and, at the same time, an act which created disciplines by making demands for specific methodologies and research programmes. It is these features which make the life sciences in this period such rewarding examples of the interpenetration of structures of thought and public action.

This approach is, of course, not without its problems, however large its possible contribution to our historical understanding of the period. It runs the risk of failing to satisfy those who would like to see a full-scale exploration of Cuvier's

Introduction

scientific thought. It also runs the risk of failing to satisfy those who like to see the historical case demonstrated by more extensive use of a comparative method, rather than a focus on a single career. But is does have the merit of focusing attention on the very ways in which an individual could stand at the crossroads of the interchanges of power. One of the major arguments of this book concerns the personalisation of intellectual and political power in this period. Until very recently historiography has tended to endorse the idea that intellectual norms and political power were mediated through, and decisively shaped by, the institutions of science rather than the personalities of science. This book aims to suggest that the reverse is more likely to have been the case. It attempts to discuss the main ways in which individuals were the carriers of systems of power and to examine the precise ways in which they operated in the shaping of Cuvier's career. The first way in which individual power was shaped was through the operation of patronage. Cuvier was regarded by contemporaries as the arch place-man, the greatest manipulator of patronage in science and in some branches of the administration, notably those of education and the Conseil d'Etat, of his day. Surprisingly, in view of the recognised importance of patronage in the shaping of careers, we possess no general study of its operation for this period, either in intellectual life or in public life in general. Comparative sociological and anthropological material is also of little use to the historian as it either tends to deal with primitive societies remote from those of western Europe, or to produce models which are only applicable to the very different circumstances of the twentieth-century state. The studies which offer most illumination of this topic from a comparative viewpoint are probably those of Jeremy Boissevain, with their sharp focus on the texture of the micro-negotiations of patronage in Mediterranean societies where the state, just as it did in the nineteenth century, tends to play a secondary role in the definition of public life.

What precise questions can be asked of the material assembled in this 'case-study' of Cuvier? In other words, what sort of general programme of research into the study of intellectual–political patronage should be outlined for the history of this period? Extended consideration is given to this theme in the concluding chapter of this book. Here it is enough to say that we need to isolate different forms of patronage (e.g. formal/informal; family/non-family). Examples of these different types of patronage are discussed at length in the chapter dealing with the scientific community centred on the Paris Museum of Natural History. We need to ask also what was it, if anything, that distinguished the exercise of patronage power in the sciences from the exercise of patronage power in the general public arena. This is one of the themes of the chapters dealing with Cuvier's early career-making in Paris, and with the difficulties of his career under the Restoration. We also need to know far more about how the patron/client relationship was established, even within the sciences themselves. The chapters devoted to Cuvier's career-making aim to do precisely that: to discuss his conscious and precisely worked-out strategies in attracting patronage support. The case of Cuvier is valuable here precisely because Cuvier was himself so aware of the difficulties and dangers of the patron–client relationship. Above all, he was concerned to avoid the dangers of reliance on any single patron in the formative stages of his career. Accordingly, he cast about to find the widest possible range of support, from Lucien Bonaparte to his future enemy Lamarck. His success in doing so was partly a function of the private learned societies then flourishing in Paris as new vehicles of sociability for the élite of the Directory; but it also indicates the range of potential patrons open to Cuvier extended into fields which would now be regarded as separate from one another. The width of the choice of patrons available to him in other words was a function of the homogeneity and fluidity of the élite that emerged after *thermidor*.

Cuvier's own role as a patron is examined in many aspects in this book. An important part of Cuvier's role as a patron in the sciences was to use his powers to insist on norms and to implement research programmes often in conflict with those of other figures in science. The degree of actual power which his positions and patronage gave him is examined in the section on scientific controversy. It gives a picture surprising to those steeped in the normal view of Cuvier as the unquestioned dominant figure in French life sciences in this

Introduction

period, of constant struggle to maintain his position. But such surprise is based on a misapprehension of the nature of personalised patronage. Precisely because such power is personalised, it is also unstable. Precisely because the basis of power is the person and not the institution or even, to some extent, the 'agreed' scientific norm (singularly lacking in Cuvier's day), it also lacked the power to produce universally agreed or accepted research programmes or methods of procedure in science. It was the nature of patronage, in other words, to produce controversy rather than consensus in science. The conflicts which notoriously marked Cuvier's career are thus not totally the product, as a moralising biographical tradition would have us believe, of his own intransigence or rigid, 'Teutonic' character; they were endemic in the scientific life of his time, and did not affect him alone.

Cuvier's patronage was also exerted over many other fields than the purely scientific. The chapter on education in particular can be read as a series of case studies in the way patronage originating in one area of activity could be transformed both by the participants, and by the pressure of outside events, into a relationship of far wider scope. It was on these micro-political resources, rather than on institutional resources, that men relied to shape careers, to draw upon for the prosecution of scientific projects, and to rely upon in times of crisis. But there was also a large informal aspect to patronage. Patronage could act as a ratifier to pre-existing, informal relationships. Patronage procured the tangible rewards of relationships of dependence. Yet all power in this society was personalised, and from this it followed too that personal, informal relationships, such as friendship, or relationship by blood or marriage, formed a medium of power which was also an emotional medium. One of the major concerns of the first two chapters of this book is the way in which friendship became the vehicle for the formation of a scientific vocation in Cuvier's case, while the theme of the family as the subject of informal patronage, is explored both in Cuvier's own case, and with comparative material, in the chapter on life in the Paris Museum.

Yet patronage itself would have been empty of content without the scientific vocation which made men undertake all the hazards and uncertainties of the intellectual life in the nineteenth century. We know curiously little about the formation of vocation in this period, in spite of the extent and frequency of its description in contemporary autobiographies. Little attention has been paid to this genre of material, and no historian has attempted a collation of the patterns of vocation-finding on anything like the same scale as has often been done for the history of the later Antique period, to take only one example. This book does not aim to provide such a comparative analysis. It does aim to provide a detailed study, in its first two chapters, of the processes of childhood, youth, and early manhood, which went into the formation of a scientific vocation in the case of Georges Cuvier. My earlier work has also suggested some ways in which we can interpret the accounts of the finding of vocation so common in autobiographies and funeral *éloges*. Here, I extend these methods into a detailed consideration of the form and content of Cuvier's own account of this period of his life, and its relation to other events omitted from his account. Formalised accounts such as those contained in the *éloges* always give the impression of a scientific vocation as something innate in the individual from his earliest youth. In this survey of the example of Cuvier I have on the contrary tried to stress the very contingent factors which drove Cuvier into making the vocational choice that he did. I suggest that in the world of the eighteenth-century small state in which Cuvier passed his formative years, pressures from powerful others may well have been so strong and so intrusive as to give the asocial world of nature a powerful attraction. This is particularly so if one realises the relative informality and social ease of the relationships entered into as a consequence of the pursuit of natural history–friendships, walking tours, teenage private learned societies–in contrast to the world of coercion in which he existed otherwise. Cuvier is almost always presented as being dominated by the search for power, and to some extent this is a true picture. But in these opening chapters, as well as in that which deals with Cuvier's life under the Empire, I have also tried to suggest that one of the attractions of science may well have been the opportunities it gave him to exercise power on the peripheries, in the outlying provinces of the Empire, in the unpatrolled hours of the otherwise highly organised Stuttgart Academy. This sort of

Introduction

power, what one might call 'powerful marginality', is also a feature of the life of science of his day. For although science, at least at his élite level, was an occupation of considerable public prestige, it was also one *in itself* marginal to the exercise of real power in his society, the sort of power that collects taxes, gathers armies and administers provinces.

A biographical study concerned with the operation of the micro-politics of patronage and the family runs the risk of ignoring, however, the major intrusion into the life of science, and of the public arena in general, of the public. This is an element which cannot be reduced to micro-political analysis, and yet which, as I suggest in Chapters III, VI and IX, cannot be excluded from any account of career-making in this period. Science was not wholly conducted in the view of an audience of peers and protégés. On the contrary, successful conquest of public notoriety was one of the major steps in the making of a career, and in the achievement of individual financial stability. This 'public' not only constituted a 'market' for science in the sense of its readiness to consume lectures in such open lecture theatres as the Lycée de Paris and the Collège de France, as well as those of the Muséum, but also in the large and growing readership it provided for books on popular science, a market from which Cuvier himself well knew how to profit. Such audiences, as I argue in the chapter on the Muséum, may well have placed enormous expository demands on men such as Cuvier and Geoffroy St Hilaire, demands which certainly influenced the structuring of their ideas about the order of nature. The public arena was also, as I discuss in my examination of the importance of controversy in Cuvier's career, itself of importance in shaping the structure of some of the most notorious conflicts of Cuvier's day. We need to realise perhaps more forcibly just how unusual it was that the conflict with Geoffroy should take place in the inner sanctum of élite science, the Academy itself. Most of Cuvier's other conflicts were conducted in the full public view, and in spite of their apparently unbridled ferocity, were in fact managed according to sets of unspoken rules about correct public utterance which varied according to an acute appreciation of the public arena involved. It was thus not only institutional position which determined the making of careers; it was also a relationship to the public. The existence of a public in the modern sense was a creation of the revolutionary era, the first era of mass politics in French history. The 'public' made possible the political innovation of the Jacobin Terror, for terror is hardly effective without a public; it made possible and likely the profound instability and violent debates of revolutionary politics as a whole; and it made both possible and likely the public controversies and shifting reputations which are one of the hallmarks of early nineteenth-century science in France.

Enough has now been said for the reader to realise that this is a polemical book, which explicitly or implicitly takes issue with many current, or recent and still influential trends, which have influenced ideas about this period of French science. It is also polemical in relation to the extraordinary biographical tradition which has grown up around Georges Cuvier. I have no desire to overweight this book with attacks on other biographers at the expense of positive enquiry into Cuvier's career and personality. In any case, I have already commented upon the major lines of the tradition in another place. In a sense the major contribution of this book to the revision of that tradition lies very simply in its description of the context in which Cuvier operated. Only such a sense of context can enable us to correct such assumptions, easy to make in its absence, that, for example, Cuvier's dominance in the French life sciences was unquestioned in his lifetime. Again, only the restoration of a detailed historical context of his life, notably absent from most accounts, will allow us the sufficient evidence to challenge the harmful demarcation between the world of science and the world of public life in general. Two further salient characteristics of the biographical tradition need to be described. There is firstly, a tendency to judge Cuvier's actions in strongly moralistic terms which are rarely applied to any other scientist. Such judgements are often invoked as the explanations of actions, notably in the case of the conflict with Geoffroy. In fact they are, of course, nothing of the kind. Explanation of actions is only possible given an adequate knowledge of context. Once this context is established then it becomes clear how strongly the whole social setting of the French life-sciences was geared to produce conflict. Secondly, much of the biographical tradition indignantly eschews ideas

Introduction

that science and politics coexist in the same universe, castigates and denigrates Cuvier's scientific achievement in virtue of his political involvement, also to an extent which is applied to no other scientist, and yet at the same time uses profoundly political terminology in descriptions of his career. Words like 'conservative' are used to describe his character and to lead easily into evaluations of his work as 'rigid' or 'authoritarian'. From there it is only a short step to the establishment of Cuvier as a scapegoat for the failure of French science to produce the 'progressive' and flexible theories of Darwin. In this interpretation, Cuvier is routinely credited with the possession of enormous power, which he is alleged to have used to hold up the progress of French science in a transformist direction. Yet such assumptions are completely unbacked by any examination of the extent of his power and the real nature of his political views. This is part of the purpose of the section of the book dealing with Cuvier's life under the Empire and the Restoration. It is hoped that the cosmopolitan liberal who emerges from these pages will make it more difficult for future scholars to use such politically loaded language as a so-called aid in the understanding of Cuvier's science. It will be apparent, in conclusion, that studies of Cuvier's life are not studies of a 'typical' scientist or intellectual of this period. He was a man too passionate, too energetic, too productive and too conflict-ridden ever to have existed near the mean of life. Just because of this, his life explores to the outer limit, beyond safe and moderate degrees, all the problems possible to the scientist in public life. He also of course contributed a few problems that were specific to himself: the problems of a Protestant in high places in Restoration France; the problems of a man born and educated outside France, who yet made his way into the élite of its capital. Yet these specific problems are also of great use and importance to the historian. Simply because Cuvier's life traversed, as no native Frenchman's did, that profoundly typical transformation of the end of the eighteenth century from life in a small dynastic state to life in a large nation-state, he retained the outsider's distance and dual vision to a higher degree than did many of his French contemporaries. Cuvier judged the French experience from a cosmopolitan viewpoint all his life. It was this that contributed objectivity and humanity to his views on society and politics. It was also this which prevented his mental and emotional life being as profoundly orientated on the pursuit of power within France as many historians have supposed. The solidarities and exclusions of the nation-state were never wholly to his liking. The cosmopolitan ethos was also one which reproduced many of the demands of the ethos of the natural sciences themselves, in its stress on the objectivity of the observer, and his freedom from the world of combination and intrigue. These were ideals which profoundly moved Cuvier, and which channelled him towards the world of science in the first place. It was the conflict between them, and the necessary world of careerism, which he handled with such adroitness, which lent his character its turbulence, and his public face its rigid self control. It was also this conflict which underlay the whole world of science in his lifetime. It was in these senses that the study of nature indeed articulated some of the most profound destinies of the individual, both public and private.

I
The cosmopolitan province

Malgré le sérieux et la froideur apparente, le tempérament de Cuvier n'était rien moins que flegmatique. Sa vie interne et cachée était comparable à la chaleur intérieure de notre globe terrestre, qui toute enveloppée qu'elle est pour ainsi dire d'une croûte froide, se manifeste de temps à autre par des tremblements de terre et des éruptions volcaniques.
(Pfaff on Cuvier, 1858)

Georges Cuvier was born in the capital city of the principality of Montbéliard, now on the Swiss borders of France, on 23 August 1769.[1] It is the intention of this chapter to examine his childhood and youth as the initial stages in the formation of a vocation, and to establish methods of interpretation, to be used throughout this biography, of the mass of nineteenth-century writing on the life of ,Georges Cuvier. Modern historians, preoccupied with Cuvier's career at the heart of centralised post-revolutionary France, have found this early period of his life difficult to assimilate into their accounts.[2] Earlier writers treated it extensively and repeatedly, but they did so through the creation and elaboration of series of *topoi* and other rhetorical devices; in fact, nineteenth-century accounts of Cuvier's early years are so highly structured in these ways that they cannot be fully understood simply as narratives. They have to be interpreted in relation to the social worlds which produced them, and as indicators of states of feeling and response underlying the events recounted in such highly formalised ways.

Within its narrow borders, Montbéliard in fact contained enough contradictions to necessitate all the harmonising devices of later rhetoric.[3] Though French in language, it was Lutheran in religion and nursed bitter memories of invasion and religious persecution by the stronger neighbour. It was tiny in extent, poor in its agriculture, domestic in the scale of its industry, parochial in its spiritual and religious concerns. Yet, on another level, its very smallness turned it outward toward the rest of the world. The combination of poverty and the high quality of Lutheran education, led the principality to export intellectual manpower all over the German states and eastern Europe.[4] This process was facilitated by the presence in Montbéliard as regents of a younger branch of the Grand-Duchy of Württemburg, to which Montbéliard had been politically united since the fifteenth century.[5] Representatives of the ruling house were not only resident in the principality; they were also allied with most of the greater dynasties of Europe and especially to those of Prussia, Russia and Austria. A rising talent in Montbéliard could, with luck, thus be fed into a network of patronage and opportunity which stretched far beyond even the boundaries of Württemburg, let alone those of Montbéliard itself. To grow up in Montbéliard was not to see life before one as a single inevitable road; it was, sooner or later, to be faced with a range of choice in one's future direction which veered between the narowest parochialism and the wildest cosmopolitan adventure.

Montbéliard itself was a resistant, limited environment which offered little accommodation to the nuances of individual reaction. The population of the town was low,[6] and kept so by the inadequacy of the agriculture of the surrounding countryside. Increasingly serious crises of grain supply from the 1760s cannot have lessened the already acute social pressures of life in such a small community.[7] Physically, the townscape was limited, enclosed, resistant to expansion. A description of 1723, for example, speaks of the town almost as a single fortress:

une comté et ville sur les confins de l'Allemagne vers le Franche-Comté. Fief de l'Empire depuis un temps immémorial, elle est divisée en vieille et nouvelle ville sur la pente d'une montagne; elle forme un carré d'une structure inégale, parce que celle qui regarde le ponent est plus longue, son circuit est d'une heure et demi; elle a quatre grandes portes, la vieille ville a de fortes murailles flanquées de tours avec un puissant boulevard du côté du midi. La nouvelle ville est assez bien fortifieé par en haut, mais elle est ouverte du côté de midi. Au reste cette partie est entourée la plupart d'un double fossé d'eau. Près de l'église de St Osvald, où se trouvent les sépultures des Princes avec des belles organes, se voit le château qui est grand et spacieux, bâti sur un haut rocher, divisé encore en vieux et nouveau château. On y trouve aussi l'arsénal, la vieille chancellerie, les archives du Prince, l'écurie, la cave, et les boutiques des tonneliers. La place est d'une raisonable étendue, pour y pouvoir planter le canon, faire voltiger les chevaux et faire toutes sortes d'exercices. Vis-à-vis des deux châteaux se trouve celui de la nouvelle ville nommée la Costa, avec une haute tour.[8]

The walls of morality were equally firm. Every three years, the General Consistory of Montbéliard met and surveyed the population of the town, 's'occupant des règlements disciplinaires'.[9] In each parish, the pastor, the mayor and the village elders met regularly all the year round to enquire into family disputes as well as into 'tout ce qui concernait l'état religieux de chaque paroisse'.[10] Even if Cuvier had not had many pastors among his near relations,[11] he could scarcely have failed to absorb the pressures in this society towards careful self-control and careful self-presentation. Anonymity and ambiguity were difficult to achieve in such a small and carefully inspected community.

Emphasis on the careful control of self-presentation was also demanded from another quarter. Political authority, in the person of the Grand-Duke or his regent, was near, and accessible. In December 1770, for example, the Grand-Duke Charles Eugene held a public audience, which, loaded with the remonstrances, complaints and suggestions of the bourgeoisie of the town, had lasted from nine in the morning till seven at night.[12] Pastors in particular found a ready welcome at the Grand-Ducal residence at Etupes, three miles outside Montbéliard itself.[13] Spiritual and political power came very near to the ordinary bourgeois. Each kind of power, to be placated and manipulated, demanded conformity of conduct to its own rules and demands. In the case of political power, upon this conformity depended not merely access to the rewards at the disposal of a minor princely family, but also, potentially, to those in the gift of the truly great. Family links, for example, brought Joseph II of Austria to Etupes for a prolonged stay in 1781, and the Grand-Duke Paul of Russia in 1782.[14] It was this resource of patronage that Cuvier's family was to exploit in his favour, and which was to set the course of his education.

The ways in which they could do this were heavily

determined by their social status within Montbéliard. Local patriotism has ensured much detailed research into Cuvier's family origins.[15] The majority of his forbears were Lutheran pastors and municipal officials. His great-grandfather Jean Cuvier had broken with this tradition to become a surgeon, just as Cuvier's father had done by adopting a military career. The family stood within the ranks of the bourgeoisie, who in Montbéliard, as in many German towns, formed a firmly defined social class, with their own yeomanry force, their own right of remonstrance with the Grand-Duke, their genealogies inscribed in the Red Book preserved by the town government.[16] In the absence of a significant indigenous nobility, they were the dominant social force within the principality. Thanks to Cuvier's father's service in the Régiment de Waldner, one of the mercenary regiments in the service of France, the family was also able to summon up the powerful protection of its commanding officer, the Comte de Waldner.[17] The relationship was formalised when Waldner consented to act as Cuvier's godfather; it was carefully kept alive by the many visits Cuvier paid as a child to Waldner's household. Christian-Frédéric-Dagobert, Comte de Waldner, whose last two Christian names were also borne by his godson, was a prominent figure in the little court at Etupes, and a highly respected soldier in the German states and in France. In spite of its low income (Cuvier's father was retired and on half pay at the time of his birth, and his mother's dowry had been tiny), Cuvier's family thus had powerful and well-cultivated connections, and an assured respect in the *pays*. Even before his scholastic career had begun Cuvier's potential for social ascension was high. The political power of court connections, and the moral authority of the clergy, secured for the family a deference which had little connection with its financial position.

However, the emotional life of Cuvier's family presented many curious features. Cuvier's mother, Anne-Clémentine Chatel, was more than twenty years younger than her husband Jean-Georges, and, though sensitive and intelligent, was often in poor health. Her emotional intensity was not lightened by increasing financial difficulties.[18] Simultaneously with the increasing food shortages which affected the whole of the region from the 1760s,[19] the French government also entered the fiscal crisis which rendered the payment of Jean-George's half-pay pension from the Ministry of War in Paris uncertain and dilatory. In 1769, the Cuviers' first child died at the age of four; this shock was translated into a relationship of unusual intensity with the child who was born in August of the same year. Though christened Jean-Leopold-Nicholas-Frédéric, and given the name of Dagobert by courtesy shortly after, the child was always addressed within the family circle by the name of the dead child, Georges; it was the name by which he always signed letters and documents as an adult. Nor was the special concern simply an emotional reflex to the death of a first child. As Cuvier's intellectual gifts became obvious, both parents may well have hoped that a successful career in the Grand-Duchy, or at the very least the assured mediocrity of a pastor's income, would rid them in old age of the increasing threat of financial insecurity. By the time Georges' brother Frédéric was born four years later in 1773, financial worry and worsening health left Anne-Clémentine with little emotional energy to spare for the new child. From the first, Frédéric attracted a smaller investment of hopes and affection. He is not even mentioned in Cuvier's own account of his childhood, which describes his own life as a child with his parents in some detail. No powerful godparents were obtained for Frédéric.[20] His formal education, which ended at fifteen, never became the intense field of parental striving and contriving as did that of Georges.

It is now impossible to reconstruct a detailed narrative of the events of Cuvier's childhood. Even his contemporaries produced their reminiscences only after his death in 1832, from memories already fifty years old, of a vanished social world. Most accounts were produced with Cuvier's later career firmly in mind, and against a scenario of ideas about how the childhood of genius should be related to its later achievements. Taken at face value, these accounts do not greatly advance understanding; one useful way to increase their significance is to analyse their structure and *leit-motiven* as indicators of the structure of adult expectations of a child in that particular society. Cuvier as the model child tells us much about what Montbéliard wanted from its children, and hence what the real pressures and demands on a child were likely to have been.[21]

The events of Cuvier's later career, for example, were clearly dominant in the anecdote recounted by Cuvier's cousin Georges Duvernoy of the small child's facility in explaining to an audience of admiring adults the mechanisms by which a travelling conjuror achieved his effects.[22] Here, one sees clearly back-projections of Cuvier's later reputation as the enemy of charlatanism, illusion and grandiose claims in science. It also conforms to a Romantic tendency to locate innate wisdom in children, women and the untutored elements of society generally; it was a tendency which crept into the ethos of science itself: talent was innate from childhood onwards, the 'naive vision' of nature an absolute gift unaltered by the impact of the social world.[23]

However, the anecdotes of Cuvier's childhood also allow us to see that pressure from that world was intense. Almost every source mentions the intensity of the relation between Cuvier and his mother, and most stress the importance of her early coaching to explain his later academic success.[24] This is also one of the few commonly recounted anecdotes of these years which receives confirmation from Cuvier's autobiography. The unanimity of the biographers on this point indicates the strength of the pressure of parental expectation for his academic success. It was a pressure strong enough to set him notably apart from other children.

Cuvier at ten or twelve was vividly described by a former school friend, a man who, despite their shared passion for natural history, spent most of his life in Montbéliard as a prosperous artisan:

Cuvier dans ce temps était d'une faible complexion; il n'était pas si agile ni si robuste que moi . . . il était toujours occupé avec lui-même; il ne jouait point avec des camarades à la paume, à l'arbalète, aux échasses; il ne se mêlait point à d'autres jeux et ne pensait qu'à des livres'.[25]

Wetzel went on to relate how, although they were inseparable companions, Cuvier always let him take the responsibility and endure the punishment if their botanising trips trespassed into school hours, or led to prolonged lapses of attention in class. Caught between the solidarities of childhood, and the desire to conserve the favour of the adult world, there was no doubt which way Cuvier turned.

Escape from this demoralising pressure of expectations from the adult world was impossible either at school, or within the family circle. His parents not only gave affection; they expected a reward. On the short term, Cuvier gave them that reward by producing a front which was carefully controlled, and which he safeguarded from threats posed by participation in the group life of other children. To reassure his parents, Cuvier made himself imitate as much as possible the careful deportment of respected adults.

It was only outside school and outside the family circle that he could find self-forgetfulness and emotional expansion of a careless and intense kind, and cease to be 'occupé avec lui-même'. At about the age of twelve, Cuvier became a frequent visitor at the house of his uncle the pastor Jean-Nicholas Cuvier, who drew his attention to a complete edition of Buffon's natural history which he had acquired for his library. This book became the great occupation of his childhood. Many years later he recalled how 'Tout mon plaisir d'énfant était d'en copier les figures et de les enluminer d'après les descriptions'. It was an activity which allowed a complete absorption in a world far removed from the pressures of family and school life. Seated in his uncle's house five miles from his home in Montbéliard, drawing in silence and with utter concentration, the young Cuvier was erecting a screen between himself and the rest of the world. With Buffon, perceptions and interests could be followed freely and whole-heartedly, undiverted by intrusive extraneous demands and the internalisation of the wishes and needs of others.

It was outside the family circle too that the child could find a more careless expression of the emotions. The evidence for this comes from an anecdote suppressed by Cuvier's biographers until John Viénot's work of 1932, perhaps because it provides an image of Cuvier as a truly childish child, not an obvious natural historian in the making. This family anecdote reveals a child totally different both from the underhand, disloyal schoolboy of Wetzel's account, and from the remote infant prodigy of the other stories. In the presence of his aunt Marie-Anne Bonsen, the wife of his uncle Paul-Nicolas Cuvier,

Cuvier became far more openly demonstrative:

Il était aux petits soins avec elle; il lui prodiguait ses caresses; il s'asseyait sur ses genoux; il l'embrassait et ne l'appelait pas autrement que 'ma femme'. Cette espèce d'enivrement lui a duré plusieurs années.[26]

At this point we should return to Cuvier's involvement with the work of Buffon to examine it, not as part of the workings of the biographical traditions surrounding his earlier life, but as a real event in the development of a scientific vocation. Local historians have made strong attempts to establish a connection between Cuvier's later fame and the local strengths of scientific and medical culture in the Principality,[27] yet Cuvier himself, writing a few years later to his friend Christian Pfaff, gloomily commented that whereas literary and theological subjects were highly esteemed and often cultivated with intelligence and learning in his native town, an interest in natural history was regarded as at best a harmless pastime.[28] The interest which Cuvier displayed in his uncle's edition of Buffon, and his collecting expeditions in the countryside, were therefore not likely to be regarded by the adults in his vicinity as any sign of the emergence of a life's vocation. Rather it was simply, once again, evidence of the young Cuvier's ability to amuse himself in a quiet and orderly way, demanding no participation from other children and posing no threat to adults.

It is thus not surprising that in choosing a career, Cuvier's parents could see only one way to continue their son's education for lucrative employment:

Le pays de Montbéliard avait depuis longtemps des bourses à l'Université de Tübingue, pour des jeunes gens qui se destinaient à l'état ecclésiastique, et l'ordre, dans lequel on les obtenait, était réglé par celui qu'on avait dans les classes au collège. Au moment décisif, un régent qui m'avait pris en aversion parce que, dans mon orgueil enfantin, je lui avais trop laissé voir que je le jugeais fort ignorant, donna la préférence sur moi à deux de mes proches parents. Il fut ainsi, sans le vouloir, la cause de toute ma fortune. Sans son injustice, je serais devenu, comme mes deux pauvres cousins, ministre de campagne, et j'aurais traîné une vie obscure. Au lieu de cela, j'entrai dans une autre carrière, et j'ai pu même rendre service à eux et à leurs enfants.[29]

Cuvier's later account tells us much about the depth of the

The cosmopolitan province

disappointment suffered by both Cuvier and his parents at this significant defeat of his career expectations. So great a disaster at that time could only be rhetorically balanced by allusion to the crushing success of Cuvier's later adult life. This structure of reversal and compensation enables us to enter into the experience of the actual achievement of success, a series of gambles, not an unbroken line of progress. Sometimes these gambles failed, and to recoup position after a failure required a correspondingly more significant regrouping of forces.

Heavy social guns were in fact mobilised by Cuvier's family. Their friendship with the Comte de Waldner had given them a purchase on the attention of the court at Etupes.[30] Once this was done, the matter rapidly arranged itself:

> Le duc Charles de Württemberg, souverain du pays de Montbéliard, y venait de temps en temps visiter le Prince Frédéric qui en était le gouverneur. Un de ces voyages eut lieu précisément à l'époque dont je parle. La princesse, sa belle-soeur, ... avait vu mes petits dessins et m'avait pris en amitié. Elle parla de moi au Duc, qui aussitôt m'accorda une place gratuite dans son Académie de Stuttgart.

Probably because of an epidemic in Stuttgart, and contrary to the impression given in his autobiography, Cuvier did not actually take up this place until two years later, in 1784.[31] The journey to Stuttgart, so magically made possible by the carefully cultivated patronage networks of Montbéliard, was also a frightening break with the familiar world. Even in 1823, Cuvier was unable to look back without

> une sorte d'effroi, à ce voyage que je fis dans une petite voiture, entre le chambellan et le secrétaire du Duc, que je gênais beaucoup, parce qu'il y avait à peine de la place pour eux, et pendant toute la route ne se parlèrent qu'en allemand, dont je n'entendais pas un mot, et m'adressèrent à peine deux paroles d'encouragement et de consolation.

Clearly, the already considerable efforts made by Cuvier to adapt to the demands of his environment would require even further intensification in these new and challenging circumstances.

Founded in 1770 by the Grand-Duke Charles-Eugène, the same who had so providentially visited Montbéliard in 1782, the Academy had been awarded university status by the Emperor Joseph II in December 1781.[32] By 1784, it had reached its full scope. In the wave of administrative rationalisation and bureaucratic expansion which swept through the small German courts in this period,[33] the Academy became a highly organised training ground for the state service. Three hundred students and fifty masters brought together from all over the German states and eastern Europe, occupied an enormous, specially designed building on the outskirts of Stuttgart,[34] and followed a formidably wide curriculum. Instruction in the polite arts of horse-riding, dancing and fencing, were accompanied by the study of history ancient and modern, law, public finance, technology, modern languages, medicine, mathematics, natural science, forestry and classics. Except for the classics, these were subjects in which Cuvier might have found it difficult to obtain formal instruction as part of a regular curriculum had he either stayed in Montbéliard, or continued his instruction in France. However, discipline was severe. Pupils were boarders without exception, wore uniform, moved at meals and between classes to words of command, and were subjected to constant inspection.[35] An elaborate system of penalties, administered by the Grand-Duke himself, was attached to faults in bearing, turnout and manners, as well as to more serious offences.

As a community the Academy could not have been more diverse. The promise that good performance in its examinations would lead immediately on graduation to responsible state employment in Württemburg, ensured severe competition for entry, which could take place at any age from eight upwards. The breadth and excellence of the instruction offered, at a time when many of the older German universities were moribund, drew pupils from all over east and central Europe.

Cuvier, the Lutheran son of an obscure half-pay officer from a small town in a tiny principality, could have rubbed shoulders with Catholic Polish counts and Orthodox Russian princes.[36] Among such a group, friction was inevitable. Without the safety-valve of long home holidays, constant surveillance was necessary to prevent its explosion. All forms of judgement of persons were dangerous; special punishments were reserved for gossip, malicious tale-bearing and slander.[37] Just as in Montbéliard, the surveillance of conduct was intense and continuous, and pressures for conformity and against the

The cosmopolitan province

making of markedly differentiated responses to others, were strongly insisted upon. Absent in Montbéliard, though, was a social feature built into the very structure of the Academy: the distinction between noble and commoner. The nobility slept in different quarters and ate different food at different tables from the rest of the pupils, amongst whom, of course, was Cuvier. Academic success, however, could gain for the commoner admission to a minor order founded by the Grand-Duke, which carried with it the privileges of nobility, and in addition, of admission to the Grand-Ducal table, and preferential employment in the state administration.

The Academy thus reproduced within itself, to a far greater degree than did Montbéliard, the highly stratified, aristocratic society of late eighteenth-century Europe. It also encapsulated one of the basic internal conflicts of later eighteenth-century government: that between the norms of an 'objective' bureaucracy functioning for the good of the commonwealth, and of the personal, arbitrary, subjective will of the absolute ruler.[38] The Grand-Duke's personal interest in the Academy was well-known.[39] Part of the building was periodically occupied by him, and his appearances at meals and in class were frequent and unheralded. As in Montbéliard, supreme political power was embodied in an easily accessible, visible, human figure.[40] It was a power capable of coming very close to each pupil. In this nursery of bureaucrats, as the career of both Cuvier and Friedrich Schiller showed, the Grand-Duke's subjective reactions had a dramatic impact on individual careers. By 1784, the Academy stood at the centre of a polemic which implicated this whole aspect of eighteenth-century government. It was attacked for the subjection of the humanity of individuals to the rigour of its military discipline; it was further attacked for the Arch-Duke's arbitrary intervention in the lives and careers of its pupils. For neither 'objective' regulation by discipline and rules, nor 'subjective' intervention by the Grand-Duke, was any guarantee of freedom, especially not when the two modes of action cut across each other within the same institution. The issue of personal self-determination within an aristocratic society lay at the heart of the discontents of the late eighteenth century, and was much present in the Stuttgart Academy.

The most powerful voice raised against the Academy on these grounds was that of a former pupil, Friedrich Schiller.[41] On graduation in 1782, he was forced against his will to abandon a literary vocation and to follow the career of a regimental surgeon by the personal interference of the Grand-Duke. Schiller's misery was acute. It turned his already apparent literary talent towards deeply felt social and political criticism. Having written his first play, *Die Raüber*, in secret, he fled from the anger of Charles-Eugène over the border into Mannheim to arrange for its production. It was an immediate and much relished success, but Charles-Eugène arranged for his extradition and forced him to return to his hated avocations in Stuttgart. In 1784, Schiller escaped for the last time, appropriately enough under the cover of the confusion caused in Stuttgart by a hunting party given by Charles-Eugène for his brother-in-law the Grand-Duke Paul of Russia. His *Cabale und Amour* of the same year satirised Württemburg, the Academy and the Grand-Duke, in terms even less disguised than those of his earlier play. It was from the date of his final escape that Schiller felt himself to be a 'citizen of the world': an idea which had deep significance for Cuvier and his circle of friends within the Academy.[42]

Even apart from the resounding success of Schiller's plays, it would have been difficult to keep from the young Cuvier the knowledge of Schiller's career and the increasing public criticisms of the Academy. Schiller's closest friends at the Academy, Boigeol, Grammont and Scharfenstein, all from Montbéliard, had still not graduated when Cuvier arrived in Stuttgart. Grammont committed suicide, unable to tolerate the pressures which Schiller himself was to claim had enclosed his youth with bars of iron. With the exception of the tacit protest of Grammont's suicide, Schiller's revolt was the most extreme ever experienced by the Academy, but contemporary descriptions of Cuvier's appearance and manner while at Stuttgart make it clear that he was affected adversely by the same extreme pressures: the unrelenting dosages of instruction, the lack of contact with the fluid human relationships of the real world, the mechanical discipline, and the total subordination of individuals to the will of the Grand-Duke. Christian Pfaff first met Cuvier at the Academy in 1787 and remained a life-long, if critical, friend. He described Cuvier at this time:

> Son visage très-maigre, plutôt allongé qu'arrondi, pâle et marqué abondamment de taches de rousseur, était comme encadré par une crinière épaisse de cheveux roux. Sa physionomie respirait la sévérité et même un peu de mélancolie. Il ne prenait aucune part aux jeux ordinaires de la jeunesse; il avait l'air d'un somnambule qui n'est point affecté de ce qui l'entoure ordinairement et qui n'y prête aucune attention. L'oeil de son esprit seul était ouvert sur le monde de l'intelligence.[43]

In a different way, Cuvier was responding to the pressures which Schiller had questioned openly and boldly. Just as in Montbéliard, his air of remoteness presented an appearance of conformity, camouflaging internal emotional reactions. That such were not lacking is borne out by Pfaff, who commented that

> malgré le sérieux et la froideur apparente, le tempérament de Cuvier n'était rien moins que flegmatique. Sa vie interne et cachée était comparable à la chaleur intérieure de notre globe terrestre, qui toute enveloppé qu'elle est pour ainsi dire d'une croûte froide, se manifeste de temps à autre par des tremblements de terre et des éruptions volcaniques.[44]

By maximising internal suppression, Cuvier was able to succeed in fulfilling the demands of the Academy with striking success, while offering as little excuse as possible for the irrational exercise of Grand-ducal power. He quickly became able to speak fluent German, and by 1787 had shown himself so academically successful as to be admitted to the order of Chevaliers and its aristocratic privileges, which included preferential admission to posts in the Grand-ducal bureaucracy. He had mounted a successful operation of conquest of an aristocratic institution from the position of a commoner. A future career in the Grand-Ducal administration seemed already clearly mapped out. This career did not necessarily include great attention to natural history for its own sake. Registered in the Faculty of Administration, Cuvier's curriculum included many scientific topics, such as chemistry, mineralogy, zoology, botany, geometry and mining. Yet these were all taught not as distinct sciences, each with an individual internal logic, but as aspects of an extended notion of *Cameralwissenschaft*, the science of government. This curriculum also included law, commerce, finance and economic theory. There is no evidence that Cuvier chose to enrol himself in this faculty because of the scientific instruction it offered; it was rarely possible at this period to make a living simply through the cultivation of the sciences. Formal instruction in natural history in the Academy was also in abeyance, because of the death of its teacher Charles-Heinrich Koestlin, and remained so until the Academy was closed in 1793.[45]

Perhaps this was the very reason that Cuvier became increasingly fond of passing his spare moments in its study, and became friendly with Johannes-Simon Kerner, the teacher of botanical drawing, who offered encouragement and the gift of a Linnaeus. Friedrich-August Marschall von Biberstein, a young nobleman, also proved to be a sympathetic companion on botanising expeditions, taking over the functions filled by the young Wetzel in Montbéliard. New species were discovered and verified, and appeared in Kerner's publications.[46]

It was during these years at the Academy that the significance of the pursuit of natural history began to change for Cuvier. Koestlin's death created a vacant niche used to construct a base of private authority. He founded a natural history society, whose members included many of the other Chevaliers, such as Pfaff and Biberstein. It organised field excursions, encouraged its members to read papers on their discoveries, and Cuvier awarded prizes and decorations to those adjudged the best.[47] For Cuvier, natural history was still, as in childhood, a way of maintaining inner balance and objectivity, but its formalised pursuit now also offered him a unique and unchallengeable position of authority over others. It was a mild, innocent-looking *revanche* for the total control to which he had himself been subjected by the Academy. Natural history as a personal area of authority at an oblique relationship with the major formal structures of power, established itself as a model for Cuvier during these years. He was able to combine his love of the natural world with the attainment of leadership over others.

Natural history also enabled him to integrate himself more

The cosmopolitan province

successfully than before into the life of his contemporaries. The enclosed life of the Academy generated an intense adolescent culture, whose basic outlines conformed to the growing ethos of sentiment in late eighteenth-century Germany. Pfaff recalled how

La vie claustrale que nous menions à l'Académie était très favorable au culte paisible des Muses, en même temps qu'elle exaltait ces beaux sentiments d'amitié auxquels la jeunesse s'abandonne avec tant de bonheur.[48]

Schiller himself had contrasted the sacred bonds of friendship and sympathy with the atomism, loneliness and mechanical regularity of the life of the Academy.[49] This was an emotional style which went well with the cultivation of natural history. Friendship was linked with the freedom and egalitarianism of life in the open, and the sentimental expansion caused by the beauties of nature, far removed from the structures of compulsion present in formalised human society. Openness to nature and its beauties was seen as a guarantee of emotional authenticity – an authenticity hardly at a premium in the Academy. Cosmopolitanism was also a strongly felt part of this ideal. As nature obeyed the same laws the world over, so the authentic cosmopolitan felt at ease in any country, and did not allow his inner stability to be shaken by such extraneous contingent factors as governments and rulers. The title of Pfaff's first work, the *Phantasien eines Weltburger auf eine Reise durch den Württembergische Alpe*[50] sums up this combination of nature-worship and cosmopolitanism. It was an ethos of vital importance in Cuvier's emotional maturing. The cosmopolitan ideal underwrote the search for liberty, liberty as an ability to maintain inner objectivity despite humanly contrived circumstance and interference. It was the denial of any possibility of such inward authenticity which had driven Schiller to his revolt, as a precondition of being able to live as a true *Weltburger*.

At the end of his stay at the Academy, Cuvier himself had come to regard it as a 'prison'.[51] The cosmopolitan ethos had enabled him to look beyond the boundaries of Württemburg, and to select other figures than the Grand-Duke on which to model himself. One such figure was Horace-Bénédict de Saussure, whose *Voyages dans les Alpes* became one of the classics of romantic attitudes to nature.[52] In his volumes, appreciation of sublime scenery was combined with detailed geological observations, and a cosmopolitan disregard for the political boundaries imposed by man on the surface of nature. In conscious imitation of Saussure, in his last summer in Stuttgart, Cuvier, with Biberstein and two other companions, undertook his own journey into the Alps.[53]

Slowly, the world was opening out, but it was still bounded by the prospect of a career in government. Cuvier had received much formal instruction in some branches of science. He had also gathered round him a group of friends and set up a co-operative programme of the description and re-definition of species which, as we will see, was to determine much of his work in natural history after his departure from Stuttgart. Intermittent instruction from Karl-Friedrich Kielmeyer had given him some appreciation of the use of the experimental method in anatomical enquiry.[54] It is still unlikely that Cuvier at this stage of his life visualised a career as a naturalist. The pressure of his parents' financial decline was strong, and however deep his inward bent, it was the rare person who could expect to be able to make a secure income out of the practice of natural history in the eighteenth century. Nor indeed had Cuvier yet acquired the degree of inner certainty necessary to state that he *had* an overwhelming vocation. That peculiar combination of inner objectivity and external incaution was hardly likely to have been acquired after years of bending to strong, externally imposed pressures from highly organised intrusive environments.

On his graduation from the Academy in 1788, however, Cuvier was abruptly informed that there was no vacant position for him in the administration of Württemburg. It was the second major reversal of his career. All his efforts to meet the demands of the Academy seemed to have gone for nothing; after all, he had not conquered social position and financial security. His situation, however, was not unusual in his generation. Institutions such as the Academy had been only too successful in turning out potential bureaucrats faster than government itself expanded. Henri Brunschwig long ago identified such abrupt *crises de débouché* as one of the roots of the Romantic mentality in Germany.[55] Above all, such shocks intensified and changed the individual's perception of himself as being distinct from others, and pressures on Cuvier to detach himself from his surroundings rather than conform to them, were gaining ground. But in the short term, he had to make money. The only means of so doing presented itself that summer in the shape of a tutoring post in Normandy about to be left by another Montbéliardais, Georg-Friedrich Parrot,[56] who was seeking better fortune in Russia. As they had brought him to Stuttgart, the international connections of the Principality worked again, with decisive consequences, to move him across Europe, to the Norman town of Caen.

II
Youth, revolution and vocation

Je ne suis entouré que de profanes, que je ne puis pas même éviter; quand j'étudierais avec plaisir un insecte, une plante, je suis forcé d'aller dans un cercle de femmes, et pour les amuser, de m'occuper de niaiseries.
(Cuvier to Pfaff, Spring 1790.)

At the end of August 1788, Cuvier set out for Normandy, and arrived in Caen in the first week of September. His previous experience in Stuttgart had not so much given him a conscious vocation, but more a set of defensive responses to the pressures of intensely experienced social and political environments. Natural history offered at once the most effective retreat for personal vision, the best way of establishing a personal reputation, and an important vehicle for friendship. But it was only the complex evolution of the Norman situation between 1788 and 1795 that was to make it possible for Cuvier to view natural history as a life-style deeply and explicitly connected with his own idea of himself, and it was only the progress of the French Revolution itself which would allow him to consider natural history not simply as a vocation, but as a possible means of subsistence.

The post in Normandy represented a desperate expedient for a young man of Cuvier's intellectual gifts, an aberration from the clear path of expectation mapped out so firmly by his education.[1] It also separated him both geographically and socially from his only friends, those he had made at the Academy. Since his post was, in the nature of tutoring posts, no more than temporary, it did not substitute another career pattern for one he had lost, but only postponed and confused the question of his final orientation. Perhaps the extraordinary tenacity with which Cuvier held on to his political and

Youth, revolution and vocation

administrative positions in his later career in France, as well as to many of his ideas in natural history, can at least partly be traced to this prolonged period of chronic uncertainty in Normandy.

For the first time, Cuvier's own comments on his situation are available to us, in the long series of letters written by him between 1788 and 1792 to Christian Pfaff, who was still completing his training at the Stuttgart Academy for a medical career.[2] These letters, of course, provide a valuable check on later accounts of this period in Cuvier's life. They are especially valuable, also, because although in no sense constituting a diary, they do chronicle very clearly the relationship between the evolution of Cuvier's vocation as a naturalist, and the evolution of his political and social attitudes. They also detail with great clarity, as do the *Diaria Zoologica* of the same period,[3] the development of his descriptive methods in natural history, and of his ideas on the ordering of the natural world.[4]

For Cuvier, the purpose of writing to Pfaff was not only to maintain their friendship, but also, as with the shorter series of letters written to Biberstein,[5] Hartmann,[6] Autenrieth,[7] and Kielmeyer,[8] to keep alive the collective programme of the Stuttgart natural history society, and to keep abreast with the anatomical researches of Kielmeyer.

The letters to Pfaff in particular, however, also have to be interpreted in terms of their recipient. Though Pfaff had been a close friend in Stuttgart, he was familiar neither with Montbéliard nor with Normandy. Detailed reference to events in these districts is thus rare in relation to Cuvier's frequent accounts of events in Paris gleaned at second hand from such newspapers as chanced to circulate in Normandy, which better fed Pfaff's demands for accounts of important political events. We learn little about events in Cuvier's family in these years, or about the slow engulfing of Montbéliard by revolutionary France which culminated in its annexation in 1793.[9] The same is true for Normandy. Many details of Cuvier's life with the d'Héricy family, his employers, do survive in the letters, but at the same time, Cuvier's letters to them reveal a relationship far stronger and more complex than that portrayed to Pfaff. More complex also were the changes in the political situation in Normandy, changes which Cuvier did not explain fully to

Pfaff, but which he exploited to gain admission to the scientific world of Paris.

At first, however, Cuvier experienced a worrying lack of definition in his new environment as compared to the rigidities of Stuttgart. He wrote to Pfaff in September 1788:

Vous ne pouvez pas vous figurer quelles sensations étranges réveille en moi le souvenir de l'Académie. Depuis cinq mois que je vous ai quittés, j'ai joui de la liberté et fait connaissance avec le monde d'une manière très agréable il est vrai. Eh bien, malgré tout cela, j'ai souvent regretté ma prison. Souvent je sens ici comme un vide que je n'ai jamais éprouvé là-bas.[11]

To this sense of personal void was added an acute social unease:

'Dans le monde, on a des connaissances, mais pas d'amis. La société est si exigeante, on est enlacé par tant de liens, qu'en somme on est loin d'être aussi libre qu'à l'Académie'.[12]

As a tutor, Cuvier's social position was definitely subordinate. His social marginality was increased by the fact that both he and his employers, the Marquis and Marquise d'Héricy, were Protestants in an overwhelmingly Catholic community. In spite of offical discouragement, persecution of Protestants was still a feature of life in Caen, and contributed to their concentration in some quarters of the town.[13] It was close to the Protestant stronghold of the rue neuve St Jean, in the hotel d'Héricy on the rue des Carmes, that Cuvier lived for most of his first two years in Normandy.[14]

In spite of its religious tensions, however, as an urban environment Caen was far more open than Montbéliard.[15] The city walls had been demolished in the 1750s. Large open spaces and private gardens broke up the street plan, providing refreshment for the citizen, and interesting possibilities of exploration for the young naturalist, especially since one of the largest of these gardens, containing many botanical rarities, was possessed by the Marquis d'Héricy's father.[16] The population of Caen, at nearly forty thousand,[17] was over ten times that of Montbéliard, and contained a far larger transient element, composed of students at the University, and travellers on the road between Paris and the Norman coast. A daily coach linked Caen with the capital. The inhabitants of Caen, in other words, were not trapped within its limits either

Youth, revolution and vocation

physically or culturally. Here, Cuvier for the first time encountered the experience of life in a large nation-state, with its greater challenges, greater resources, greater and more confusing repertoire of possible roles.

In spite of his initial dislocation, Cuvier quickly discovered and exploited the resources of the town in natural history. Denied access to the botanical garden by the absence of its director Desmoueux in Paris, he gained his objective by a monetary transaction with the under-gardener.[18] The garden was a prize indeed, and an essential working tool; in 1786 it had possessed two and a half thousand species of plants, [19] classified according to a mixture of the systems of Linnaeus and de Jussieu.[20] A private collection in the town containing ninety-two species of fish was also opened to him,[21] as was a collection of oriental birds kept in an unnamed *château* outside the town.[22] He obtained admission to the University Library very shortly after his arrival, [23] where he was able to consult a complete Réamur; further handbooks on insects were available in the library of the Academy of Belles-Lettres.[24] Through a combination of his own efforts and the contacts of the d'Héricy family he made the acquaintance of the antiquarian the Abbé Gervais de la Rue, and of the University librarian, François Moysant, a distant relative of the d'Héricy family.[25]

Cuvier orientated himself quickly in Caen not only to adapt to yet another strange environment, but also to be able to maintain full control over the programme of natural history which he had established in Stuttgart, and which he had agreed to continue with his friends there even in his absence. Cuvier's view that Stuttgart was the real focus of his life was in fact very slow to shift, and it was a long time before Cuvier could see himself as anything but a transient cosmopolitan in the French setting. The d'Héricy family had in fact originally planned that he should take his pupil, Achille d'Héricy, on a tour of Europe in 1792, a tour which would naturally have included a long stay in Stuttgart for the improvement of Achille's German.[26] At first, therefore, Cuvier's post had seemed to threaten no loss of mobility or isolation from intellectual companionship, but as the political situation within France worsened, the project was gradually shelved. Yet even a year later, Cuvier still regarded 28 April 1789 as a private festival, the 'anniversaire de mon départ de Stuttgart'. It was only in 1790 that in great depression he admitted that '... je perds tout espoir de me fixer en Allemagne'.[27] The gradual weakening of the links with Germany did not, on the other hand, immediately result in a decision to build a career in France; in 1792, still ready to follow the classic course of the Montbéliardais, he entered into negotiations for a post in Russia.[28] Less than three years before his arrival in Paris, he could see nothing before him but perpetual exile from his friends and homeland, 'enfin une triste perspective pour l'avenir'.[29]

The problems of Cuvier's future could in fact only resolve themselves by a decisive modification of the situation in which he found himself in the Caen of the *Ancien Régime*. At first sight, it was an environment markedly less restricted than that of Stuttgart. The d'Héricy owned the town house in Caen, and two small *châteaux* in the country between Caen and Fécamp: that at Auteville, which they seem rarely to have used, and that of Fiquainville, where Cuvier and the family were to spend most of their time after 1791.[30] Before that date, the d'Héricy led an active social life in Caen, in which their tutor found himself included. His German contacts in fact led him to assume a certain conversational prominence as a fount of knowledge on the affairs of central and eastern Europe.[31] Cuvier's remarks in his autobiography on the solitude of his years in Normandy, though true in a deeper sense, in the most obvious way apply only to the years of the Terror and after.

Even when the d'Héricy moved to the country in the summer, their social connections were peculiarly appropriate for Cuvier. The largest landowners in the district around Fiquainville were not the d'Héricy but the Grimaldi family, princes of Monaco and Counts of Thorigni in Normandy. Their castle at Valmont, which still stands, dominated the countryside around the d'Héricy property.[32] The Grimaldi family were related to the Duc de Choiseul by the marriage of his daughter Thérèsa to Prince Joseph Grimaldi.[33] Choiseul had been one of the commanding officers of Cuvier's father's regiment, and was a frequent visitor to the court at Etupes, as were the princes of Monaco.[34] The ruling family of Württemburg was also personally represented in Normandy by a younger and morganatically married brother of Charles-Eugène.[35] So in Normandy, in spite of its remoteness from Germany, Cuvier remained surprisingly close to that pattern of international aristocratic patronage which had been so decisive in determining his education.

Yet, at a deeper level, even before the decline of the political situation in France, Cuvier was beginning to find both this world and that of the Norman nobility neither interesting nor satisfying to him. His social position was far inferior to that indicated by his education and intellectual capacity. His situation was not only worryingly temporary, but also of considerable intellectual restriction. The libraries and collections of Caen, though excellent for a provincial town of that date, were all too easily worked out. Cuvier's age, nationality and lack of publications, as well as his social status, debarred him from membership of local learned societies such as the Académie des belles-lettres. After a while, Cuvier discovered that the polite society of Caen was in no position to satisfy his needs. By 1790, gloom and frustration were at their height. He commented enviously to Pfaff:

Tu as des ressources qui me manquent; tu peux t'occuper continuellement de l'objet de tes études, et tu as des amis qui peuvent te donner des conseils. Moi, au contraire, je ne suis entouré que de profanes que je ne puis pas même éviter; quand j'étudierais avec plaisir un insecte, une plante, je suis forcé d'aller dans un cercle de femmes, et pour les amuser, de m'occuper de niaiseries. Je dis niaiseries, parce que dans de telles réunions (la politique exceptée) on ne peut en effet pas dire autre chose; et je dis femmes, parceque la plupart des hommes ne méritent pas un autre nom.[36]

Cuvier was beginning for the first time to be able to define himself as different from and antipathetic to, the aristocratic society which in Germany had provided the focus of all his ambition. The major definition of this difference came through his resentment of the interruption in his studies in natural history at the expense of the social demands of an aristocracy on its subordinates. To be a man meant to be independent of social restriction. Yet there was still little Cuvier could have done to turn natural history into a full-time pursuit. It took the events of the revolution to cut through the network of social and economic relationships which restrained Cuvier's social ascent and to break the psychological restraints which had prevented him evaluating his ardent leisuretime pursuit of natural history as a vocation rather than a retreat.

As the revolution moved through increasingly radical phases, events in Paris were quick to find an echo in Normandy. The University of Caen was closed in 1791, following the unanimous refusal of its teaching staff, including Cuvier's friend the Abbé de la Rue, to swear loyalty to the civil constitution of the clergy. Simultaneously, riots triggered by food shortages after repeated bad harvests started to turn specifically against the aristocracy as enemies of revolution and justice.[37] The royal troops were unable to control disorder and, in one of the most violent of the early riots, their commander was murdered. The aristocracy of Caen took equally violent counter-measures after this catastrophe. Cuvier himself was pressed into service by the Marquis d'Héricy, who had armed his servants 'd'epées, de fusils et de pistolets'. Meanwhile, the commander's head 'fut promenée par toutes les rues avec de la musique'. Naturally and unheroically, Cuvier ended up by hiding in a neighbouring house, rather than encounter this murderous cortège.[38]

Soon, conflict divided the d'Héricy family itself. Its older members rapidly and notoriously became involved in counter-revolutionary movements.[39] For the younger generation, the position was less clear-cut: their sympathies with reform were heightened by their disadvantaged positions as Protestants, and they did not join the movement of emigration which increased steadily after the execution of Louis XVI in 1793. On the other hand, their relationship to notorious counter-revolutionaries, and their noble status itself, made their position difficult to maintain as the revolution took on an increasingly radical character. Abruptly, social life ceased, as the ideas of the Marquise in particular became unacceptable to her more conservative aristocratic friends.[40] In 1791, she and the Marquis separated; it is not clear whether it was because of genuine incompatibility, or as a common gambit of those years to safeguard property rights by turning over control of estates to the wife, as part of her settlement, which would otherwise have been confiscated on the emigration of the husband.

Youth, revolution and vocation

Political sympathies amongst Cuvier's own friends had also polarised: the Abbé de la Rue, after the refusal of 1791, went sadly into exile in England; Moysant, on the other hand, had become one of the leading agitators amongst the progressives.[41] Planning for an ultimately unsuccessful but large-scale counter-revolutionary *coup* was in progress in the older branches of the family.[42] By 1791, it had become imperative to leave Caen. In February of that year, Cuvier, his pupil Achille, the Marquise, and intermittently the Marquis, took up permanent residence at Fiquainville, a few miles from the sea, near Fécamp.

It was here that a real solitude could be experienced. The social obligations of Caen had vanished. Achille's education did not consume the whole day. For the first time in his life, Cuvier possessed large tracts of time to use exactly as he pleased. The whole meaning of solitude changed.[43] It was no longer a defence, an uneasily held barricade against massing social pressures. Polite evaluations of the importance of social performance became meaningless. Solitude could be valued for itself, utilised as an intellectual resource, and asserted as a mark of superiority. In the heart of the Norman countryside, Cuvier was able to utilise many of the most salient features of the cosmopolitanism he had encountered in Stuttgart. The objectivity of the true cosmopolitan enabled him to judge all human societies with impartiality; in the circumstances of the Revolution, it also gave him the ability to construct roles for himself which had not previously existed in the society around him, and which had little to do with its former structures of renumeration or hierarchy. This freedom was enhanced by the opportunities of life in a large state as compared with a small one; for the first time, Cuvier was not obliged to regulate his conduct in conformity with the demands of a very present supreme power. It was then that Cuvier first seriously started to act out the role of field naturalist. First came the costume. It was made up, he wrote triumphantly to Pfaff:

d'un long et large pantalon, et d'une camisole avec des manches d'une étoffe très légère. Le *vasculum dillenianum* ne manquera non plus et tu peux croire que la *capsulacum aciculus* jouera un grand rôle.[44]

A few months later, only a dithyrambic Latin could adequately *describe the feelings of release generated by his collecting expeditions in the woods, or on the nearby seashore, maxima fruens libertate.*[45]

This great liberation from social definition also allowed Cuvier to redefine his scientific links with Stuttgart, and in doing so to redefine his attitudes towards pursuing a career in France. It was not easy to maintain in revolutionary France the Linnean-style programme of description of species which had been decided upon as the continuing work of the Stuttgart natural history society. Time and distance were gradually diluting the friendships of the Academy. After many anguished rebukes to Pfaff and Biberstein for their failures in correspondence, Cuvier gradually took upon himself the whole work of the project.[46] The very stagnation of his career in comparison with theirs – Pfaff was pursuing medical practice and Biberstein a combination of diplomacy and travel in Russian Asia – meant that he alone had leisure to continue the Stuttgart programme to its full extent. It was part of his new role, into which he flung himself with ardour. His expeditions in Normandy, recorded in the letters to Pfaff and in the *Diaria Zoologica*, with which they partially overlap, resulted in the description of over three hundred distinct varieties of birds, plants, insects and molluscs. Through Pfaff, he was also able to obtain the text of most of Kielmeyer's current lectures at the Academy,[47] a stimulus which led directly to the shift in his own work from 1792 away from a purely descriptive approach to a more general interest in the establishing of relationships between anatomical form and physiological function.[48]

Cuvier's increased freedom also allowed him to reconsider the problems of classification. It was both easy and necessary to attack the inadequacies of the Linnaean system, but at this stage, not surprisingly, Cuvier's strongest ideas on these topics were negative ones. Contemporaries supported many competing systems of classification, or none at all.[49] It was necessary for anyone who wished to make a positive contribution to the philosophy and practice of classification first to work through and criticise the ideas of others. In 1790, he came very near to Buffon's argument that species, classes and orders of all types were simply useful and necessary abstractions for the naturalist, without any objective existence in nature. To Pfaff's

Youth, revolution and vocation

enquiry of what then did constitute the order of nature, he could only give a vague and unhelpful reply.[50]

He knew already, though, what order of experience he wished to base classification upon, even if he could not as yet produce positive ways of doing so. He rejected the assaults on his sense of reality offered by the Naturphilosophie to which Pfaff tried to convert him. Reality and logic were the essential constituents of his new freedom to realise a cosmopolitan objectivity:

Je cherche déjà depuis longtemps, sans y parvenir, à me faire une idée de la force plastique de la nature; la métaphysique est surtout nuisible quand, d'après la méthode de Platon, elle s'enveloppe de métaphores poétiques. Je crois, je vois, que les animaux aquatiques ont été créés pour l'eau et les autres pour l'air. Mais qu'ils soient les rameaux ou les racines, ou do moins les parties d'une même tige, encore une fois, c'est ce que je ne peux pas comprendre.[51]

Throughout his life, Cuvier's views on the primacy of certain forms of perception in the formation of systems of observation and classification of the natural world, of the necessary dominance of logic and objective vision, were to be held with tenacity. It was the tenacity of one who has also fully experienced the distortions of vision and self-perception which were the necessary consequences of conformity to the demands of highly charged small-scale societies.

In these years, Cuvier also began to systematise his attitudes towards the social world, but here, the achievement of a freer vision was not unaccompanied by sarcasm and anger. He began to repudiate the validity of the hierarchical groupings mirrored in the Stuttgart Academy, on whose conquest he had himself expended so much time and energy. In March 1790 he remarked to Pfaff unfavourably on the administration of the Academy, and especially that 'c'était déjà un tort de faire des distinctions de naissance'.[52] More and more, Cuvier turned for support in his role as natural scientist to a form of the cosmopolitanism he had adopted in Germany. When Pfaff dared to imply that there were national rivalries in science, Cuvier lectured him sternly: 'le vrai philosophe cherche la vérité partout où elle peut, elle veut apparaître'.[53]

Two years later Cuvier gave Pfaff his opinion of the nobility in no uncertain way:

Ici, à la campagne, je ne vois presque pas de nobles, et depuis que je ne fréquente plus cette classe ignorante et souvent méprisable, ma manière de voir sur la révolution a changé; car les connaître au fond et les voir tous les jours fait qu'on trouve bien tout ce qui paraît les atteindre.[54]

It is also interesting to note from this passage that in the 1790s, at least as far as the upper classes went, Cuvier was far from being a social conservative. Many later commentators have accused Cuvier of a 'natural' or innate conservatism,[55] and have drawn conclusions from this about the rest of his philosophy of natural history, especially the idea of the fixity of species; but once Cuvier's social attitudes are precisely situated in his personal development, and in contemporary political events, the picture becomes somewhat different. Like most other people in France during the Terror, Cuvier saw a return to order as the only hope for the preservation of society;[56] but this did not mean that he wished for the return of the *old* order: it was after all, precisely its collapse which had given him his first taste of genuine personal freedom. Cuvier realised that he depended upon radical change in the nature of society and the distribution of its resources for the realisation of his now intensely felt self-conscious vocation. Psychologically it was only when he was able to cease devoting his main energies to fulfilling the demands of aristocratic society that he was able to throw himself fully into the part of the solitary, self-sufficient, cosmopolitan seeker after the truths of nature.

With this repudiation of the attitudes of Stuttgart and Caen, came an intensification of Cuvier's efforts to find a way to Paris. Since 1791 he had been in contact with some Parisian *savants*, and his reading had kept him in touch with the major developments of the learned world.[57] In the next year, his first article was published.[58] He established friendly relations with Lacepède by letter. Two long letters on the anatomy of the skate established Cuvier's credentials as an anatomist, as did his criticisms of previous work on the anatomy and classification of fish by Linnaeus, Bloch and Gesner. When, in 1793, Lacepède was ousted from his post in the newly constituted Muséum national d'histoire naturelle for political reasons, Cuvier felt close enough to him to write a long letter of sympathy.[59]

Youth, revolution and vocation

By 1793 Cuvier was certainly in correspondence with some leading figures in the world of French natural history, but in order to get to Paris he needed personal acquaintance with a figure of influence in the new world of non-aristocratic patronage which was appearing in the capital. Before the abolition of the aristocracy, Cuvier would certainly have tried to secure a post in Paris through the Grimaldi and Montbéliard connections, but in the France of 1793-5, this way was not open to him. The methods by which Cuvier did finally get to Paris were complex and curious, and have been carefully distorted, perhaps by Cuvier himself, and certainly by later biographers.

The remaining evidence for this episode poses considerable problems. Cuvier's letters to Pfaff come to an end for no obvious reason in the summer of 1792. Between 1792 and 1795, letters either to or from Cuvier are fewer in number than for any other period, with the exception of that of the Hundred Days. The surviving version of the autobiography is completely blank for the period 1792-3, largely due to excisions by Madame Cuvier.[60] It was not until 1866 that Charles de Beaurepaire revealed that from 10 Novermber 1793 until 19 February 1795 Cuvier had acted as secretary to the commune of Bec-aux-Cauchois, in which Fiquainville was situated.[61] This episode in Cuvier's life does not appear in the 'autobiography', in any reported letter or conversation by Cuvier himself, nor in the writing of contemporary biographers such as Duvernoy and Lee who had been close friends of Cuvier. Even by the 1830s it seemed to be impossible to admit that Cuvier had filled any public office, however minor, during the period of the Terror: to do so would have altered, as we shall see, the interpretation of the episodes which led to his arrival in Paris.

As one of the few educated non-aristocrats of the region, Cuvier was an obvious candidate for the post of secretary. It gave him an independent base of power and responsibility for the first time. The post carried with it the salary of 30 livres a year, a small sum, but one which chained him to no individual patron. It also carried with it powers of appointment on a communal level, powers which Cuvier used to bolster the weakening position of the d'Héricy family. Elected on

23 September 1793 (3 frimaire an II) as one of the inspectors of the forced loan of that year, he used his position to save the d'Héricy surplus grain from requisition by the authorities of the *département*. On his further election as regional officer for the manufacture of saltpetre – a vital ingredient for the gunpowder of the revolutionary wars now being fought by France – on 20 March 1794 (309 ventôse an II), he saw to it that it was his pupil, Achille d'Héricy, who oversaw the gathering of the raw materials, and who had the authority to denounce those who did not comply. By December 1794, the position of the *ci-devants* had improved to the extent that Cuvier was able to recommend M. d'Héricy himself as the most worthy citizen of the commune, on account of his advanced agricultural methods. Cuvier had certainly started to make up for his exclusion from power in *Ancien Régime* France. He had used the circumstances of the revolution to create a situation where his employers were dependent on him and no longer he on them. In 1794, his increasing local prominence enabled him to put his talents as a naturalist before the government representatives and Parisian literary figures Garat and Ginguéné, to whom he was recommended by the district of Montivilliers as the most gifted young man within its circumscription. Cuvier was translating an administrative position into a demonstration of his public independence which should match his new freedom to involve himself with natural history. He was also translating a political position into the opportunity to gain access to a cultural resource – the ability through Garat and Ginguéné, to raise his status in Paris in circles which knew him only as a naturalist.

Most accounts of the way Cuvier got to Paris, however, centre on a quite different story, which lacks independent documentary confirmation. The story runs as follows: around 1793, Cuvier set up, either at Valmont or at Fécamp, an agricultural debating society, to pre-empt the formation in the locality of a *société populaire*, or *sans-culotte* group. His manoeuvre had the desired effect, and popular passions were duly restrained. One of the members of the debating society was the Abbé Henri Tessier, a well-known agronomist, hiding at Fécamp under an assumed name and in lay costume, and acting as surgeon to the regiment stationed there. Tessier's

Youth, revolution and vocation

contributions to discussion were so brilliant that Cuvier guessed his true identity. After confronting him with his discovery, he assured the alarmed Tessier of his discretion and protection. In gratitude, and impressed by Cuvier's powers as a naturalist, Tessier arranged for him to give a botanical course at the military hospital in Fécamp. This gave Cuvier his first teaching experience. Tessier also recommended Cuvier to his scientific friends in Paris who, in some accounts, included Geoffroy St Hilaire and in others de Jussieu. In Paris, Cuvier's genius was rapidly recognised, and an invitation to a post at the Muséum national d'histoire naturelle inevitably followed.[62]

Cuvier's autobiography also poses many problems in this respect. The printed version of it contained in Flourens' biography derives from a abbreviated version of Cuvier's original manuscript, prepared by Mme Cuvier. The original is now lost. Both existing versions are cut at this point. This is all the more odd, as there seems no obvious reason why an anecdote which reflects only credit on Cuvier should have been excised. Just as puzzling is the way the Flourens printed version produces a footnote at the point where the text is cut, which relates the Tessier story in its canonical form. If the story were already there in the text, it would seem pointless to remove it, and then retell it in a footnote. It may be that for some reason, Cuvier's own original version of the story had caused unease both to Mme Cuvier and to Flourens, and that the latter substituted a more acceptable version in his footnote.

When the Flourens version of the Tessier story is measured up to literary criteria of consistency provided by independent sources, the problems only increase. The story does not tally with specific facts, and when it is told by other writers than Flourens, it seems to lack the consistency of a firmly established account.

It has already been established that Cuvier had in fact no need of Tessier as an intermediary between him and the Parisian scientific world; Olivier, Haüy, Lacepède and Lamétherie were all familiar with his work in greater or lesser detail, and Garat and Ginguené in a more general sense. Lee's statement that it was through Tessier that Cuvier entered into correspondence with the *savants* of Paris is thus patently untrue.[63]

Internal examination of specific texts of the story only increases doubts. Lee, a close friend of Cuvier, tells the story in two versions at two widely separated places in her work.[64] In the earlier version, the society meets at Valmont, and Tessier puts Cuvier into contact with Lamétherie, Olivier, Lacepède, Geoffroy St Hilaire, Millin de Grandmaison; he then writes about his 'discovery' of Cuvier to Parmentier. In the later version, the location of the society is left uncertain between Fécamp and Fiquainville, and Tessier alerts the *savants* of Paris to the gifts of Cuvier by a letter, not to Parmentier but to de Jussieu, of 11 February 1795.[65] Given the dating of this alleged letter, it is difficult to see how Cuvier could have been so rapidly provided with a Parisian post as to be able to resign from his position as secretary of the Bec-aux-Cauchois by 19 February. The timetables of the Tessier story and of the official record of the Bec-aux-Cauchois seem, in other words, to be incompatible.

The story of Cuvier and Tessier must perhaps be treated with caution as a narrative of real events. Perhaps a better understanding of this period in Cuvier's life is to be gained by asking what function it serves by its inclusion in the biographical canon, and what might be its relation to attested events. The political purpose of a story about Cuvier outmanoeuvring, in a peaceful way, an association of *sans-culottes* are obvious; it established an image of Cuvier as an impartial figure reconciling party strife; it set him outside the highly charged political field of the Revolution. Lee supresses the involvement with the administration of Bec-aux-Cauchois completely, or at least was never told of it. Even in her retouched account however, there is little correspondence with the real world. There *was* a *Société populaire* at Fécamp,[66] but its proceedings, of a ferociously anti-clerical and anti-aristocratic character, went on without a halt throughout the years of the Terror. It seems likely, though not certain, that Cuvier gave a course on botany in Fécamp at this time,[67] but there is no proof except Tessier's own alleged letters to de Jussieu and Parmentier that it was through his mediation.

These are the only nuggets of fact extractable from the Tessier story. The story is more important for what it obscures than for what it reveals. Firstly it fills in the period of the

Youth, revolution and vocation

Terror so completely that Cuvier's involvement with the administration of the Bec-aux-Cauchois is obscured. It therefore also obscures Cuvier's use of that position to rise in the world, as well as his use of Garat and Ginguéné, radicals who later fell out of favour with Napoleon, to gain independence from his employers and advertisement in Paris. Cuvier must be seen to have risen by means of objective, overwhelming merit, rather than through that mediation of merit through politics which the ideology of science in the nineteenth century found so deeply offensive.[68]

Lastly, the Tessier story seems to absolve the enquirer from further research into the timing of Cuvier's arrival in Paris, and the chains of patronage which lay behind it. As we have seen, it constructs a timetable for this event which is difficult to reconcile with the implications of contemporary official records. By 1847, Isidore Geoffroy St Hilaire had clearly shown that the accepted dating of Cuvier's appearance in Paris as April 1795 was questionable.[69] By 20 April of that year, Cuvier and Geoffroy had already prepared and read a joint paper for the Société d'histoire naturelle in Paris. Geoffroy himself said that he met Cuvier only two months after the latter's arrival in Paris, in other words in early February. Why then did Cuvier only resign from his post at Bec-aux-Cauchois on 19 February? The only explanation which will fit both these facts is that Cuvier left Fiquainville for Paris very early in the new year of 1795, but, uncertain for some weeks whether or not he would be returning, did not resign his position as communal secretary. By 19 February this uncertainty was resolved: by mid-March (23 ventôse) he was reading a paper to the Société Philomatique. Cuvier's autobiography states that he went to Paris with his pupil Achille d'Héricy, ostensibly to let Achille see the sights of Paris, but also to explore the faint hope of a post at the Muséum. In Cuvier's account, the Muséum was hesitating in the face of what looked like the inevitable necessity of hiring the anatomist Richard as assistant for the aging Professor of comparative anatomy, Mertrud.[70] The collapse of Mertrud's health made his replacement an urgent matter; on the other hand, Richard was likely to be a difficult colleague. When Cuvier arrived in Paris at an unspecified date in 1795, it was only with the *'espérance'* that the Muséum would turn to him as a way out of its difficulty.

The very fact that Cuvier took Achille to Paris with him, and also left his lovingly constructed herbarium behind in Normandy shows that at that point he had made no formal break with his employers.[71] In spite of the assertions of contemporary biographers, Cuvier had received no clear call to Paris and fame: he was undertaking another gamble.

Other evidence also suggests that Cuvier's visit to Paris might have had still further objectives than the education of Achille, or the obtaining of an innocuous post in natural history for himself. Cuvier's lodging in Paris was in the hôtel de Matignon, the former town house of the Grimaldi family. Surviving letters to the d'Héricy in Normandy in 1795 are couched in a veiled terminology scarcely appropriate to describe the process of educating Achille or of lobbying for a renumerated post, and more appropriate to the progress of a secret mission whose details could not be discussed openly in writing.[72] Evidence such as this does not lend itself willingly to the reconstruction of events. The most likely possibility however is that Cuvier came to Paris very early in the year to lobby on behalf of the d'Héricy and perhaps of the Grimaldi as well for the release of sequestrated property and the removal of their relations' names from the list of *émigrés* deprived of civil rights. In the more ordered society of the Directory, such first steps in the regrouping of the old upper class were slowly becoming possible. Cuvier's contacts with such political moderates as Lacepède, who returned to Paris in 1794,[73] and Millin de Grandmaison, made him a likely candidate for this task. If this is so, it certainly helps to explain the rapidity with which Cuvier entered into the social world of such figures as Talleyrand, who was later to buy the Matignon palace, and of Larévellière-Lépeaux, one of the members of the Directory itself.[74]

It does, however, seem clear that the biographical tradition surrounding the years 1793-5 of Cuvier's life has performed a systematic function of obfuscation. Above all, it exists to lift Cuvier, as a natural philospher in the making, out of the realm of the political. In doing so, it also lifts the Paris scientific world, which so nobly co-operated to find Cuvier a succession of jobs that year, out of the political. Fuller discussion of the

Youth, revolution and vocation

pattern of Cuvier's employment will be found in the next chapter, but it is worthwhile to consider, in conclusion, why Cuvier should have found so much willing help in Paris. He was certainly a gifted naturalist, who had benefited by a rigorous and systematic German education, and seven years of increasingly intensive field work and reading in Normandy, but this is not the whole story. Gifted young men are often neglected. The answer lies more in the curious distortions of the scientific patronage networks which had resulted from the Terror. Normal methods of recruitment to the scientific community by its established figures had collapsed after the abolition of the Academy of sciences in 1793, and the dispersal, imprisonment and death of many of its members.[75] In the calmer period beginning in 1795, patrons needed to re-establish their positions; new protégés were at a premium. At the same time, the events of the Terror had allowed potential protégés to lay immense and indissoluble purchase on potential patrons. Geoffroy St Hilaire rescued both Haüy and Daubenton from imprisonment, persecution and, in the case of the former, almost certain death. The story of Cuvier and Tessier points in the same direction. In this situation, strange reversals of the normal predictable patterns of power in the scientific community took place. The old became dependent upon the young, and because of this, the young, very early, found themselves in positions of great influence. Geoffroy gained a chair at the Muséum, thanks to the efforts of Haüy and Daubenton, at little more than twenty; Cuvier was admitted to the Institut at the very end of 1795, at the age of twenty-six. In these circumstances, there was competition for recruits between older patrons, and the links of patronage became dispersed and shifting. Hence the indeterminacy in the biographical tradition about who actually did summon Cuvier to Paris, who exerted effective patronage for him at any given point over any given issue.[76] Cuvier exploited this situation, as we have seen, by spreading his demands between many different potential patrons. This gambit had the further advantage that he himself, unlike Geoffroy, never appeared as the protégé of one man more than another. He was tied to no one, and owed no overwhelming debts. In fact, at least in the case of Tessier, it was he who was the creditor, and Tessier's efforts on his behalf were simply his just reward.

Cuvier's Norman years saw him undergo two contradictory processes. The first was that intense discovery and exploration of solitude as a guarantee of vocational and personal authenticity. The second was the equally important experience, however much he might have denigrated it, of socialisation in the flexible, cultured, aristocratic society of Caen. However much he might have deplored his enforced attendance in the *soirées* of the town, there remains the fact that he did attend, and that he acquitted himself well. Yet the contradiction between these two processes may well have been, at this stage, if not in the future, more apparent than real. Each of them, in their different ways, contributed to increase Cuvier's maturity.

However, we are still left with the question of how and why Cuvier's intensified vocation became transmuted into the quest for a Parisian post. Some elements of the explanation are obvious. By 1795, Achille, Cuvier's pupil, was aged seventeen or eighteen, and in the nature of things would not require a tutor for much longer. Cuvier thus urgently needed another post. The Revolutionary wars made it difficult to leave France. Cuvier already had valuable scientific contacts in Paris, and had gained, through his experience in the Bec-aux-Cauchois, confidence in manipulating the French political scene. The events of the Revolution had also meant that Cuvier had been able to free himself from the inner demands of conformity imposed by an aristocratic society, and was set free to pursue his life in a world no longer shaped by the dominance of one social class over economic resources, political power, and social communication. On all these counts it would seem natural for him to turn his passionate interest in nature into a post with an income, and to go to the place in France where all careers are made, particularly by the anomalous: to Paris.

III
The conquest of the city

Mais voilà cette chienne de ville, où les distractions s'entassent sur les distractions, et où l'on est sans cesse entraîné par milles affaires. (Cuvier to Camper, 1799, Camper papers, Amsterdam University Library.)

Cuvier arrived in Paris at the beginning of 1795. By the end of the year he had been elected to the newly-formed Institut de France and had achieved not only the beginnings of a scientific reputation, but also public recognition and social success.

The purpose of this chapter is to suggest the precise ways in which Cuvier achieved what seems so surprising a feat. This is especially necessary since contemporary biographers showed little interest in this topic.[1] The major difficulty in the way of this project, however, comes from the state of the evidence. Correspondence and papers from this crucial period in Cuvier's life are rare, especially for the years 1794–6. It is impossible to check many of the statements made in the otherwise quite full account in the autobiography. The scarcity of documentation also often means that explanations for known events cannot be forthcoming: how, precisely, for example, did Cuvier attract the patronage of Lucien Bonaparte? It is questions of this order which are most difficult to answer, and can often only be answered in terms of probability rather than certainty, through the examination of independently produced documentation, and the interrogation of the biographical tradition itself along the lines established in previous chapters. It is fairly certain that this shortage of documentation was deliberately created, either by Cuvier himself, or by his family after his death, for it is hardly likely that so active a life, one so crowded with personal contact, sociability and scientific activity should have left so little record for this period. It is difficult to suggest a specific reason for the disappearance of documentation in the way such as exists for the similar shortage of material for the years 1814–15. In speculating upon this problem, however, we may remember Henri Beyle's comment to Cuvier's stepdaughter, Sophie Duvaucel:

Vous avez vu quelques très jeunes gens faire de grands fortunes. Soyez convaincue que quelles que soient les phrases et les apparences, pendant deux ou trois mois de leur vie ils ont été comme Julien ... Je vous assure que personne n'a fait une grande fortune sans être Julien.[2]

The author of *Le rouge et le noir* is in fact warning not only his correspondent but we ourselves to look behind the secular 'miracles' made possible by a chaotic society and an expanding state, and behind the words used to mark and to disguise their achievement.

The record of the positions actually held by Cuvier between 1795 and his appointment as Permanent Secretary of the First Class of the Institut in 1803 shows not the easy conquest of permanent success, but rather a fluctuating and often frenetic employment in many different and often temporary positions (see appendix). It is the record of a man snatching at employment for reasons partly financial and partly produced by the nature of the Parisian world in which he found himself. To assess Cuvier's rise to prominence, we thus have to describe how that world was constituted in general, and then go on to sketch some problems which affected Cuvier more specifically.

The first problem facing anyone hoping to become known in Paris was that of finding and dominating many different kinds of social arenas. Social and political change since 1789 had affected the life of the capital in such a way that opportunities to gain visibility and reputation through appeals to topics of public interest, such as science, were both more numerous and more hotly contested than they had been under the *Ancien Régime*.[3] In the post-revolutionary public world, men came to the fore because they could sway crowds and public meetings; proficiency in oratory and a public 'presence' were the prerequisites of success. It is not surprising that so many of the prominent figures of the Revolution were drawn from the academic or legal professions. The task before Cuvier in his public lectures at the Muséum, the Lycée des arts and the

Collège de France, was not simply to convey scientific information; it was also to create an impression on the public. It was undoubtedly to this end that Cuvier modelled his lecturing style upon the stage presence of the well-known actor, Talma,[4] and concentrated on a strongly visual presentation emphasising the production of actual specimens, and the making of rapid freehand drawings at the blackboard.[5]

Cuvier's lectures formed the high point of a spectrum of rational but spectacular entertainment which was increasingly important in Parisian life in this period. The growth of a reading public for science also facilitated the making of a career in Paris. Specialist journals sprang up in large numbers; scientific books for a general audience were also printed in increasing numbers.[6] Cuvier's own description of the animals in the menagerie of the Muséum was consciously undertaken to profit from this trend and to supply the needs of those who 'n'avaient point les ouvrages classiques d'histoire naturelle'.[7] Public interest in science was also reflected in the large number of references to it in the new journals of general culture, such as the *Décade philosophique* and the *Magasin Encyclopédique*.[8]

The stronger public face of science, however, did not mean that the position of those who aspired to a career in the 'highlife' of science had necessarily become any easier. The expansion in the public interest in and consumption of science had not been matched by a corresponding expansion in the possibilities of employment in the institutions of scientific research.[9] The making of a career was not the unproblematic process which it has often implied to be by later commentators wedded to a vision of the Empire as a golden age of French science and the emergence of its professionalisation.[10] The early years of the Revolution had seen a strong attack on the practice of science from those who thought that its institutions and, in particular, the Académie des sciences lacked sympathy with the practical science of ordinary men, and displayed an elitist disdain for untutored insights into nature which did not fit into its prevailing orthodoxy.[11] The argument for the vindication of the democratic intellect against oppressive élite corporations had culminated in the closure of the Académie des sciences, and contributed not a little to the execution of

Lavoisier. In other words, a considerable 'consumption' of science co-existed with a measure of public dislike and mistrust of those who produced it. It was not simply a distrust which came from the left. Counter-revolutionary commentators were never tired of suggesting a link between the horrors of the Terror and the popular *journées,* and the spread of half-understood 'philosophical' ideas amongst the lower classes. Such men saw the existence of intellectuals as a symptom of social upheaval. *Savants* were uprooted and displaced persons, like Cuvier himself, 'Des hommes jetés hors de rang par les événements, privés de toutes resources et de toute espérence.'[12] Such prejudices did not diminish even in the relative calm of the Consulate. As a contemporary observer pointed out:

'Il s'est établi insensiblement, parmi même les personnes éclairées, une sorte de préjugé contraire aux savants, aux littérateurs, et généralement aux individus qui cultivent ou protègent avec zèle les sciences et les arts, comme s'ils n'avaient en vue que de troubler l'ordre public en excitant parmi les différentes classes de citoyens un esprit de fermentation contraire à la sureté et au repos publique.[13]

To both right and left, in fact, the *savant* represented a scapegoat figure. The contemporary debate over the responsibility of men of learning for the Revolution made it an uphill struggle to define the social role of science in neutral and acceptable terms. It made it even more difficult to talk coherently about the social role of science. To argue for its diffusion amongst society as a matter of public utility, for example, was to recall only too clearly the radical democratic attack on the old learned corporations. The only way such arguments could be conducted was to refer science to the endorsement of the state.[14] This contemporary rhetoric, taken for reality in many modern accounts, has led to an over-emphasis on state-funded scientific institutions as a component in the scientific life of this period.[15] A truer and broader picture might be formed by examining the confusion induced in the scientific role by the conflict between science viewed as a cultural commodity in demand amongst a wide public, and science as a body of knowledge cultivated by a small body of men often holding posts in state-funded institutions. The audience for science had extended, but it was also disunited: there was no guarantee that state, scientific community and

The conquest of the city

broader public would use the same criteria of what they wanted from science, or who they conceived the authentic scientist to be.[16] In these circumstances, the working out of an identity as a scientist was no simple matter. Cuvier could no longer go on with the playing out of the purely 'a-social' elements in the official ideology of how the true *savant* behaved. In particular, the glorification of fieldwork and of a constructive stoic solitude, the 'great enjoyment' of the freedom from the pressures of human society, had drastically to be revised. The making of a career in Paris could in fact only be achieved by the sacrifice of the ability to live through the ideology of science in its pure form. It was in Paris that Cuvier first really confronted all the conflicts which surrounded the gap between the apolitical ideals of science and the making of a scientific career in a rapidly changing and highly political metropolitan society. It was this conflict which led Cuvier, after much internal stress, to make certain choices about the kind of scientist he wished to be, and the kind of science that he wished to produce.

Cuvier had become used to isolation and independence in his years in Normandy, and these were traits which he carried over into his early years of career-making in Paris. Cuvier was careful not to link himself too closely to any patron, but would tend rather to manoeuvre between many different acquaintances each able to help him in a specific way. This can be seen quite clearly if we list the patrons involved in obtaining particular posts for Cuvier in these years.[17] This simple tabulation of available information reinforces the suggestion of contemporary accounts, that Cuvier had been careful to become dependent on no single patron for his translation to Paris. Thus, as we have seen, the story of Cuvier's discovery by Tessier, and his subsequent reception in Paris by Geoffroy and Millin, has the effect of denying that Cuvier owed his fortune to the intervention of any single powerful figure. In this way, the making of Cuvier's career can be strongly contrasted with that of Geoffroy, whose son and first biographer is at pains to stress the extent of Geoffroy's moral dependence on Daubenton.[18] This was also the reason that in spite of severe financial pressure, Cuvier refused the salaried position of a pupil at the Ecole normale, preferring to sit unpaid with

Laplace and the other professors; as he said later, 'Je ne voulus point me mettre dans une position inférieure à celle où j'étais arrivé'.[19] Cuvier was determined to be no man's particular client.

In fact, Cuvier's first temporary post, at the Commission temporaire des arts, brought him into contact with a far wider range of potential patrons than that which could have been provided by the Muséum.[20] At the same time, his immersion in a wide range of private scientific societies meant that he could show off his gifts at their meetings without having to acknowledge dependence on any particular group or individual.[21] It was within their walls that Cuvier established substantive claims to recognition in science. It was also in these societies that he was to make valuable friendships, including that with the geometer Lacroix, and with his future colleague at the Muséum, Alexandre Brongniart.[22] It was all a way of preparing his path for election to the Institut at the end of the year, and a way not peculiar to Cuvier.[23] These were actions which maximised Cuvier's freedom of manoeuvre, and preserved him from the possible consequences of an immediate plunge into the tangled patronage politics of the world of Parisian scientific institutions.

This was a patronage system in crisis. The events of the Revolution and more specifically of the Terror (1793-4) had not only destroyed the scientific community centred on the old Academy of Sciences, abolished in 1793, but set up deep political and personal tensions between its remaining members. As it became known that plans were afoot to create in the First Class of the new Institut de France some kind of equivalent to the old Académie des sciences, competition between patrons for the allegiance of promising protégés, who would bring credit to their names and styles of doing science, became heated. This competition was not without justification. A rapid count of elections to the First Class between 1795 and 1814 shows that fewer than one half of such elections went to men connected with the old Académie des sciences.[24] In these circumstances it is not surprising that Cuvier's entry into the Muséum may not in fact have been easy. The decision to employ Cuvier rather than Richard was probably not unanimous, and left a legacy of distrust of Cuvier at least from

The conquest of the city

Haüy, and probably from Daubenton and Faujas de St Fond as well.[25] Fears that the apparently docile protégé Geoffroy, the firm supporter of two of the oldest members of the Muséum, might be outdistanced by the new arrival and increase the lustre of his supporters Lacépède and de Jussieu, seem to have been strong. The way in which Cuvier was elected to the Institut at the end of the year 1795 bears out this interpretation. It is marked by the hard bargaining caused by the situation in the Muséum. The electing core of Cuvier's section was composed of Lacépède and Daubenton. In spite of contemporary expectations they excluded Geoffroy from election, and included Richard, the man whose post Cuvier had taken. An evening-up between the two sides had taken place, very much at the expense of Geoffroy.[26]

Lack of correspondence makes it difficult to reconstruct with certainty, the remainder of Cuvier's social contacts. However, a check of a wide range of contemporary memoirs certainly provides some results; it shows that Cuvier had managed to generalise his social impact over a wide range of different social *milieux*.[27]

These ranged from the liberal Protestant banking circles of Mme Gauthier and Benjamin Delessert, through to the right wing, with the Pastoret family, and into the world of science, politics and administration represented by the Prony and Lavoisier connections. Cuvier in fact had become highly socially visible. The personal contacts achieved through the scientific societies had been transformed into membership of the *salons*, and enabled him to maximise his social status and to turn it into powerful support for his scientific career.[28] It was Lucien Bonaparte himself, for example, who secured his appointment to the Collège de France. In later years, the employment of this kind of range of patronage may well have become increasingly rare. Biot, for example, made his way by reliance on a single patron, Laplace. Cuvier's early progress is far more reminiscent of that of his friend Joseph-Marie De Gérando, who also appeared in Paris from the provinces after a difficult and broken career, and relied heavily on support from patrons outside his own specialised field of interest in philosophy, patrons such as Louis de Fontanes and Lucien Bonaparte.[29] It seems likely that in the years after 1795, the operation of patronage became more rigorously demarcated. The foundation of the Institut National was a crucial element in this process because it endorsed the position of many prominent figures in the scientific community, and offered a closely controlled single arena for the evaluation of the merit both of themselves and of their protégés; in fact it re-established and formalised ways of ascribing merit. But in the year 1795 itself, the situation was still fluid enough to allow outsiders such as Cuvier, drawing on patronage from many different sources, to achieve position and reputation. Cuvier's most important social contact of all, however, may have been the dramatist Antoine Vincent Arnault. Arnault, a brother-in-law of the astronomer Delambre,[30] Cuvier's colleague as Permanent Secretary of the First Class of the Institut from 1803 till 1822, was also a member of the Société polytechnique, which Cuvier joined in 1795.[31] Arnault, the holder of a senior post at the Ministry of the Interior, was close to Talleyrand, and to Bonaparte himself. It is likely that it was through Arnault that Cuvier encountered his future wife Anne-Marie Coquet de Trayzaile, widow of the tax-farmer Philippe Duvaucel, executed in 1794. Arnault was almost certainly the lover of her sister, Laure Brack.[32] In 1804, Arnault appeared as one of the witnesses to Cuvier's marriage.[33] It is striking that, with the exception of de Jussieu, and immediate members of Cuvier's family, all the other witnesses were also part of Arnault's circle. They included Cuvier's patron and colleague, Antoine Fourcroy, and the financier and future *régent* of the Bank of France, Joseph-Basile Ducos. Ducos, for a while an advanced Jacobin, had met Fourcroy and Arnault in Paris in 1791.[34] These were all men on the make, men whose original Jacobin commitments had softened to an extent to allow their accommodation with the régime of the Directory, the world of finance and government, swayed by political and amorous intrigue. It was a world in many ways very close to that described for Julien Sorel by Stendhal.

It is curious that Cuvier's marriage, his social relationships outside the world of science, and his family relationships, so important to any rising patron, should have been so neglected in our picture of his Parisian life. Let us take the marriage first.

There is no account of the marriage in the 'Autobiography'.

Duvernoy, undoubtedly in possession of first-hand information, suppressed it while his account of Cuvier's life was at proof stage.[35] There are few retrospective comments in the correspondence of Anne-Marie's better-known daughter Sophie Duvaucel. Contemporary commemorations of the marriage, while elegant, are not informative.[36] Exhaustive search for the contract of marriage has failed to produce results.[37] It seems likely that such a thorough concealment was undertaken, for similar reasons to that of the obfuscation of Cuvier's social contacts; that an exploration of the family and social relationships surrounding his marriage would diminish the 'scientificness' of Cuvier's life. It is in fact noticeable that of all the members of Cuvier's extensive family it is only Sophie Duvaucel who is regularly and fully mentioned by his biographers and it is significant that such attention is paid to someone who until Cuvier's death was his faithful assistant and hostess. Those who pursued careers outside Cuvier's immediate control, like the generals Walther and Brack, or like the politician Coulmann, are erased from a record primarily concerned to emphasise Cuvier's individual power and importance with the world of science.

The importance of family relationships also immediately becomes apparent when we examine the way Cuvier constituted his own group of protégés once he had reasonable security in Paris. Frédéric, his brother, was the first to arrive. After his establishment in Paris in 1797, he was kept busy preparing a catalogue of the collections of the Muséum. In 1804, he became keeper of its menagerie. Then came Georges Duvernoy another compatriot, and a distant relative of Cuvier, whose work was vital to the publication of the *Leçons d'anatomie comparée* in 1805.[38] Then Charles-Louis Laurillard, another Montbéliardais, who from 1804 held the post of *aide-naturaliste* at the Muséum, and was later director of its anatomical laboratory. Unofficial helpers drawn from among his family and compatriots included his nephew Charles Cuvier, and his distant cousin the young St Simonian, Ferdinand Curie.[39] Cuvier's position as automatic patron for other Montbéliardais making their way in Paris meant that he had ready to hand the nexus of a group of collaborators and assistants whom he could place in advantageous institutional positions. A carefully cultivated provincial network exercised in fact a sort of multiplier effect on Cuvier's own efforts to gain a strong position in Paris. Montbéliard, however, expected a return. When the schools of Montbéliard needed more money, it was Cuvier whom his native town deputed to take up their cause with the Conseil d'Etat. When conflicts over the exploitation of the forests of Alsace again threatened their interests, it was again Cuvier who had to raise the matter with the Ministry of the Interior.[40] It is facts such as these which should lead us to beware of treating patronage as something that happened only in Paris. On the contrary, it was also a link between provinces and capital which was capable of determining careers and interest groups.

However, Cuvier was not the only member of his family successfully to traverse the *montée à Paris*. Especially on his mother's side of the family, the Consulate and Empire witnessed only one more case of the conquest of Paris by a provincial élite. In particular, the career of General Walther, the son of provincial legal officials, who rose through the ranks to become a general and a trusted collaborator of Napoleon, and was buried in the Panthéon, is a case in point, as, later, was that of Walther's son-in-law the politician J. J. Coulmann. Although there is no direct evidence on this point, it is not inconceivable that Walther's rapid rise, and the close friendship of his wife with the Empress Josephine, may well have aided Cuvier's own rise to prominence, and his rapid acceptance in the circles of patronage controlled by the Bonaparte family,[41] as much as did Arnault.

The rise of General Walther may well also have facilitated Cuvier's entry into the world of Parisian Protestantism and Protestant finance. In 1803, in fact, he was chosen to act as a member of the body which was to elect the newly established Consistory of Paris.[42] In the same body was his cousin General Walther, his publishers Treuttel and Würtz, and the banker Bartholdi, who was later to become Walther's son-in-law.[43] Cuvier's entry into this group may well have also been facilitated by his friendship with the financier, Ducos, as well as, slightly later, by his friendship with Mme Gauthier, the daughter of Benjamin Delessert. In the next generation, the marriage of J. J. Coulmann, and the appointment of Frédéric

Cuvier *fils* as *sous-régent* of the Bank of France, were to continue the strong implantation of the Cuvier family in the world of the *Banque Protestante*.[44] In fact, Cuvier's family rose to national importance by exploiting the traditional Protestant professions in France: science, banking and the army. But Cuvier's family connections would have been useless without his own efforts. In fact, Cuvier's career in these years is marked by frenetic activity. Partly, the intensity of the way he lived came from attempts to reconcile the demands of the many different arenas in which he operated. Partly, it came from financial pressure. By 1803, as a rapid survey of figures shows, his income was well below the median range of income in the more prosperous quarters of Paris.[45] Lacking inherited wealth or real estate, he was totally dependent on literary income and the salaries from his various positions, although his free lodgings at the Muséum must have aided his position considerably. Nonetheless, the pressure to raise income by extra office-holding remained heavy, and increased after his marriage to a woman who brought him four children from her previous marriage. The search for office and the pace of publication which mark Cuvier's whole career may at least partly be explained quite simply by his need for money. The achievement of office unconnected with teaching posts was particularly important because such income did not fluctuate: lecturing income, on the other hand, tended to be affected in some cases by numbers of students inscribed for the course. It is also such factors which made Cuvier's appointment as Permanent Secretary in 1803 important to him even beyond the power it offered him within the scientific world: it was permanent, its income was high and fixed, and unlike his posts in education, it carried no obligation to undertake long and arduous journeys away from Paris.

Cuvier's response to the different areas of Parisian life in which he moved was far from being an undifferentiated one. It seems clear from contemporary comments that he controlled some forms of scientific association far more easily than he did others. Most confident was his reaction to the world of the private scientific societies. Cuvier had, after all, been promoting such societies since his Stuttgart days.[46] The comparatively friendly and relaxed atmosphere of such societies was a far cry from the tense manoeuvres of the Institut, as many contemporaries made clear. The members of the Société philotechnique, for example, '... bien que l'égalite de mérite n'existât pas plus chez eux qu'ailleurs, vivaient entre eux sur le pied d'une égalité qu'un banquet fraternel restaurait tous les mois'.[47] To some extent, the ideal of scientific community as a breaking down of class divisions to produce a community of interest, was a reality in the private societies.[48] It was a world, as Pfaff noted, which produced a confident, witty and convivial Cuvier.[49] But in this period, community was often the last thing produced by the institutions of science. In the Muséum, for example, Cuvier often appears domineering, aggressively insensitive to the claims and sensibilities of his colleagues, or simply confused and uncertain. His opening lecture at the Muséum reveals a great uncertainty of tone. Speaking to an audience composed of colleagues and students, he indulged in wild swings of tone and self-presentation. After a ritual eulogy of Daubenton, who was present in the audience, he proceeded to a prolonged self-depreciation which contrasts uneasily with the demanding and forceful self-portrait of this period presented in the autobiography. Embarrassingly prolonged, such abnegation may well have caused many of his potential students to indulge in a literal questioning of his capabilities. However, this section in turn was succeeded by the promulgation of a programme for natural history of enormous scope. Wildly changing tack, he swept away the claims of the systems of the past, whose authors he had just eulogised at length. For the new legislator of science, their systems were important only as they had produced 'facts': 'Peu importe le but de ceux qui ont receuilli ces faits, pourvu qu'il puisse s'en servir pour le sien'.[50] Exaggerated humility and exaggerated arrogance, fulsome references to living members of the Institut, and ultimately dismissive treatment of the dead, encapsulate all Cuvier's uncertainties in an uncertain environment.

The conflicts which may well have surrounded Cuvier's entry into the Muséum were soon added to by Cuvier himself. The breakdown of his relationship with his friend and colleague Geoffroy St Hilaire was one of the decisive themes of Cuvier's entire life. Its final and public stages in its last two years were to leave an enduring mark on his scientific

The conquest of the city

reputation and his power as a patron. In this earlier period, its effects on the style of Cuvier's science were crucial. It has often been asserted that there was little overt conflict between Cuvier and Geoffroy until the end of the 1820s.[51] In reality, the first stages in the disintegration of their relationship came much earlier.[52] In 1799, Geoffroy and Cuvier responded very differently to offers to accompany Napoleon on the expedition to Egypt. Cuvier made the same rapid calculation of position which had accompanied his refusal to become a pupil at the Ecole normale:

Mon calcul fut bientôt fait. J'étais au centre des sciences, et au milieu de la plus belle collection, et j'y étais sûr d'y faire de meilleurs travaux, plus suivis, plus systématiques, et des découvertes plus importantes, que dans le voyage le plus fructueux.[53]

This calculation was largely correct. Berthollet, for example, who did accompany Napoleon, certainly gained a close personal relationship with the future Emperor, and from that, lucrative positions and landed endowments, but he also lost to Fourcroy, who stayed in Paris, control of research directions in chemistry, and of its major organ, the *Annales de Chimie*.[54]

Geoffroy, however, departed with eagerness to Egypt. After the first few months of French success, marked for the *savants* on the expedition by the establishment of the Institut d'Egypte and many successful field expeditions, things began to look less promising. Geoffroy contracted severe opthalmia, and for a month the future of his sight hung in the balance. The British navy broke through the French hold on the Mediterranean, and by blocading Alexandria trapped the army in Egypt, and threatened to seize the scientific collections formed by the French. Napoleon deserted his main force, slipped the blockade, landed in France at Fréjus, and began the rapid journey to Paris which ended with the coup of brumaire. The *savants*, with the rest of a plague-stricken army, were left to sit out heir fate in the desert. There was no guarantee that they would ever return home. Geoffroy's letters to Cuvier at this time make painful reading.[55] In danger of losing his sight and his collections, if not his life, Geoffroy pleads with Cuvier to reassure him of the continuation of their friendship and collaboration. It is now impossible to decide whether Cuvier in fact answered these pathetic appeals or whether he simply ignored them, but whether his letters were lost or never written, it is unlikely that their relationship recovered from this degree of tension. It is in fact, more than likely that Cuvier did not reply to Geoffroy for it is noticeable that there are no references in other letters to his intentions to write to Geoffroy. Why did Cuvier behave in such a brutal way? Part of the answer must be that in rejecting Egypt and rejecting Geoffroy, Cuvier was rejecting a whole way of doing science. Geoffroy's tales of hardship and travel pointed up the choice between natural history as fieldwork, and natural history as work on the dead specimen in the Muséum. The first was, of course, far more in conformity with the ideology of natural history, which glorified the solitary field observer and direct contact with nature. The second, Cuvier's choice, had little such support, but was far more useful, as Cuvier himself points out, in the rapid establishment of a scientific reputation and a scientific system. This was a division in scientific styles of which Cuvier was highly aware. A few years later, reviewing a work by Humboldt, he pointed out:

Il y a pour l'ordinaire autant de différence entre les idées et le style du naturaliste voyageur et celle du naturaliste sédentaire qu'entre les talents et les qualités nécessaires à l'un et à l'autre. Le premier, parcourant avec plus ou moins de rapidité une multitude de contrées diverses, est frappé successivement par un grand nombre d'objets et d'êtres intéressans; il les observe dans les lieux même où les plaça la nature, dans leurs vrais rapports avec ce qui les entoure, et dans toute la plénitude de leur vie et de leur action, mais ne pouvant donner à chacun d'eux que quelques instans qu'il n'est pas toujours maître de prolonger à son gré; privé de la faculté de comparer chaque être avec ceux qui lui ressemblent et d'en fixer rigoureusement les caractères, privé même faute de livres de la possibilité de consulter ceux qui ont vu les mêmes choses avant lui, il ne conserverait de ses observations que des traces isolées et fugitives, si au courage et à l'activité nécessaires pour le genre de vie auquel il se consacre, il ne joignait la mémoire la plus inaltérable, et ce génie élevé qui saisit avec promptitude les rapports les plus éloignés des choses. Le naturaliste sédentaire ne connaît il est vrai les êtres des pays lointains que par des récits plus ou moins sujets à l'erreur, et par des enchantillons plus ou moins altérés; les grandes scenes de la nature ne peuvent être senties par lui avec la même vivacité que par ceux qui en ont été les témoins; il lui échappe mille circonstance [sic] délicates de moeurs et d'habitudes qui l'auraient frappé s'il eut été sur les lieux; mais ces

The conquest of the city

inconvéniens sont compensés par bien des avantages. S'il ne voit pas la nature en action, il en fait passer tous les produits en revue devant lui; il les compare entre eux aussi souvent qu'il est nécessaire pour arriver à des résultats certains; il choisit les questions qui traîte; [sic] il en circonscrit à son gré l'étendue: il met à les examiner tout le tems qui lui plaît; il rassemble de toute part les faits qui s'y rapportent; le voyageur ne parcourt qu'une route étroite; ce n'est vraiment que dans le cabinet que l'on peut parcourir l'univers en tout sens, mais il faut pour cela une autre sorte de courage; celui qui tient à un dévouement sans borne pour la vérité et qui ne permet d'abandonner un sujet que quand au moyen de la réflexion, de l'observation et de l'érudition on l'a éclairé de tous les rayons que peut fournir l'état momentané des connaissances.[56]

It has seemed worthwhile to quote this passage at length because it delineates so clearly what was involved in the scientific style of which Cuvier became a major proponent; it also shows how Cuvier himself conceived of this style as existing in opposition to that of the field naturalist, rather than as something which could be combined with it, as Geoffroy was to attempt to do.[57] The degree of the removal of this style of science from that endorsed by official ideology led Cuvier to have to argue specifically for it as a style *not* connected with cowardice and lack of nerve. The rejection of Geoffroy, the rejection of field natural history, and the rejection of the 'great enjoyment' of emotional authenticity built into the ideology of fieldwork, were all interconnected, and were all to saddle Cuvier with guilt and confusion. His election to the Institut at the expense of Geoffroy caused satisfaction mingled with guilt, leading to an exaggerated emphasis in Cuvier's 'Autobiography' on his gratitude to his former collaborator:

Ce fut avec un vrai chagrin que je me vis ainsi passer avant Geoffroy qui avait été le principal auteur de mon avancement. Je n'ai pas cessé dès lors de faire tous mes efforts pour que l'Institut réparât cette injustice.[58]

The last assertion is demonstrably untrue. Cuvier's guilt and confusion led to increasingly harsh and marked rejection of Geoffroy's pleas for a renewal of their friendship, and for aid in specific circumstances. When the Institut was reorganised in 1803, Cuvier's seat became vacant by virtue of his appointment as Permanent Secretary. Geoffroy wrote to him to ask him for his endorsement as Cuvier's successor in the First Class, but even the intervention of Laplace in Geoffroy's cause was insufficient to make Cuvier act with sufficient force, and it was not until 1807 that Geoffroy was to secure election.[59] By 1811, the enmity between the two men had become sharp enough for Mme Cuvier to send her husband, during his absence in Holland, detailed reports on Geoffroy's activities in Paris, particularly when these seemed to threaten the progress of Cuvier's own protégés.[60]

In choosing sedentary natural history, Cuvier had also been driven by the need to make a career in Paris, a need which was intensified by the frustrations which had dogged him ever since he had failed to gain a post in Württemburg. But to be driven by the love of power in the human world, and at the same time by the wish to achieve personal authenticity by direct contact with nature, is to be continually exposed to emotional and intellectual conflict. Cuvier's actions towards Geoffroy were the measure of his inner perturbation. It is not surprising that such inner conflicts should have found their outlet in bad physical health, and in frequent references to close friends to feelings of unhappiness and unease. Overwork was certainly a strong contributor to such feelings of depression.[61] More mysterious are the frequent references of this period to 'Des chagrins particuliers, qui tiennent à mon état moral ... chagrins d'un genre qu'un philosophe n'ose guère avouer'.[62] Such worries were acute enough to lead to severe collapses of energy. Often, he was 'réduit à un tel état que rien au monde ne m'intéressait plus, et que sans les efforts de mes amis ... je perdais pour toujours l'énergie que j'avais autrefois'.[63] Fears of death were encouraged by his weak physical state.[64] Although for his friends outside Paris, he often painted a rosy picture of his inclusion in the true community of *savants*,[65] in reality his efforts to gain recognition in a world of science far removed in character from the idealised picture of the ideology of science, had left him with a picture of human society as little better than that of the brutes:

nous retrouvons parmi eux le même spectacle que dans le monde; quoi qu'en aient dit nos moralistes, ils ne sont guère moins méchants ni guère moins malheureux que nous; l'arrogance des forts, la bassesse des faibles, la vile rapacité, de courts plaisirs acheté par de grands

The conquest of the city

efforts, la mort amenée par de longues doulours, voilà ce qui règne chez les animaux comme parmi les hommes.[66]

Cuvier's vision of the animal world was deeply coloured by that of the human society in which he was forced to make his way. Such sentiments are not those of a man simply actuated by the need for power; they are those of a man coming to realise the high price to be paid for success in the political world. Nor could he gain reinforcement from more intimate relationships. His friendship with Geoffroy was not succeeded by any other of comparable intimacy. The death of his mother in 1793 and of his father in 1797 were succeeded by that of his sister-in-law in 1801, an event which deeply depressed Cuvier and which overshadowed the rest of Frédéric Cuvier's life.[67] Contemporary accounts agree that Cuvier at first had little success in his attempts to find a wife. He was certainly rejected by Alexander Brongniart's sister Emilie as well as by Laure Brack before he was able to make the definitive choice of her sister Mme Duvaucel.[68] Even the achievement of this marriage may well have been accompanied by a repudiation of another kind. Evidence exists which allows the conjecture that Cuvier had contracted an informal liaison, which may well have resulted in two or more children, and which it seems likely that he felt compelled to terminate as his marriage approached.[69] Concern at his 'état moral', in this cousin of so many pastors, was probably connected with feelings of guilt raised by his treatment of Geoffroy, the insecurity of his personal and professional relationships, and by the collapse of the vision of science which had sustained him in Stuttgart and Normandy.

Many of these conflicts were irresolvable. However, Cuvier does seem in the end to have succeeded in at least creating a *modus vivendi* which would allow him to pursue his career without the same high degree of stress as that which is obvious before 1803. The first stage in this stabilisation came from his appointment as Permanent Secretary for the physical sciences of the First Class of the Institut. It is difficult to establish that Cuvier had any part in the reforms of the Institut of that year. The new constitution of the Institut, which gave greater autonomy to each class in the matter of elections, made the office of Secretary permanent, altered the internal financial arrangements of the Institut and abolished the class of moral and political sciences, was based on reports prepared by the Minister of the Interior, the chemist Chaptal.[70] Heated discussion had broken out in the Conseil d'Etat over an earlier scheme put forward by Antoine Fourcroy, with the help of Laplace, Roederer, Dacier and Vien.[71] The effect of the new measures was to scatter the members of the Third Class, the stronghold of Napoleon's opponents the *Idéologues*, amongst the remaining classes. Not surprisingly, such measures aroused great hostility within the Institut. Luckily, it seemed that Cuvier's absence in the south of France at the time of these changes would detract from the odium that might otherwise have fallen to him as one of their principal beneficiaries. As his friend Candolle pointed out to him:

Peut-être même est-il avantageux vu la tournure que les choses ont prises, que vous ne vous soyez pas trouvé ici pendant que ces changemens ce sont arrangés; votre position vous eût peut-être forcé à vous en mêler et la généralité des membres de l'Institut ont vu d'assez mauvais oeil ceux qui ont provoqué ces changemens.[72]

Whether or not Cuvier set in motion these changes in the Institut, he was certainly extremely concerned that he should gain the post of Permanent Secretary. The strong impression of lofty disinterest on this matter given by Duvernoy's versions of his correspondence with Cuvier at this time, should be compared with the urgency conveyed in Viénot's fuller edition of the same letters.[73] It is clear that Fourcroy strongly backed Cuvier for this post.[74]

It was not an easy position for Cuvier to fill. He was one of the youngest members of the Institut, and certainly one of the most recently arrived in Paris. He had never formed part of the old Academy of Sciences. He had to justify his right to organise men far senior to himself, and in his funeral *éloges* on departed members, to describe men often far better known to his audience than they could have been to him. He achieved acceptance by the use of rhetoric, a rhetoric concentrated in the funeral *éloges*, and wielded far more skilfully than that of his opening lecture at the Muséum. Cuvier played on the more emotive aspects of the ideal of community, often so lacking in the reality of scientific life, to suggest a continuity between the Academy of Sciences and the Institut, and to include himself, implicitly, in that continuity. He described to his audience the first session of the Institut:

> what tears of joy, what mutual and pressing enquiries on each others' misfortune and exile ... what unhappy reminiscences of those of their colleagues who had fallen victim to the executioner; what sweet emotion for those who, still young, sat for the first time by the side of men whose genius they had long respected, and who learnt by this moving scene to know their hearts.[75]

By describing his audience to themselves, Cuvier rectified his relationship to them. It is this function which made Cuvier regard the *éloges* as one of his most important forms of literary production: they stabilised his position within the Institut, and ensured that it accepted him. Stabilisation of his role within the Institut also led to a gradual decrease in the variety of forums which Cuvier had previously used to increase his visibility. In 1804, he resigned from the Société philotechnique and ceased to play an active role in the Société philomatique. He also found substitutes to give his courses at the Athénée de Paris and at the Collège de France.[76] His scientific papers had begun to appear only in specialised journals after the foundation of the *Annales* of the Muséum in 1802. Collaboration with Geoffroy had ceased in 1799. Increasingly, Cuvier was ceasing to be a public *savant* and was orientating himself towards the production of specialised science for an audience of his peers. As Cuvier said to his Italian friend Fabbroni, the appointment as Permanent Secretary had left him in Paris 'perpétuellement fixe'.[77]

In conclusion, several important points emerge from a study of the early years of Cuvier's Parisian career. The first is that success in science did not stem wholly from the use of means within *science*. Cuvier's support came as often from the inside as from the outside of organised science; it was also made possible by a growing consumption of science by the broad public. Secondly, it is also possible to say that such a way of achieving success may well have been highly dependent on the very specific circumstances obtaining in Paris and amongst the Parisian élite in the period after the fall of Robespierre and before the seizure of power by Napoleon. Thirdly, the degree of stress which Cuvier experienced in making his way in this world was heightened by the combination of the fluidity of patronage, the inability of institutions to guarantee security, the absence of a clear public role for science, or of any prevailing intellectual synthesis. All these factors meant that a successful career depended to an unusual extent on the ability to master the many different forms of sociability which had sprung up since the end of the *Ancien Régime*. It also depended quite literally on the ability to assume a rôle: Cuvier's guides were not only other *savants* but also the great actors of the day, whose example enabled him to develop the public visibility so essential to success in this society.

IV
Problems and opportunities of the Empire: science and the Imperial University

> L'habitude où l'on était de regarder l'Allemagne entière comme un seul pays; la facilité avec laquelle on passait du service d'un prince à celui d'un autre, avait aussi donné à la partie politique de l'Allemagne plus de tendance au cosmopolitanisme. On s'attachait à la justice universelle plus qu'aux intérêts particuliers d'un état, on jugeait stoïquement chaque question comme si elle avait eu lieu entre les nations étrangères.
> (Cuvier, quoted in Duvernoy, 1833, p.147).

The years after the fall of Robespierre witnessed the first effort by the French state to construct a virtually complete system of education, a field formerly dominated by the Church. This meant not only that the state assumed responsibility for the organisation of teaching, but also that it defined more or less closely the content of what was taught. For the first time, in fact, the state became implicated in the staking out of subject areas, and the validation of some lines of enquiry at the expense of others. Now, education itself came to be inextricable from the goals of the state, and successful learning, uniformly tested, gradually became a prerequisite for employment by the state.[1] Georges Cuvier's investment in this new system was heavy and prolonged.[2] The purpose of this chapter is to assess this involvement as a factor in the stabilisation of Cuvier's position as a public figure, in the formation of his political ideas, and in the working out of the close but ambiguous relationship between science and power already foreshadowed by the end of his time in Stuttgart.

Cuvier's relationship with state education cannot be explained simply in terms of careerism. It is, of course, true that the administration of education on this scale was the only wholly new area of activity undertaken by the French state in the period before 1814. It was therefore less dominated by the great patronage dynasties, in many cases of pre-1789 origin, who still possessed great power in the more traditional areas of state operation, such as public finance.[3] Figures in education, such as Louis de Fontanes and Antoine Arnault,[4] tended, on the other hand, to be associated with the newest patrons of all, the imperial family, and to have been implicated in its cultural politics. As we have seen, this was a setting already familiar to Cuvier himself. Education was obviously, also, a particularly attractive field of administration for men already possessing a high degree of formal instruction and of commitment to cultural pursuits.

However, these advantages were to be less in evidence as this period progressed. Education, like all other civil administrations, was deeply affected by the financial chaos of the Empire which reached new heights after the Russian campaign of 1812. The new administration's jurisdiction and administrative relationships had been so badly defined at the outset that conflict with local authorities and central ministries was the rule of its existence rather than the exception. The very novelty of the administration made it in fact a less than perfect instrument for advancement on the stage of general politics. The precise nature of Cuvier's involvement in education, with its long break between 1803 and 1808. can only be explained by reference to several other factors. Firstly, Cuvier could obviously manipulate for the purposes of his own patronage a position in the administration of education, but even here, we need to look very closely at the nature of the motives which governed such exercises of patronage before we can understand the kind of position that Cuvier was trying to build for himself. Secondly, Cuvier's own attitude towards systems of state education must be carefully explored. It is worth remembering that only in terms of French history was such a system a novelty. In central Europe and the German states the struggle for control of education between Church and State had already been joined long before 1789. Education for state service by the government had been the dominant idea in Cuvier's own training in Württemburg; success in examination held by state-financed universities was the prerequisite of entry into government service in Prussia.[5] The Austrian Empire, under both Maria Theresa and Joseph II, had already experienced both violent political struggles over this issue, and partial success by the state in imposing its own system at the expense of that of the Church.[6] In the United Provinces, private societies had already scored great success in providing accessible, effective, generally secular education for the working class.[7] In terms of the experience which Cuvier brought to bear on his career in France, a state administration of education was a familiar idea. Paradoxically, Cuvier gained rapid mastery of a French institution precisely because of his education outside France. It is therefore not surprising to find that a revaluation of his own educational experience also took place. The Academy in Stuttgart, condemned as a 'prison' in 1788, is treated by the autobiography of 1822 as the source of all his success in French official life.[8]

The evolution of the Napoleonic educational system was complex. The Revolution had suppressed the universities, and confiscated the property of the teaching orders upon whom the provision of most secondary education had depended. The Directory which came to power in November 1795 did not bring back the teaching orders, but introduced a new system of secondary education through *écoles centrales*, one for each *département*. The curriculum and philosophy of these schools was strongly influenced by the intellectual school known as *idéologie*, many of whose adherents, such as Destutt de Tracy, Cabanis, Garat, Ginguené and Paul-Louis Roederer, saw in Napoleon a strong but moderate successor to the Directory, and supported the *coup* of *brumaire* 1799.[9] In return for their support Napoleon gave many of them public positions and continued for the time being to endorse the existence of the *écoles centrales*. The theoretical bases of their curriculum had largely been provided by the Destutt de Tracy.[10] For him, the training of the senses ranked as high as the training of logical power, and was to be achieved by the study of such subjects as natural history to train close observation, and manual subjects to train the co-ordination of hand and eye. De Tracy's belief that knowledge derived entirely from external stimulus in fact made such training a crucial moral objective, since knowledge of good and evil could thus only be acquired by accurate reasoning from well-perceived sense-impressions.[11] As Napoleon's domestic policy moved in a steadily conservative direction, towards a reconciliation with the Church, and the maintenance of internal pacification through agencies of social control such as propaganda through education and religion, *idéologie* began to pose a threat. Its treatment of sense-impressions placed a strong emphasis on individual perception as the heart of the moral life; at the same time, its materialistic implications were also obvious. Neither was very welcome to a ruler trying to enforce domestic peace through the encouragement of uniformity of opinion, and to base the social control of the lower classes in particular on the acceptance of the moral code taught by the Catholic Church.[12] The Concordat of 1802, and the proclamation of a life tenure of the Consulate of Napoleon, signalled the end of the moderate, secularising republicanism typical of the early days of the Revolution, and the beginning of decisive moves by Napoleon against the *idéologues*. Cabanis, de Tracy, Ginguené and Garat lost their official positions. In 1803, the Third Class of the Institut, a stronghold of *idéologie*, was disbanded, and its members dispersed amongst the other sections. The *écoles centrales* were abolished, and work begun by Fourcroy on a new plan for state education. This new plan was to culminate in the establishment of the Imperial University in 1808, a body which attempted to control all levels of education, except the primary, through France and the Empire. At secondary level it substituted the *lycée* for the *école centrale*, and at university level it established separate Faculties of sciences, law, theology, medicine and letters in Paris and selected provincial towns to supplement the *grandes écoles* established by the Ancien Regime and the revolution. The *lycées* in particular were, in comparison to the *écoles centrales*, far more restricted in the social range of their pupils, and in the scope of the curriculum. Modern languages, history and the philosophy of law, for. example, all disappeared in favour of a renewed concentration on such safe subjects as classical languages. In theory, science was guaranteed an equality of status with literary topics, but in practice became increasingly restricted to the subjects necessary for preparation for the entrance examination of the Ecole Polytechnique.

In 1802, Cuvier was appointed an *Inspecteur-général des études*, and sent to the south of France to organise the new

Problems and opportunities of the Empire 73

lycées at Bordeaux and Marseille, to inspect other schools in Provence, and to examine masters and pupils hoping for places and positions in the new institutions. Fourcroy and Fontanes were both influential in securing this post for him.[13] It was a post with some advantages. Its salary was double that which Cuvier was later to draw as permanent secretary of the First Class of the Institut. It also carried enough patronage for him to be able to recommend relatives and compatriots such as Duvernoy, and friends such as De Gérando for posts within the new organisation of education, not to mention the Norman protégés of Mme d'Héricy, and old comrades from Stuttgart.[14]

Yet his reaction to the post was strongly negative. His tour in the south of France, from November 1802 to April 1803, was successful in its objectives, and useful in the opportunities it gave to gather new species of fish and molluscs from the Mediterranean,[15] but his letters back to close friends in Paris were full of complaints. The long journeys over bad roads, the boring receptions in full uniform, the long oral examinations of crowds of ill-prepared schoolboys and their scarcely better-instructed masters, often inspired him with disgust.[16] However, Cuvier did not resign his post after only a year for reasons of this order. Far more prolonged and difficult tours outside France were to mark his employment in the Imperial University after 1808; nor did he seem to consider it impossible by that time to combine the office of Permanent Secretary with that of an Inspector-General. The hypothesis which must be examined therefore, is that Cuvier resigned as Inspector-General in 1803 because the post was uncongenial to him for other reasons than those of pure inconvenience. His strong surviving consciousness of being an outsider to French life by birth, religion and education had made it impossible for him to be an uncritical observer of the regime of the Consulate and Empire. Grandiose schemes of conquest by France meant for him the destruction of the security of his friends and colleagues abroad. The cosmopolitanism of the late eighteenth century seemed to have achieved a hideous caricature in the aggressive expansion of the Empire. The extraordinarily rapid expansion of the French state in Europe led to the creation of a mentality where human will and desire seemed to have no limits. Cuvier had signalled his distance from this ethos by his refusal to participate in the Egyptian campaign. Like his old friend De Gérando, he could see this time not as one of glory but of egoism, an egoism which would ultimately undermine man's knowledge of the world:

> In an age of egoism, it is so difficult to persuade man that of all studies, the most important is that of himself. This is because egoism, like all passions, is blind. The attention of the egoist is directed to the immediate need of which his senses give notice, and cannot be raised to those reflective needs that reason discloses to us; his aim is satisfaction, not perfection ... Perhaps he fears that in penetrating the mysteries of his being he will ensure his own abasement, blush at his discoveries, and meet his conscience. True philosophy, always at one with moral science, tells a different tale. The source of useful illumination, like that of lasting content, is in ourselves ... [and] brings a man to a better awareness of all the bonds that unite us to our fellows, to the re-discovery of the inner root of his existence, of that identity of common life actuating us all.[17]

Such introspection could alone provide the basis of an objective knowledge of the external world, whether human or natural. In such statements of these, the basic hopes of *idéologie* were strengthened by the far older precepts of stoicism. Those who agreed with De Gérando moved consciously against the self-image of the age, a self-image which the glorious gestures of Napoleon's propaganda reinforced daily.

In these circumstances, intellectual projects of resistance to the emotional climate of the regime carried some political overtones. De Gérando asked the real élite of the Empire, its clear-sighted men, to declare themselves against the false élite of those blinded by egoism:

> 'Ne faut-il pas que toutes les âmes qui se sentent un peu d'élévation luttent avec énergie contre cet esprit de calcul et de personalité qui devient si général?'[18]

It is not surprising that the counter-offensive to the style of the regime should have concentrated, in cultural terms, on projects of observation, such as that embodied in the Société des observateurs de l'homme. Founded in 1799, its first members included Cuvier and De Gérando, as well as many former members of the Third Class of the Institut, such as Destutt de Tracy, and aimed to promote knowledge both of distant societies and of the working of the mind of individuals.

Problems and opportunities of the Empire

An instance of the latter was the investigation into the Wild Boy of Aveyron conducted by Itard; of the former, were the anthropological enquiries sparked off by the voyages of exploration of Baudouin and Peron, to which both Cuvier and De Gérando contributed.[19] In these enquiries, the building of philosophical systems was seen as an outdated form of enquiry, leading only to the fruitless vanity and partisanship of their possessors; only unprejudiced observation could correct the perceptual disorders caused by egoism.[20] The programme of the Society pointed out that

'l'homme deviendra le sujet de travaux d'autant plus utiles qu'ils seront dégagés de toute passion, de toute préjugé et surtout de tout esprit de système.[21]

The defence of observation of the facts against the spirit of system which Cuvier was later to undertake in his conflict with Geoffroy, and with Lamarck, was not based on intellectual obscurantism, or a refusal to confront the essentially modern question of defining 'the facts', but on his struggles in the Consulate and Empire to refuse to distort perception by the egoism valued so highly in political society.

It is important, however, to know how Cuvier's intellectual allegiances influenced his public position. How was it that his connections with many tendencies critical of the imperial regime were compatible with his repeated employment by it? Cuvier's position, however, was not unique. The same question could be asked of De Gérando, and of Roederer, who sat out the Empire far from the centre of events, as Minister of Finance in the puppet kingdom of Naples. It could also be asked of two betrayers of Napoleon, Talleyrand and Fouché, neither of whom, even in the heyday of the Empire, could be said to have developed a sincere belief in the value of its existence, or a strong conviction of its durability. The reason for their employment by Napoleon was that, like Cuvier, they possessed overwhelming talent in a particular field. The great problem faced by Napoleon in the formation of a new governing class was in fact the shortage of capable individuals in a state whose old ruling class had collapsed and dispersed during the Emigration, and whose territory was increasing at a dizzying speed. To forge a new ruling class, Napoleon introduced the policy of the *'amalgame'*: a deliberate mixing in government of men of widely different political views, to damp down the remnants of revolutionary conflicts, and to attach men of all parties to the regime through their enjoyment of its rewards. Through this policy Napoleon abandoned the possibility of coercing his unstable ruling class beyond a certain point, without ruining the possibility of achieving a working government even in the short term: and to an over-extended military Empire, the short term can often appear the most crucial.[22] In these circumstances, many men torn between disagreement with the style of the regime and excitement at its potentialities, pursued careers which were marked with paradox. It is therefore not surprising that when Cuvier publicly attacked the Consular regime for its glorification of the 'egotistical' values of power and glory at the expense of those of the intellect, he should both have been continued in his office, and received support from a wide audience of the élite. Cuvier's Stuttgart friend Christian Pfaff left an eye-witness account of the public reading at the Institut of Cuvier's 1801 *éloge* of the agronomist Gilbert:

I shall never forget the effect which this piece produced in a numerous and brilliant audience when they realised that in praising Gilbert, Cuvier was attacking the new Sejanus of our times. Especially deafening applause greeted his statement that 'Already the men who worship power hardly make the barest offerings of respect to genius, so much does the power which shapes thought appear to them inferior to the power which dispenses fame and fortune'.[23]

It is unwise in fact to underestimate the strength of the hostility of the Napoleonic élite to many features of the regime; it was precisely the extent of this hostility which meant that the Empire was marked by fierce ideological struggles within that class. Possibly the most famous of these controversies, and the most directly concerned with the regime's attitude toward the intellectual life, was triggered by the publication in 1802 of Mme de Staël's *De la littérature considérée dans ses rapports avec des institutions sociales*, which drew prolonged criticism from Louis de Fontanes, a rising literary figure, and future Grand-Master of the Imperial University. The political implications of Mme de Staël's book could hardly have been clearer:

Problems and opportunities of the Empire

On dit que les lumières et tout ce qui dérive d'elles, l'éloquence, la liberté politique, l'indépendence des opinions religieuses, troublent le repos et le bonheur de l'espèce humaine. Mais que l'on reflechisse sur les moyens qu'il faut employer pour arrêter la tendence des hommes vers les lumières! Que l'on se demande comment empêcher ce mal, si c'en est un, à moins de recourir à des moyens affreux en eux-mêmes et définitivement infructueux... Comment l'indépendence religieuse ne conduiroit-elle pas au libre examen de toutes les autorités de la terre?[24]

The second stage of the debate soon followed when Fontane's intimate friend Chateaubriand published his *Génie du Christianisme*, in 1802. It was an instant popular success, all the more so since its elaboration of the more facile of the arguments from design to justify the existing social order and the Catholic Church coincided neatly with the signing of the Concordat between Napoleon and the Pope, and the re-establishment of the connection between Church and State broken by the Revolution. Fontane's laudatory review of the book was reprinted in the official *Moniteur* to coincide with the festivities marking this event.[25] The *Décade philosophique* counter-attacked with a long and considerably less laudatory review spread over three issues in June and July of the same year.[26] The struggle for the values of reason and the *libre examen* continued when Roederer used his own *Journal de Paris* to attack all those who joined in the denigration of '... Toutes les idées philosophiques de tout un siècle, ... tout le siècle qui nous a vu naître.'[27]

The result of this polemic in fact was to set up a series of polarities: between faith and reason, science and religion, fact and imagination, reason and emotion. They were polarities which made a broad cosmopolitan view of the external world, whether human or natural, based on self-knowledge, very difficult to maintain; they also contained a strong hint of anti-intellectualism. In 1807, Cuvier commented with some force on this tendency:

Je ne m'amuserai pas à répondre à ceux qui voudraient faire croire que l'esprit des sciences est contraire à celui de la réligion. Je veux bien ne pas douter qu'ils soient réligieux, mais font-ils l'honneur à la réligion de dire qu'elle s'accorde mal avec les seules vérités non contestées auxquelles l'homme soit encore parvenues?... Le poète seul, disent-ils, est toujours en contemplation devant le beau moral et idéal... D'ailleurs, on raisonne toujours comme si la science excluait la littérature, du même comme s'il était possible qu'un savant ne fut pas lettré.[28]

If we have established Cuvier's sympathy with many forces in disagreement with the imperial regime, it has also become, however, even harder to understand his reasons for re-entering the administration of education in 1808 as Inspector-General and member of the Council of the Imperial University. It was certainly not due to any great reconciliation with official values. In the same year, for example, Cuvier experienced the greatest difficulty in obtaining official sponsorship for the printing of his report to the Emperor on the state of scientific knowledge, because officials at the Ministry of the Interior objected to its lack of specific references to God and religion:[29] the triumph of faith was conspicuously absent from his public statements. Cuvier had of course maintained the interest in educational theory implied in his close relationships with Guizot's circle and with such foreign experts as the German Joachim Campe.[30] As we have seen, it is also true that complete conformity was not a prerequisite for employment by Napoleon. Thus it becomes a matter of determining what it was that Cuvier saw in the organisation of 1808 that he had found to be missing in the organisation of 1802–3. The most obvious answer is an imperial dimension of activity. In 1802, French territories had possessed no common scheme of educational organisation; in 1808, it was the very function of the new Imperial University, created between 1806 and 1808, to provide such a plan, to adapt indigenous educational institutions accordingly in the non-French provinces of the Empire, and to supervise their operation. In the absence of direct evidence on the mechanisms of Cuvier's appointment we can only speculate on its advantages both to him and to the imperial regime.[31] The creation of an Empire with a large number of Protestant or German-speaking subjects certainly made it advisable to have at least one Protestant member of the Council. Cuvier's scientific reputation also made him useful in the re-organisation of the teaching of science under the aegis of the University. He still remained a striking exception to the general character of the appointments made by Fontanes in the first days of the new organisation. Such men as Philibert and Guéneau de Mussy, for example, shared Fontanes' hopes for the eventual return of the monarchy.[32] Another Inspector-General, Jean Joubert, was a close friend of Chateaubriand's mistress, Mme de Beaumont, and had collaborated with Fontanes on the articles attacking Mme de Staël.[33] Another member of the Council, Henri Coiffier de Verfeu, who was to accompany Cuvier on his first Italian tour of 1809–10, had emigrated at the same time as Fontanes, in 1793, but was only allowed to return to France in 1802.[34] These were all men closely personally linked to Fontanes, and who had often gained their literary reputations by supporting Fontanes' campaign against the values of the Enlightenment, and in favour of a conservative regime. In this sense, the establishment of the Imperial University in 1808 completed the movement which the signing of the Concordat, the attack on Mme de Staël, and the publication of the *Génie du Christianisme* had begun. Cuvier thus stood somewhat apart from the governing ethos of the Imperial University, and its attempts to implement through education belief in Empire and Church.[35] We are thus forced to the conclusion that Cuvier may well have been appointed for those very qualities.

There are certainly many signs that the French, at least in some civil administrations, realised that different attitudes were needed to obtain co-operation in the conquered territories of the Empire from those that could be used inside France itself. Not only was Cuvier already in possession of a large international network of contacts within institutions of learning, as well as governments, he was also a living example of the success possible within the French system for men born and educated outside France. Cuvier had also acquired a high reputation for tolerance, tact and objectivity.[36] This was a reputation which fitted in well with the contemporary ethos of science which above all approved of the capacity for objective observation, and which made no manipulative claims within the field of human political relationships. In the era of the *amalgame*, to be able to call up a neutral self-presentation as a man of science was of considerable advantage in public life.

Cuvier's appointment to the Imperial University, which was duly followed by special responsibilities for science and for the conquered provinces, thus had considerable potential advantage for the Imperial administration. For Cuvier himself, its advantages were also considerable. Because this was an imperial and not a national organisation, its geographical coverage was in large part identical to that of his own network of scientific patronage. Though the University he could intensify and extend these contacts. His power over appointment to university posts could only increase his power over those dependent for their livelihood on such positions. In terms of his scientific work, Cuvier's ability to tour Europe at the expense of the Imperial University in order to reorganise existing educational institutions also meant that he had the possibility of seeing collections of specimens outside France that would otherwise only have been known to him by drawings and plaster casts. In fact, the special nature of Cuvier's responsibilities within the University allowed him at this point both considerable personal advantage and the exercise, as we will see, outside France, of many of those values which had their origin in a reaction against the values of the imperial regime.

We must now examine Cuvier's actions within the University. His autobiography manages to give the impression that he played a dominant role within the new organisation.[37] Certainly, he played the major part in the foundation in 1809 of the new Faculty of Sciences in Paris, and personally chose its first members, thus also achieving at one stroke an enormous increase in his powers as a patron.[38] It is also clear that Cuvier used his position within the Imperial University decisively to influence the type of education within the Protestant faculties of France and Switzerland towards a far broader training for the ministry than had hitherto been available, and contributed greatly to the modernisation and humanisation of the Protestant churches.[39] On other grounds, however, we may dispute his claim to have dominated the Councils of the Imperial University. It is firstly, difficult to see how Cuvier could have enjoyed such prominence, given the sheer length of time that he was absent from Paris on missions of inspection and reorganisation for the University.[40] Cuvier's assertion is also difficult to substantiate for another reason. Records of the decisions of the Conseil of the University pay little attention to the recording of the discussions which led up to them.[41] We thus have no means of knowing how influential Cuvier was even when he was physically present at its meetings. Writings produced by Cuvier which were not intended as biographical material suggest rather that while in Paris he felt excluded from real responsibility by the inner groups of Fontanes' friends. In 1820, recommending reforms in the University, he thought it advisable that any new structure should:

éviter toutes les plaintes qu'a pu occasioner la dénomination exclusive de quelques favoris, en choissisant dans le Conseil et dans les Inspecteurs-Généraux des commissaires entre lesquels ils partargeront la préparation des travaux.[42]

It seems far more likely that it was during his tours outside France that Cuvier felt most able to act with independent responsibility in accordance with his own views. Objectivity, cosmopolitanism in the eighteenth-century sense, and the ability of the truly balanced man to mediate between conflicting interests were all called into play. All these ideal ways of behaving also of course were reinforced by the neutrality and objectivity which Cuvier projected as part of his role as a man of science.

Cuvier's first tour, decreed on 18 October 1810, took him to the United Provinces and to the Hanse towns of north-western Germany.[43] A special objective was the examination of primary education in the United Provinces, with a view to assimilating it to the French system.[44] Instead, so impressed was Cuvier by the Dutch system that he recommended it should be introduced into France. The report on this question by Cuvier and by his fellow Inspector, François Noël, was instrumental in ensuring the preservation of the Dutch system.[45] It also influenced most other projects for the reform of primary education for the next twenty years.[46] Long after his return to France Cuvier was to continue to fight for subsidies for the Dutch schools.[47]

In Holland, in fact, Cuvier encountered a world highly sympathetic to his own values. The pedagogical theory behind the Dutch system was based partly on the work of his friend Joachim Campe.[48] The private society, the Maatschappij tot 'Nut van't Algemen, founded in 1784, whose efforts lay behind the great scope of the primary school system, had begun its work as part of a crusade to reconstruct the moral economy of the Dutch nation. Cuvier's report bears strong marks of his reading of works by the society on this topic.[49] Cuvier's expressed view of the Dutch system, in other words, was considerably shaped by the Dutch themselves, and bore little relation to the exploitation of Holland by France which was otherwise the hallmark of the relationship between the two states. He had in fact long disapproved of the economic and social consequences of this exploitation, consequences which made the work of the schools even more necessary than before.[50]

For Cuvier, the encounter with the outstanding success of the Dutch system was a turning point.[51] It demonstrated that the attempt to maintain a moral order on the basis not only of the individual but of the social class was possible even under the most adverse economic and political conditions. From this point on, his interest in primary education was to be second only to his interest in the teaching of science, and to share its force as a moral and emotional programme as well as an intellectual one. His long struggle under the Restoration to obtain a system of free, secular elementary education for the poor, was a legacy of his experiences in Holland. Cuvier's acute apprehension of the fates awaiting the children of the poor without education was very different from that of the Emperor, who saw primary education for the poor not as a means of social and moral salvation but of social control.

Cuvier's journey into Germany, which included a visit to Stuttgart,[52] produced a renewed evocation of the cosmopolitanism which had been the most valuable legacy of his education:

L'habitude où l'on était de regarder l'Allemagne entière comme un seul pays; la facilité avec laquelle on passait du service d'un prince à celui d'un autre, avait aussi donné à la partie politique de l'Allemagne plus de tendance au cosmopolitanisme. On s'attachait à la justice universelle plus qu'aux intérêts particuliers d'un état, on jugeait stoiquement chaque question comme si elle avait eu lieu entre les nations étrangères ...[53]

It was also obvious that Cuvier regarded the German universities as in some ways superior to the French.[54] Cuvier's missions in Germany and in Holland were therefore not conducted in a spirit of imperial conquest. Instead, they served to reinforce in him a sense of difference, to accentuate his feeling of dislike for the effects of imperial rule on the subject nations, and to make him cling harder to the values inculcated in him by his training outside France. The rejection by the Imperial University of his recommendations concerning the Dutch primary system, at least kept clear the differences between him and the rest of the Conseil.[55]

Other benefits had in any case been amply reaped from the tour of Holland and Germany. Working feverishly in the intervals of his official duties, Cuvier had become familiar with German collections of fossils just in time to include them in a new section with the reprinted essays making up the *Recherches sur les ossemens fossiles des quadrupèdes* published in 1812.[56] Links of patronage had also been strengthened. French plans to rationalise the Dutch university system included the abolition of the tiny University of Franeker, where Cuvier's friend and collaborator Adriaan Camper held a chair. While the rapacity of the French financial bodies in Holland, backed by the orders of the Emperor, allowed no stay of execution for the University itself, Cuvier was able to secure Camper's appointment as Inspector of the Academy of Leyden. A similar success was scored by the appointment of Cuvier's correspondent Brugmans to the rectorship of the same Academy in 1811.[57] At its most efficient, Cuvier's exercise of patronage could thus establish a maximum of overlap between scientific contact and political dependence, and by its specifically science-based origins, establish a field of influence which no other competitor was likely to be able to enter.

Often, however, the situation was less clear-cut, and more interesting. The French conquests did after all create genuine conflicts of interest. Cuvier's contacts with his collaborators in the German states had often been hindered by the fears of his correspondents that their information would lead to the seizure of their collection as part of the scientific and artistic plunder of the Empire. In answer to such fears Cuvier could only deprecate such practices, point out that he was in no position to change the policy behind it, and promise to do his best in individual cases.[58] It was not a strong position. Cuvier's wish to define himself as different from the administration which employed him also arose from these very direct tensions which the expansion of the Empire placed upon his role as a man of science of international standing. It was important not to be totally identified with the all-conquering French state which had placed so many of his friends and collaborators in positions of discomfort and insecurity.

In natural history, perhaps more than in any other scientific discipline, the exchange of tangible objects or information about them, in the shape of specimens, casts, drawings and verbal descriptions, was of crucial importance in research. Priority in classification of unknown species was a vital element in scientific renown. Under these circumstances, collaboration in the large-scale classificatory works favoured by Cuvier could only proceed upon a basis of mutual trust, mutual repayment of services, and compensation for possible loss of priority. The practice of nautral history itself thus forced Cuvier to lay great emphasis on projecting an unthreatening, non-imperialistic self-presentation.[59]

Between 1809 and 1810, and again in 1813, Cuvier was absent in Italy, aiding the integration of the Italian universities into the imperial system. Italian responses to the French were extremely diverse. Within individual states, the French occupation had often sharply divided the ruling class. It is therefore not surprising that Cuvier's reactions to the Italian states he visited should have been very variable. In Genoa, the ruinous finances of the University, the weakness of its teaching and the desertion of its students had been accentuated by a combination of French greed and aristocratic hostility to an institution which they saw as an instrument of French irreligion.[60] Conversely, Cuvier's hostility to the Genoese nobility rapidly became extremely strong. In Turin, the situation of the university was not so desperate, and Cuvier found much to admire in its organisation, and to recommend as a model for the French. After pointing out the striking similarities between the state organisation of education in Piedmont before 1789, and that of the Imperial University, he went on to recommend the introduction of the Piedmontese qualification of *agrégé* as a substitute for nomination to university chairs through patronage.[61] At the same time,

Problems and opportunities of the Empire

however, Cuvier seems to have found few of the Piedmontese aristocrats restored to power by the French personally congenial. Here he differed from his friend De Gérando, who soon became a family friend of Prospero Balbo, the Rector of the University of Turin, who was to be Cuvier's companion on the rest of his first Italian tour.[62] It may well be that Cuvier's Protestantism was regarded without enthusiasm in the two regions of Italy which were among the most hostile to the occupation of the Papal states by the French, and their imprisonment of the Pope, the abolition of the religious orders and the seizure of Church property. The Imperial University, in its role as a substitute for the teaching orders was particularly likely to attract Catholic hostility.

In Tuscany, however, a very different situation prevailed, and Cuvier seems to have felt far more in sympathy with the ideals of the scholars and teachers he encountered. In the former Grand-Duchy, definitively annexed to France in 1808 after the collapse of a series of puppet regimes, the strongest supporters of the French were those men who owed their rise to power under the old regime to their involvement in the reforming policies of the Hapsburg Grand-Duke Peter-Leopold. Peter-Leopold's departure to Vienna in 1790 for his coronation as Holy Roman Emperor on the death of his brother Joseph II, and the political reaction in Tuscany against enlightened reform which occurred in response to the French Revolution, had both rendered the position of his former supporters extremely precarious. It was therefore not surprising that they should seek to recoup something of their former position, and to restore the reforming legislation abolished by the Regency Council of the 1790s, through collaboration with the French regime.[63] In Tuscan terms, French policy on religion in particular, was very similar to that pursued by Peter-Leopold who, like his brother in Austria had struggled to subordinate Church to State, and to gain control of education from the religious orders. Cuvier himself attached far more importance to the preservation of the legacy of enlightened despotism than to the imposition of the French system:

Presque partout l'on trouve encore des traces manifestes des gouvernements bienfesans [sic] auxquels ces parties de l'Italie ont été si longtems soumises, et que ce sera un devoir pour l'Université

Impériale de faire ensorte par sa protection que l'Italie ne puisse pas se plaindre, cette fois, comme elle a eu si souvent sujet, d'avoir encore été envahi par des barbares.[64]

At the very time when the Enlightenment and its values were under attack in France itself, Cuvier was able to give recognition to the achievements of Enlightened regimes in the peripheral territories of the Empire, and to do so precisely because these were the peripheries; here, viewpoints which were out of favour at the centre could be expressed under the mask of a wise adaptation to local conditions. Cosmopolitanism rather than imperialism could be stressed.[65] In fact, Cuvier's report from Italy ended up by undercutting the very principle of the Imperial University's existence, that of the provision of a uniform system of instruction for the territories of the Empire:

Chacun de ses pays, qui jouissait autrefois d'une existence souveraigne et indépendante, avait aussi son système particulier d'instruction publique, et les différens [sic] qui pouvaient y exister alors ont été fort augmentées suivant l'époque à laquelle ces pays ont été acquis par la France ... il fallait donc pour chaque pays des mesures différents.[66]

Cuvier's sympathy with the enlightened Italy was not simply demonstrated by written expressions of support, but was shown in his use of his personal authority and powers of patronage. Cuvier's relationship with the Tuscan *savant* Giovanni Fabbroni is a case in point. The two men had first met in Paris in 1799, when Fabbroni had been the Tuscan representative at the international commission on metrication. Fabbroni's whole career had been bound up with the implementation of the policies of Peter-Leopold, and he had collaborated with the first French government in Tuscany of 1799. It was therefore not surprising that he was viewed with hostility by more conservative elements who gained control of the puppet kingdom of Etruria. In 1803, there were moves to take away his office of Director of the Natural History Museum in Florence, an office personally conferred on him by Peter-Leopold. By mobilising support within the learned community Cuvier was able to hold off such threats for a while. When Fabbroni at length did lose his post in 1807, Cuvier's reaction was sharp. At his instigation, Portal, de

Jussieu, Fourcroy, Larmarck, Haüy, Geoffroy St. Hilaire, Vauquelin, Thouin and Lacepède signed a letter of protest to the royal family of Etruria and Laplace, fortified by his wife's close friendship with Napoleon's sister, Eliza Bacchiochi, now princess of Lucca, wrote individually to her on Fabbroni's behalf.[67] Although all these efforts were ultimately unavailing they did not prevent Cuvier gaining corresponding membership of the Institut for Fabbroni, and they show the strength and density of the patronage relationships which Cuvier could bring to bear on a single problem.

Such a demonstration of forces also of course, increased Cuvier's prestige as a patron able and willing to support his clients at moments of crisis, and had the effect of tying Fabbroni even more closely to Cuvier. Support from a man of Cuvier's status could only endorse Fabbroni's own, and so bolster his position in Tuscany. Both men had a very conscious knowledge of the way exercises of patronage could influence opinion. Fabbroni did not mince words to Cuvier:

Il m'est important, essentiel même pour cela, qu'on sache ici d'une manière authentique mais qui n'ait d'autre source qu'une spontanéité généreuse, que vous, que vos illustres confrères avez daignez [sic] m'accorder l'honneur de votre estime. Cela seul peut, à mon avis, déformer efficacement la perversité des intrigues.[68]

In the context of the Empire relationships of patronage and friendship had an even greater importance than mediation of individual conflicts. It was only a web of patronage, friendship and scholarly collaboration between France and the conquered states that could provide a counterweight to the great problems posed to individuals by collaboration with the French regime.[69]

In the imperial situation, where great and well-founded resentment could so easily arise between French and non-French collaborators, it was also essential for naturalists such as Cuvier to insist as far as possible on those attitudes which they held in common with their foreign colleagues, if such scientific contacts were not to collapse. Many later commentators have implied that the Empire was a golden age for French science; what they have overlooked are the problems caused to science by the very fact of imperial conquest, which turned the pursuit of scientific relationships on an international scale within Europe above all into the manipulation of personal relationships between Frenchmen and others, against a background of the harsh conflicts of interest involved in the relationships of France with its conquered provinces.

In these circumstances it is not surprising that Cuvier should have emphasised his community of political outlook with his Tuscan friends and collaborators. Both Cuvier and the Leopoldine group were agreed, for example, that education must no longer be entrusted to the Church.[70] When the conservative Rector of the Academy of Pisa began increasingly to support the teaching orders in the primary and secondary schools, to the disgust of his subordinate Santi, it was Cuvier who resolved the conflict in favour of the Leopoldine group, by breaking up the staffs of the offending schools and sending them to posts where lay teachers were in the majority.[71] Meanwhile, within France itself, the Imperial University had already come under investigation for what Napoleon considered its excessive favour to the religious orders.[72] With the weakening of Fontanes' position on this point, Cuvier could express in his reports his dislike of the teaching orders either within or without the University:

Il nous paraît dangéreux pour l'Université de consacrer l'existence des congrégations enseignantes comme corps particuliers, même en supposant que ces corps soient admis dans son sein, et lui soient affiliés par quelque liens que ce soit. Le seul corps, la seule corporation doit être l'Université elle-même.[73]

In Italy, in fact, Cuvier could give free expression to the attitudes most opposed to those endorsed in practice by the leadership of the Imperial University. More than this, his power as a scientific patron and the strength of his connections in Tuscany, enabled him on occasion completely to bypass the powers of appointment possessed by Fontanes, and to favour his own protégés. In 1812, for example, the chair of surgery in the medical faculty at Pisa fell vacant. Fabbroni's friend, Prince Neri Corsini, who was also a friend of De Gérando, recommended Fabbroni's nephew Paolo Uccelli for the post. Uccelli was also the son of one of Fabbroni's supporters during the period of political reaction in the 1790s. Cuvier, without previously referring the matter to Fontanes, gave a favourable report on Corsini's candidate, and Uccelli was confirmed in his chair in November 1812, against the claims both of the son of the former holder of the chair, and of a third candidate strongly supported by members of the Senate in Paris.[74] In this case, a tightly knit circle of friends and collaborators had so strongly determined an appointment that outside forces had no influence on the process of nomination. Cuvier, by ratifying the choice of the Italians without throwing the matter open to discussion in Paris, had increased his independence from the centre, and increased his power as a patron in the locality. In other words, non-conformity to the attitudes of the Imperial University when carefully cultivated amongst his Tuscan circle, could reap great rewards in the shape of an independent area of patronage free from the interference of the centre.[75]

Cuvier's trip in 1813 to Rome was brief, and overshadowed by the death in Paris, during his absence, of his small son Georges.[76] In the following year, the French were forced to withdraw from the Papal states. Hostility to them had been so great that even the efforts of tolerant and intelligent men such as De Gérando and his friend the Prefect Camille de Tournon had made very little impression on the state of affairs in Rome.[77] Hampered at every turn by the rapacity of the French financial agencies, and by the resistance of the Romans, Cuvier's attempts to reform universities and schools met on this occasion with a similar fate.[78]

Elsewhere, however, Cuvier's work was more durable. In both Holland and Piedmont (which after 1815 included the former republic of Genoa), the French structure formed the basis of the educational system of the restored governments, and was very often in the control of the same men. In Tuscany in particular, Fabbroni's friends experienced a return to official favour.[79] For Cuvier himself, the benefits of working within the Imperial University were not negligible. The combination of his scientific prestige and his special responsibilities for the Italian universities, allowed him to extend and intensify his power of patronage to the extent that it was often he and not Fontanes who effectively controlled appointments. Yet without the genuine sympathy of outlook which existed between him and his Italian clients, particularly in Tuscany, such power need not have outlasted the Empire. In fact, these Italians remained one of the greatest single channels of information for the edition of the *Recherches sur les ossemens fossiles des quadrupèdes* which Cuvier published in 1824.[80] Cuvier had also pursued his responsibilities within the University in a highly individual way. The man who had refused to go to Egypt now used the University to stay out of France for very long periods of time. While he was away, his actions and recommendations struck at the principle of centralised uniformity which informed the Imperial University, which his hold on the foreign business of the University enabled him to create areas of patronage, nominally within the operation of the University as a whole, but actually subject to him. In the circumstances of the Empire, such an arrangement was necessary to him as a naturalist if his chain of contacts and collaborators in Europe was not to be broken by suspicion and dislike of the French. Cuvier in fact was able to present himself as above all the mediator between the centre and the periphery in the organisation of the Imperial University. This laid the foundations for his later presentation of science as a mediating force in society.[81] Once again, Cuvier had created a situation in which he stood at a tangential relationship to the structures of power which employed him. Cuvier never expressed the view that the Imperial University should not exist: he simply acted, once within it, as though its major assigned function, the provision of social and political control through uniform educational institutions, did not exist as a serious objective for him; a point of view which he was able to argue all the more convincingly in that most of his work was concerned with the conquered provinces of the Empire and not with France itself.[82]

In 1813, Fontanes secured Cuvier's appointment as a Maître de Requêtes in the Conseil d'Etat, apparently to strengthen the University's voice in the central administration. This at least is the explanation given by Cuvier, and it may well be partly true.[83] It is also a move that in Fontanes' terms might have seemed a graceful way of removing Cuvier, after his return from Rome, from too frequent intervention in the affairs of the Conseil of the University. That Cuvier retained his connection with both the University and the Conseil d'Etat after the collapse of the Empire in the following year, was an unforeseen result of Fontanes' patronage. Cuvier avoided declaring himself for one side or the other under the Hundred Days;[84] the very length of his absences from Paris under the Empire, and his lack of enthusiastic endorsement of its values, made him appear a safe candidate for employment by the Bourbons. In this, he was not unique. Even foreigners such as Fabbroni were offered employment by the Bourbons. Employment under the Empire, so long as it was not accompanied by avowed Bonapartism or republicism, was no obstacle to employment by the regime which appeared after Waterloo.[85]

By 1815, Cuvier was in a far stronger position than he had been in 1802. For this the very existence of the Imperial University is largely responsible.

The experience of the Empire was also crucial to Cuvier in another sense. It led him to develop an ideal of science which was deeply marked by reaction against the 'age of egoism'. The illusion of human power in this world could be corrected by the experience of the study of nature: 'Une fois élevé à la contemplation de cette harmonie de la nature irrésistiblement réglée par la Providence, que l'on trouve faible et petits les ressorts qu'elle a bien voulu laisser dépendre du libre arbitre des hommes.'[86] Because nature is completely apart from man, contemplation of it brings with it restoration of a sense of order and proportion into the disordered inner world of its observer: 'Assez étendue pour suffire à l'esprit le plus vaste, assez variée, assez intéressante pour distraire l'âme la plus agitée, elle console les malheureux, elle calme les haines'.[87] The separation of man from nature which Foucault has isolated as Cuvier's basic achievement in science[88] came about not only because of the logic of Cuvier's approach to living beings, but also because of the need to establish one area of experience at least as free from the peculiar distortions of the personality which occurred in an imperial age. By the end of the Empire, Cuvier believed in good *idéologue* style that the power of the contemplation of nature to order the inner world of its observer, meant that the study of natural history was also a paradigm of correct thought:

Cette habitude que l'on prend nécessairement en étudiant l'histoire naturelle, de classer dans son esprit un très grand nombre d'idées, est l'un des avantages de cette science dont on a le moins parlé, et qui deviendra peut-être le principal, lorsqu'elle aura été généralement introduite dans l'éducation commune; on s'exerce par la dans cette partie de la logique qui se nomme la méthode, à peu près comme on s'exerce par l'étude de la géometrie dans celle qui se nomme le syllogisme, par la raison que l'histoire naturelle est la science qui exige les méthodes les plus précises comme la géometrie celle qui demande les raisonnemens [sic] les plus rigoureux. Or, cet art de la méthode, une fois qu'on le possède bien, s'applique avec un avantage infini aux études les plus étrangerès à l'histoire naturelle. Toute discussion qui suppose un classement des faits, toute récherche qui exige une distribution des matières, se fait d'après les mêmes lois; et tel jeune homme qui n'avait cru faire de cet science qu'un objet d'amusement, est surpris lui-même, à l'essai, de la facilité qu'elle lui a procuré pour débrouiller tous les genres d'affaires.[89]

By 1815, Cuvier had tied his idea of doing science to the regulation of the economy of the individual, to an ideal or ordered thought, and to a self-presentation which in the circumstances of the Empire aimed to emphasise an idea of the scientist as a cosmopolitan mediator. In doing so he effectively served his own very various purposes. He even managed to produce a view of science which could balance his own great ambitions for power and notoriety, and his deeply pessimistic view of human society, with a salutary idea of human smallness in confrontation with nature. What this view of science and the role of the scientist could not do was to act with effect in the world of metropolitan national politics with which Cuvier was increasingly closely concerned after 1815.[90] It was after this date that he was truly perpetually, if not comfortably fixed within the confines of a nation-state.

V
The Restoration and the crisis of patronage

Il vaut mieux être des écrasants que des écrasés.
(Cuvier to Stapfer, P. A. Stapfer, *Briefwechsel*, ed. R. Luginbühl, p. 54)

Au milieu de cette opposition universelle des pauvres et des riches, de cette jalousie des particuliers, cause principale des troubles des états, de cette jalousie de nations, source presque unique de leurs guerres, l'industrie et la science sont les médiateurs naturelles
(Cuvier, 1816, pp. 29–30.)

In 1815, France was transformed. The collapse of the Empire and the return of the Bourbon dynasty did not bring back the *Ancien Régime*. Instead, the new system of 'constitutional' government imposed by the victorious allies was not only new to French experience in itself; the unfamiliarity of its institutions and their wide electoral base, in comparison with the Napoleonic regime generated a new political instability, and allowed a far freer expression of social and political conflict than had been possible in the tightly controlled political society of Napoleon. It was impossible for public figures such as Cuvier not to be affected by these developments. By the end of his career, in fact, Cuvier was faced with increasingly serious challenges to his authority, which culminated in his famous conflict within the Academie des sciences itself, with his colleague Etienne Geoffroy St Hilaire. This chapter will not recapture the details of these events. It will, rather, try to establish that this conflict was in many ways similar to others experienced by Cuvier in public life in this period, which were symptomatic of changes in the nature of the French governing class, and its relation to culture.[1] More precisely, it will be argued that Cuvier's combination of authority in natural history with a significant role in what would now be defined as general politics, forced him to experience the paradoxes and ambiguities surrounding the exercise of power in this society.

It was, after all, in relation to science, that Restoration society created one of its most complex ideologies: complex in its relation to reality as actually experienced, in the way it influenced the self-perception of individuals, and in the ways it could be manipulated to meet the demands of new situations by new groups while formally denying any such function. By examining the ideology of science as one amongst others at this period we may reach a fuller understanding both of the way in which the Restoration used ideologies, and of the way in which this affected individual careers such as Cuvier's.[2]

The official ideology of science in this period, no less than before, established a strong disjunction between public or political life and that particular form of culture known as natural science. The political, full of rapid change, unforeseen consequences, and dubious morality was opposed to the scientific, where knowledge was supposed to accumulate steadily in accord with its own inner laws, observed by men remote from the world of combination and advantage.[3] The special status of science, in other words, was guaranteed by its 'mythical' nature, outside history and change. It was a view which drew strength both from the very degree of the public insecurity of science in this period, and from the difficulties experienced by contemporaries in defining the nature and extent of the political or public sphere,[4] difficulties deepened by the unfamiliarity of their new political system. By the very strength of its desire to separate science and the political, contemporary historiography betrayed the pervasive influence of this uncertainty: it seemed impossible to contemporaries to define either science or the public realm except negatively: science was where the public world was not; the public world was that which was outside science. There was no other way of saying where science ended and the public realm began except by using moral criteria (purity, disinterest) rather than appealing to the nature of the real world. As the political crisis of the Restoration deepened, the ability to maintain this 'mythical' view of science, to assert the impossibility of change and confusion in at least one sphere of life, an ability vested in the official culture of science rehearsed in the Paris Academy of

The Restoration and the crisis of patronage

Sciences, was to be increasingly challenged by those who chose to inject an overtly political element into the language they used to describe science. Neither science in general nor the career of Georges Cuvier in particular escaped that struggle for the control of public language which accompanies social struggle and is the forerunner of revolution.

Both in his lifetime and after his death, our picture of Cuvier has been determined by this insistence on the necessity of separating science and the political sphere. The mixture in his own life seems to have posed a self-evident problem, to be faced up to and examined by conscientious biographers in the same way as an accusation of scandal. In accordance with the ideology, Cuvier could only be validated as a scientist by the denigration of his public involvement. At best, the actual conjunction of the two realms could be glossed over by assertions that scientific work, after all, was rational activity incarnate, and therefore supremely fitted a man for the tasks of public administration. Alternatively, scientific activity could be viewed as a foreground to a background of somehow less substantive public activity. Other interpretations have attempted to draw analogies between Cuvier's alleged political views and his alleged scientific conservatism, usually linked to his adherence to the doctrine of the fixity of species in the debate with Geoffroy St Hilaire.[5] In other words, neither modern nor contemporary historiography has proved capable of overcoming the assumption of a discontinuity between science and the public realm which was so deeply embedded in the mentality of the early nineteenth century. This is a rhetoric and an assumption which has profoundly shaped the attitudes of commentators towards the reality of the scientific pursuit in the public world.[6]

More than any other single source, it is Geoffroy's account of his conflict with Cuvier[7] which focused attention on the issue of Cuvier's alleged conservatism in politics, and linked it with his adherence to the fixity of species. In doing so, as will be seen, Geoffroy was in fact inserting a deliberate appeal to radical interests into his account of a technical scientific debate. However, we cannot evaluate the novelty of his approach, the justice of his accusation, or its real significance for contemporaries, until we have evaluated the political context in which Cuvier operated. We need to ask how Cuvier's personal baggage of posts and relationships, the 'public space'[8] he covered, contributed to the kinds of conflict in which he became involved. We also have to answer the question in particular of how and why his scientific pursuits contributed to the likelihood that he would be drawn into conflict, and how public estimation of his public and scientific roles may have affected his self-perception and his presentation of the role of science in society.

After 1815, the restructuring of France's international role was translated for her élite into a restructuring of career patterns and expectations. The constitutional settlement guaranteed by the Charter created a political world more complex than that of the Empire, while at the same time, the ending of imperial expansion reduced the possibility for men such as Cuvier to be able to construct their own pockets of power remote from the control of the centre. This reduced freedom of manouevre may well be one of the factors which increased Cuvier's political vulnerability in this period. The Charter guaranteed a freedom of the press which was very extensive by the standards of the Empire. At the same time, a system of government through representative institutions such as an elected Chamber of Deputies, was established on a far wider, though still hardly inclusive, electoral base largely determined by property qualification. Politicians now had to take account, therefore, of new forces such as a political press, and of a larger, less homogeneous political class. It must be emphasised that the Charter had in no sense initiated party politics in any modern sense.[9] This was the problem. The collapse of common assumptions after the Revolution, and the splintering of viewpoints under the Empire, made coherent party programmes difficult to achieve. Nor was it easy for politicians at national level to locate their public. Defined only in terms of property qualification, and subject to the influence of movements of opinion among the far wider group reached by the political press, this electorate was a fluid and nebulous affair. At the same time, as government and bureaucracy expanded throughout this period,[10] the prizes to be gained by correct moves in the political game in Paris gradually increased. To succeed in the new politics it was necessary to be

The Restoration and the crisis of patronage 97

able to appeal to two audiences at once: to an amorphous electorate and to the tightly-knit group of known individuals who were one's political peers and superiors. This was a duality which Geoffroy's attack on Cuvier, with its appeals both to a wide audience of patriotic Frenchmen of common sense, and to his scientific peers, was later acutely to reflect. Public culture shared the problems of public life.

Nor did the representative system guarantee political stability. At the same time as the necessity for elections transmitted into central politics shifts of opinion in the electorate at large, the preservation of clientèle systems in the central governing élite meant that electoral defeats of significant political figures often led to purges of their dependents in the bureaucracy.[11] In this atmosphere firm political principle was not at a premium.[12] It was not only the interpenetration of politics and bureaucracy which made stable political parties difficult to achieve; it was also the interpenetration of public and private. In the society of the élite in Paris, family ties, friendships and scholarly relationships cut across both ideological lines, and less strongly, across the lines of patronage. The continual social mixing of the élite in the *salons* and in the marriage market contributed to this process. Of course there were groups and coteries; but in the words of a contemporary self-defined outsider, François Raspail, the concentration of the political world on Paris meant that 'Les coteries se trouvent donc réunis dans la même enceinte de murailles, aux portes du même pouvoir, sur les banquettes des mêmes académies'.[13]

Contemporaries did not wholly endorse the political world which they had to some extent created, and from which they certainly knew how to profit. One of the major problems they identified was precisely their own inability to form firm party lines.[14] The Revolution had destroyed old ideas of Church and state, and the ensuing collapse of public values had opened the way for the minute fragmentation of opinion which made it possible for every faction to strive for the realisation of a programme of its own.[15] Cuvier himself was aware of this problem: 'On a dit que dans ce siècle les mots magiques ont perdu leur force, que c'est par lui-même, par sa propre supériorité que le pouvoir doit se rendre respectable.'[16]

But Cuvier never made clear how precisely a strong state could be achieved, given the instability of actual politics. In practice, only very small groups of men, such as that known as the *Doctrinaires* which included Cuvier's friends Guizot and Royer-Collard, were able for very long to maintain a coherent position.

It was the patron, not the ideologist, who wielded power in normal politics. This situation, inherited from the Empire, was now intensified by increasingly fierce competition for posts in government. Internal competition amongst the élite rose as patrons found themselves with many protégés competing for the same post.[17] Conflict became so heated that textbooks on how to solicit for favours and positions began to be published.[18] From amongst those who, even with the handbooks' help, were unsuccessful in gaining positions in government, a recognisable Bohemia began to form.[19] Others now realised that to influence opinion it was not necessary to enter formal politics, and turned to political journalism. It was from this milieu that some of the fiercest adversaries of official science, such as François Raspail, were to emerge.

Even deeper discontents fuelled the revolutionary secret societies of this period, such as the Carbonari.[20] Composed partly of army officers disappointed by the collapse of the Empire, partly of students and journalists critical of the society around them, and partly by Republicans disappointed both by the Empire and by the constitutional monarchy, the Carbonari produced a series of attempted military coups, which culminated in their attempt to take Strasbourg in 1822.

All this seems very far from the world of the Academy of Sciences in Paris. Yet Carbonarism in fact touched Cuvier very closely. Its stronghold was in his home region of Alsace, whose permanent hostility to the capital was increased by the liberalism of the province in face of the increasing conservatism of the Restoration.[21] More specifically, known Carbonari included members of Cuvier's family and entourage, such as Alexandre-Jacques Bertrand, his commentator and correspondent, and his nephew Ingénu Japy, who was involved in the conspiracy at Belfort in 1820, and helped to spread secret workers' associations in the new factories of Montbéliard.[22] Most notorious of all was the involvement of his nephew

The Restoration and the crisis of patronage

Antoine-Fortuné Brack, dashing half-pay cavalry officer and devotée of Napoleon, in the attempted rising at Strasbourg.[23] Even for someone as apparently secure as Cuvier, family and regional relationships could still transmit the shockwaves of violent discontent with the existing order. If Cuvier *did* devote his political career to the repression of disorder,[24] he was fighting something which had come near his own existence, and which came as much from his own class as from the 'people' he is alleged to have feared.

From the foregoing discussion of the public life of the Restoration, it would seem unlikely that Cuvier's public life could ever be that calm 'background' to scientific achievement pictured by many writers. The nature of the surviving evidence, however, poses some problems when we turn to a more detailed examination of Cuvier's own public career. The autobiography, completed in 1822, has little to say about events after 1817. The archives of the Conseil d'Etat for this period were burnt under the Paris Commune in May 1871.[25] The bulk of Cuvier's day-to-day work in the Université de France, the successor to the Imperial University, lies scattered among the holdings of the Archives nationales. As his collaborator Laurillard remarked long ago, its interpretation poses problems by the very specific nature of its subject matter.[26] The papers surviving in the Institut de France, however, do contain some detailed analyses of policy relating to education and religion. The combination of these with his recorded public statements on government policy in the Chambre des députés, while, as Commissaire du roi, launching discussion of new bills, may offer the best chance of reconstructing his political opinions.

Contemporary memoirs, even by his colleagues in government, offer little in the way of serious appreciation of Cuvier's public role.[27] The discussion with which this chapter began should indicate at least some of the reasons why Cuvier's contemporaries could not have produced 'non-mythical' assessments of Cuvier's public life which really integrated his natural history and his politics. But the effect of the contempory use of the ideology of science was not merely to produce silence; it also provided Cuvier's enemies, both insiders and outsiders, with a well-defined and publicly acceptable means of attack upon his public life. There was no need to prove or allege corruption or incompetence; all that was necessary was to point out that no true man of science would engage in politics; that therefore Cuvier was no true man of science; that his scientific reputation must therefore have no real basis; and that therefore he was not entitled to any kind of public reputation; any that he had gained must be the product of machination, time-serving and ambition.[28] This 'argument' is of course illogical. It betrays fundamental confusion about the public role which the natural sciences should occupy. It also carried considerable emotional force with contemporaries and was repeatedly used in public attacks on Cuvier in relation to many distinct issues. In this era of faction, the need to keep one area of life free from the doubt and flux of politics was very great; correspondingly so was the need to attack anomalies which threatened the ability to do so.

If the very numbers of Cuvier's posts[29] made such attacks a constant hazard, it was also true that each administration with which Cuvier was connected was also the focus of considerable public unease. The Université de France, for example, was small in terms of the numbers it employed and the budget at its disposal.[30] The extent of its autonomy was always uncertain, as it oscillated under different ministries between complete independence and subordination to the Ministry of the Interior. All these conditions made it peculiarly liable to administrative purges and executive frustration.[31] The ideological implications of its existence were also attacked from many quarters; its provision of an alternative to the religious schools led it to be attacked by conservatives and Catholics in particular, as did its claim to the monopoly of the control of education and hence of the moral – and ultimately social – guidance of the lower classes. Cuvier was to be at the forefront of attempts to preserve the autonomy of the Université,[32] and to extend and improve elementary, secular education for the poor by the encouragement of teaching systems on the Lancastrian model, the *enseignement mutuel*.

The Conseil d'Etat enjoyed no more peaceful a condition. Its very political and legal importance rendered it more liable to attack. Conservatives resented it as a Napoleonic creation, while liberals viewed its judicial powers as potentially the

The Restoration and the crisis of patronage

instrument of ministerial despotism.[33] Extreme conservatives joined in the attack when the Conseil confirmed the titles of those who had bought land confiscated from aristocracy and Church under the Revolution. Every year, as the Chamber discussed the government budget for the succeeding twelve months, many supported motions to refuse further subsidies to the Conseil.[34]

The administration of the non-Catholic religions was also a controverted field. Protestant and liberal fears of the Catholic Church gaining total control of education were balanced by conservative fears about the loss of basic freedoms of choice if education were to become completely under the control of a secular state. Cuvier's role in the administration of the Protestant religions, as has recently been pointed out, is difficult to describe in terms of any really coherent large-scale policy, except that of securing the improvement of Protestant institutions wherever possible, and of resolving the disputes between Protestant groups which became more frequent as the more obvious forms of outside persecution became less,[35] but if little can be learned about Cuvier's religious attitudes from his involvement in the administration of religion, it is, on the other hand, clear that he was acutely aware of the threats to his position in public life which arose from his own Protestantism. In 1821, for example, he grimly pointed out to the Chamber of Deputies that his religion disqualified him in effect from holding ministerial office, because of the constant danger that he would be drawn into more or less engineered clashes with Catholic opinion.[36]

It might be that Cuvier was unduly sensitive on this point: after all his Protestant friend François Guizot duly became Minister of the Interior in 1830, though admittedly only after the revolution of that year; nor did Cuvier's religion stop the First Minister Richelieu from offering him the same position in 1817.[37] He was probably justified, on the other hand, in thinking that his Protestantism could be used more easily to draw him into public conflict. For example, when Cuvier tried to secure the appointment of his nephew Charles Cuvier to the chair of history at Strasbourg in 1822, it was over three years before the appointment was ratified, such was the opposition of Catholic interests.[38] The ultra-conservative reaction of those years only underlined the fragility of the religious toleration guaranteed by the Charter. When Benjamin Constant tried to end the scandal by speaking in Charles Cuvier's favour in the Chamber, it was of course interpreted as part of a Protestant conspiracy, and Cuvier's superior in the Université, the Abbé Fraysinnous, leant a sympathetic ear to the Catholic version of affairs in Strasbourg,[39] and also procured in 1824 the permanent leave from his post at the Collège royal in Nancy of another relation of Cuvier, the Pastor Rodolphe Cuvier.[40] At the same time, Cuvier's Protestant protégés in science experienced repeated difficulties in obtaining university posts.[41] Through his religion, in fact, Cuvier was attacked in the two sets of human relationships most dear to him, and most publicly valuable to him: his family and his protégés – and of course the two groups were not entirely free from overlap. When the general political situation was unfavourable to supporting Protestant toleration, Cuvier's grip on patronage was bound to weaken, and his presence in the public arena became precarious.

In an even more intimate sense, the attacks on his religion, taken with the attacks on him as a naturalist in public life, were damaging to the confidence needed to sustain a public role. The most important props of life – family, religion and work – became sources of public vulnerability. Since the arguments made by his enemies against science and Protestantism in public life were not and could not have been susceptible to logical statement, they were also not susceptible to logical rebuttal. Attacks had simply to be endured. If Cuvier's demeanour often seemed frigidly reserved, part of the explanation must surely be the fierce personal attacks of Restoration politics.

The damage to confidence was in fact considerable. Naturally Cuvier was a fiercely ambitious man: the effort he had expended on his social and intellectual ascent, the scope of his intellectual projects, and his actual accumulation of power, do not suggest a man with modest goals. His refusals of possible power thus become all the more striking and must be carefully examined. Under the Empire, as has been seen, they were rare, and as far as can be ascertained, often motivated by private disagreement with the objectives and style of the regime.

The Restoration and the crisis of patronage

At first, confidence was maintained under the Restoration. When the Ministry of the Interior was first seriously proposed in 1817 he accepted the idea without hesitation.[42] In 1818 as the Richelieu ministry drew to a close, Cuvier was still being mentioned in the context of the Interior,[43] though this time often with strictures on the offence his appointment might cause to Catholic interests. In 1819, Cuvier refused what he had eagerly accepted in 1817, for reasons which remain unclear, but, in the light of his original acceptance, are unlikely to have been motivated by fears that political involvement would interfere with scientific work.[44] Slowly, a displacement of confidence was taking place. By the 1820s he had become very vulnerable to a kind of over-persuasion that could deflect him from his own convictions. Charles Cuvier provided an eye-witness account of one such occasion:

Au commencement de 1820, je fus témoin, pendant plusieurs semaines, des obsessions qu'on faisait subir à M. Cuvier, dans le sens de la réaction. M. de Mirbel entre autres venait à chaque instant le travailler et lui écrivit tout un faisceau de lettres dans ce sens. M. Cuvier refusait toujours d'entrer dans cette voie ... On ne l'accepta pas et l'on ne cessa de l'obséder pour le décider à défendre à la tribune, au nom du roi, la nouvelle loi que préparait M. Décazes, et qui devait renverser celle que M. Cuvier avait autrefois défendue avec honneur. Le dimanche 12 février 1820, les émissaires se succédaient, et M. Cuvier résistait toujours, se promenait dans la bibliothèque et paraissait fort agité. Mme Cuvier me le fit remarquer avec angoisse. Le lendemain 13 février, le journal annonça tout à coup que le duc de Berry venait d'être assassiné dans la nuit par Louvel, à la sortie de l'Opéra. Cette nouvelle frappa M. Cuvier. Il y vit la confirmation de tout ce qu'on lui avait dit au sujet de parti révolutionnaire. Il prit la plume et écrivit au ministre: 'La douleur m'a vaincu. Je suis aux ordres du roi.' Voilà comment il fut amené contre son gré à défendre à la tribune la nouvelle loi, démarche dont il fut blâmé, et dont je viens comme témoin oculaire de faire connaître l'origine.[45]

The nature of the political attacks to which Cuvier was subjected certainly undermined his inner confidence, which could not draw undiluted strength from his family, his work or his religion; but we can say more than this about the impact of his private and family life on his public position in what was, after all, an age when politics and private life were closely knit. Cuvier could not rid himself of his family's Protestantism, any more than he could prevent some members of it, as we have seem, from participating in extremist political movements. He could also not use his family in any positive sense, to advance and extend his connections in the political world. The most obvious way to do this was through marriage. Neither of Cuvier's sons survived childhood; only one of his daughters, Clémentine, did so, and she was to die a few weeks before her marriage could take place; significantly enough, Cuvier's son-in-law was to have been Charles Duparquet, not a naturalist, but a colleague in the Section of the Interior at the Conseil d'Etate. It was not in natural history that Cuvier felt most in need of strengthening his position by a carefully planned alliance.[46] Though his family in the wider sense was clearly rising socially, after the domestic tragedy of 1827 Cuvier could reap the relatively distant benefits of the marriage only of other family members' children. He would henceforth be forced to rely to a much greater extent than most of his competitors on the loose links of friendship and patronage for defence and advancement.[47] As political difficulties increased after the conservative swing of 1822 and the accession of the reactionary Charles X in 1824, such links came under ever-increasing pressure. It is not surprising that Cuvier should often have encountered failure in his public life. As a reaction against weakness in some aspects of his public life, he over-compensated in others. Forced to retreat from the politics of the marriage market, he accumulated, as contemporaries held, 'more posts than any single man had the right to';[48] he did so with the same, no doubt, irritating insistence on the capacity to do so conferred on him by his superior German education which we have already seen him utilise under Napoleon. He made little secret that he regarded the French as amateurs in the field of public administration,[49] but his plans to encourage its rational study, to systematise it by insertion in the state educational system, and to legitimise it by making qualifications in this field the prerequisite for state employment, in fact to set up an equivalent of the present Ecole Normale d'Administration (ENA) came to nothing due to what he darkly called 'la routine et la pédanterie'.[50]

He also encountered failure in another long-standing project, that of the reform of the standards of science, the creation of an agreement on what good science was by enforcing these

The Restoration and the crisis of patronage

standards through qualifications granted by state educational institutions. In the whole period between 1809 and 1830 only 434 candidates gained the *baccalauréat* in science, and in the period between 1809 and 1843 only 163 qualified for the doctorate.[51] During the great reaction of 1822, Cuvier scored only qualified success, for while he succeeded in preventing the banishment of the Faculty of Medicine to the provinces to calm its unruly students, he was not able to prevent the closure of the Ecole normale.[52] Nor could he really be said to have halted the increasing influence of the Church in secondary education, which had already aroused his hostility under the Empire. The numbers of schools run by religious bodies rose from five hundred in 1809 to 21,118 in 1827.[53]

The many instabilities in Cuvier's public position made his firm hold on a number of political opinions all the more remarkable: it would have been so much easier to have had none at all. Cuvier's political ideas thus cannot be seen as somehow less substantive than those he developed in science. Nor can alleged 'conservatism' in one of these spheres be seen simply as a reflex of conservatism in another. It is not proven that ideas relate to each other across different experiences in simple analogical ways; nor, indeed, that by the standards of his time Cuvier was a 'conservative'. His closest links were not with the conservative groups of his time, the Catholics, the divine-right monarchists, the men formed by the Emigration, but with the tiny group known as the *Doctrinaires*. Of these five or six men, Cuvier was closest to Royer-Collard, Director of Public Instruction until his resignation in 1819, and to Guizot.[55] To Guizot's book on education in the French state, Cuvier was to contribute the first four chapters.[56] For both these men, education by the state posed some of the major problems of their era, and simultaneously offered their solution. Neither man saw these problems as basically concerned with procuring 'social justice' for the lower classes. If both expended great energy and incurred considerable political risks to spread elementary education of an accessible, secular type among these classes, it was for reasons which had much more to do with the restraint of factionalism amongst the upper class in the interests of the strong state:

L'ignorance rend le peuple turbulent et féroce: elle en fait un instrument des factieux, et partout se trouvent ou surviennent des factieux empressés à se servir de cet instrument terrible ... quand le gouvernement a pris soin de propager à la faveur de l'éducation national sous les rapports de la réligion, de la morale, de la politique etc. ... les doctrines qui conviennent à sa nature et à sa direction, ces doctrines acquièrent bientôt une puissance contre laquelle viennent èchouer les écarts de la liberté d'esprit et toutes les tentatives séditieuses. Ainsi se forme l'esprit publique, ainsi s'entretient un véritable patriotisme, ainsi se fortifient et se consolident les sociétés et les trônes.[57]

However, it also became clear that the Restoration state was not willing to play the role assigned to it in education, and was content to turn elementary and even large numbers of secondary schools over to the control of the religious bodies. It was a private initiative, the Société pour l'Instruction élémentaire, which provided the first effective challenge to the return of the Church to the field of education. Founded during the Hundred Days, it included Cuvier, Guizot, Royer-Collard, and their common friends Maine de Biran and De Gérando among its first members.[58] To achieve the quickest results in the minimum time, it decided to use the Lancastrian or monitorial system of instruction. As the pupils taught each other at the minimum of expense and with surprisingly solid results, the idea spread well beyond Paris, and a network of associations soon covered almost the whole of provincial France.[59] Cuvier's intervention not only secured the licensing of its schools in Paris but also a subsidy of 50,000 fr. from the budget of the Ministry of the Interior.[60] For several years it seemed that the Society was achieving its objective of offering an alternative to clerical conservatism and to state indifference to the problem in the political culture of France posed by the educational needs of the poor.

However, it was precisely this degree of success which aroused in the end the unrelenting hostility of the Church and the conservatives. As politics as a whole moved further towards the right after 1822, these were views increasingly supported both in Paris and the provinces. In 1821, Cuvier for the first time had to fight hard and long to retain the subsidy against attacks in the Chamber.[61] Although he was successful, it was a stand which was undoubtedly remembered against him, and which contributed to his fall from the office of Grand

The Restoration and the crisis of patronage

Master of the *Université* in June 1822. The political views which Cuvier held and acted upon, therefore, implied no separation between the cultural world and the political. That they did not conform to modern ideas of the fight for social justice does not any the less place them in contemporary terms with the liberal rather than the conservative wing.[62] They were views which he held publicly even though sôme of them proved harmful to his career. In Cuvier's view, culture had to be shaped in the public context. It was not only that he had the idea that the state could shape intellectual disciplines, as we have seen in the case of science and administration; it was that culture had become politics in a much deeper sense. In a world where 'les mots magiques' had lost their force, cultural justifications of power had to be fashioned if either naked tyranny or prolonged instability were not to result: '... l'écrivain qui en alienant les sentiments du peuple vent faire que l'obéissance n'ait plus de mobile que la force matérielle, cherche autant qu'il est en lui à changer la monarchie en tyrannie'.[63] Such cultural politics were the only way in which the obstacles caused by the character of normal politics to the creation of a strong state could be overcome. Restoration political society needed its myths, not simply as instruments of class domination or as vehicles for conflict between different sections of the political classes, but also for the more benign and constructive purpose of being able to proclaim the possibility of neutral ground in a factionalist age. Whoever controlled the public exposition of such myths of reconciliation, purity and life without politics, and could thus proclaim the existence of neutral ground, was in a position to gain great public authority. Such control formed both the substance of Cuvier's only non-controverted position, that of the Perpetual Secretaryship of the Academy of Sciences, and of his views on the importance of culture in the French state: the scientific myth promised neutral ground as no other could.[64] These considerations go far to explain why Cuvier was particularly likely to be hostile to attempts such as Geoffroy's to insert the language of actual politics into the language of science, to convert neutral ground into yet another battlefield.

This concern to maintain the separateness of science, to maintain the myth of the possibility of neutrality, formed one of the most basic features of one of the great political controversies of the period, that centred on the retention of the *cumul*, or the ability to hold, and receive salary from, more than one government post at the same time. This was of course a debate fuelled by the fierce competition for government posts already referred to; the existence of the *cumul* obviously restricted the number of these vacant at any given point, as well as making it difficult to establish a firm *cursus* for the reward of merit.[65] But the attack on the *cumul* was not simply a question of outsiders versus insiders; it was also a question of which kinds of authority were seen as harmful to or incompatible with each other. A whole chemistry of power was being redefined. Cuvier was quickly singled out as the greatest and most notorious *cumulard*. Almost all written attacks upon him return to this point.[66] In the debates on the *cumul* in the Chamber of Deputies, it was he who was singled out unmistakably.[67] The actual instability in Cuvier's public position did not stop contemporaries citing him, together with Laplace, as examples of men whose concentrations of power – at the expense of the young – could only be explained by servility and time-serving.[68] In terms of the scientific community, the scale of Cuvier's office-holding was indeed exceptional;[69] in terms of the political community as a whole it was less so.[70] What was unique was his concentration of combined intellectual and political authority, which constituted a standing affront to contemporary demands that the *savants* should confine themselves to the purer – if poorer – air of the library and laboratory.[71]

Cuvier refused to do this. The variety of his posts enabled him to exercise patronage in almost every corner of the French political world,[72] while the success of his *salon* before 1827 enabled him to cultivate personal contacts with every shade of opinion, from the ultra-Catholic Ferdinand de Bertier to the liberal economist Charles Dupin,[73] and young men such as Henri Beyle and Prosper Mérimée who made their living from more or less critical journalism.[74] To operate successfully in this world of personalised power, it was necessary to cultivate social contact.

It was also in such social forums that the first stages of the battles between Cuvier and his scientific adversaries were

The Restoration and the crisis of patronage

fought. Outright confrontations were rare, but as Lamarck lamented, '... avec quelques monosyllabes employés à propos, un sourire même et un clin d'oeil, un air de dédain, passant promptement à autre chose, on produit tout l'effet désiré'.[75]

This was a society whose politics were proverbially confused and unpredictable, and yet where the slightest nuance of gesture and expression in the individual was used with precise significance and so interpreted by an expert audience.[76] The society of dissimulation and deference which such tactics maintained was one which was easily disrupted. Its very personalised, private nature meant that it could also be severely disrupted by private events. The extent to which family grief over Clémentine Cuvier's death in 1827 hampered Cuvier's ability to muster friends and colleagues in informal social events such as his weekly *salon*, is an example of this. Secondly, these ways of operation stood at some distance from other increasingly important sources of opinion, such as the newspaper and periodical press. Not that these were media whose importance went unrecognised by Cuvier; his care, for example, to place a sympathetic protégé at the head of the scientific section of the *Journal des Débats*, was sharply commented upon by Geoffroy St Hilaire.[77] The danger of the press, however, lay in its capacity to capture the official language of sections of this official culture, and turn it to its own purposes of dissent and attack. In the case of individuals closely identified with the sciences, this was a serious threat, because of the reliance of science on its mythology to guarantee its public position. Cuvier's position as Permanent Secretary of the Academy of Sciences, upon whom devolved the writing of all its official corporate utterances, its speeches to the monarch and its eulogies of departed members, was particularly closely associated with the shaping of the language of official science and its mythology. Officially, science was an apolitical activity, conducted by dedicated and solitary interrogators of nature who avoided the corrupting influence of human society and intrigue. Both François Raspail, and less subtly, Geoffroy St Hilaire were to modify this ideal in such a way as to turn it into a means of attack on the official world of science. To do so, however, called into question the whole idea of science as a distinct laudable activity with its own defined standards of procedure: an ideal, as we have seen, to whose realisation Cuvier had devoted much effort through state educational institutions. In terms of this objective, the myth of apolitical science had a valuable function, which was to assure for science a claim to constitute neutral ground, and therefore to stabilise its status by removing it from the sphere of political conflict. In this sense it is entirely correct to link the conflict between Cuvier and Geoffroy with the preparation for the 1830 revolution. The terms of the debate, at least on Geoffroy's side, indicated a widening politicised area, and a declining ability on the part of his opponents to restrict that area. The maintenance of neutral ground was after all vital to the continued existence of a political class otherwise torn relentlessly between the demands of their clientèle systems on the one hand, and the need of political institutions on the other, for relatively stable ideological groups. To sacrifice neutral ground meant to sacrifice the possibility of effective, rapid action in the political world.[78]

The first step in Raspail's attack on official science was to 'capture' one of its characteristic expressions, that of the funeral *éloge*. Raspail's *Annales des Sciences d'Observation* were accordingly never complete without their counter-*éloge*.[79] It was the perfect vehicle from which to preach to the young scientist the virtues of neglecting the dictates of the Academy for those of his own 'voix intérieure'. Above all, the young should aim to keep free of the clientèle systems: '... ne devenez ni des disciples complaisans, ni des admirateurs interessés. Vérité dans les faits et liberté dans les systèmes, telle doit être votre dévise.'[80] Using the language of official science itself, Raspail could erect a whole gallery of anti-heroes, such as Lamarck, of whom he wrote:

peu façonné à l'intrigue et aux ménagemens de l'ambition, il exprime ses grandes vues avec hardiesse, et sans les accomoder aux goûts des pouvoirs divers qui ont passé successivement devant lui; il lutta contre des aversaires qui, devenus plus puissants que lui, ont semblé l'éclipser de l'éclat que leur prêtoient le journalisme et les faveurs ministérielles.[81]

In his *éloges* Raspail celebrated young or obscure men from a position critical of the official structures which usually

The Restoration and the crisis of patronage

produced such appreciations, and turned the conventional endorsement of scientific aloofness into an attack on the careerism and intrigue which seemed to him to control the world of official science. In his explicit and direct attacks on the structures of scientific authority, he relied for support, in fact, on the rhetoric of official science and its praise for unworldliness as the mark of the true scientist.

Geoffroy's politicisation of this rhetoric went further and was less subtle. 'Faisons vraiment de la science', he demanded in his conflict with Cuvier[82] and then proceeded to attempt at least partly to validate his own researches against Cuvier's by blatantly political analogies. As the conscript armies of 1793 had conquered the Rhine provinces against all orthodox military predictions of failure, so he too would overthrow the inhibiting *Ancien Régime* of science.[83] More, opposition to transformism would reveal France as scientifically backward; at all costs, 'faisons que nous ne restions pas en arrière'.[84]

Raspail and Geoffroy also prepared the way for the outbreak of conflict in another way, by using the printed word to establish much clearer line-ups of individuals on specific issues than existed in reality. In real life, many individuals moved easily from collaboration with Geoffroy to collaboration with Cuvier almost up to the outbreak of public hostilities in the Académie des sciences.[85] This loose pattern of allegiance was, as we have seen, typical of political society at large at least in Paris. Although the line-ups produced by Raspail and Geoffroy bore little relation to the real structure of relationship between the individuals they mentioned,[86] these groups were comprehensible in terms of the moral rhetoric of science employed in this new way by men who self-consciously defined themselves as 'outsiders'.

By politicising the language of science in this way, Geoffroy and Raspail rendered it almost impossible for Cuvier and Geoffroy to find any common language with which to discuss their differences. However, even the increasing force with which the opponents of official science used its own rhetoric against it, does not explain many of the specific features of the 1830 debate. Nor is it enough to point to the imminence of revolution as somehow causing the hostilities between Cuvier and Geoffroy.[87] In terms of their intrinsic intellectual differences, debate, if not conflict, between Geoffroy and Cuvier had been possible since the early years of the Empire.[88] The Restoration certainly saw a lifting on previous restrictions of critical expression, which helped to make *public* conflict more likely. As political tension increased sharply after 1825, liberal or even 'outsider' opinion was also more likely to define itself in terms of patriotism and concern for the public good against the old clientèles interested only in the maintenance of their own power. However, the very existence of these clientèles prevented for a long time the formation of clearly defined, permanently opposing groups. If polarities did not exist, then they had to be constructed, as we have seen Geoffroy and Raspail in the process of doing.[89] Although these line-ups may not have corresponded to any set of relationships within the real world, they did mark the fact that the old clientèle systems were themselves shifting. Cuvier's social coverage was drastically reduced by the closure of his *salon* in 1827, and his public standing in a Catholic reactionary monarchy was always in dispute, as we have seen. At the same time, his public positions were already too prominent for him to reconstruct them in terms of outsider politics, as Geoffroy did. Geoffroy's attack in fact had the best of both worlds. It was expressed in terms of the patriotic populist rhetoric which political tension had placed to the fore as the mark of opposition to the established government. This allowed Geoffroy to use the reputation for liberalism which he had acquired in the 1790s, and imply that Cuvier, because he was his adversary, must therefore be conservative.[90] At the same time, Geoffroy's public challenge was made possible by very specific movements within the world of organised science, which a real outsider would have found less easy to exploit. Firstly, the collapse of Laplace's hold over physicists in the Institut led to the rebuff of the attempt by his protégé Biot in 1822–3 to gain election as Permanent Secretary in succession to Delambre. A long feud also began between Biot and François Arago, whom he considered to have engineered his defeat.[91] Henceforward Arago led a recognisable faction of younger men within the Institut. His hostility to Cuvier became apparent when he supported the candidature for membership of Cuvier's former protégé and bitter enemy Blainville against that of

The Restoration and the crisis of patronage

Cuvier's own brother Frédéric, in 1825. Arago's election as Perpetual Secretary on 7 June 1830 only made matters worse, and he and Cuvier quarrelled violently over several issues. One of them, significantly enough, was that of the admission of the general public as spectators of the Académie's normal sessions; it was a general public to which Geoffroy was constantly to appeal within his own conflict with Cuvier.[92]

The balance of forces was also shifting within the Muséum. Without outright conflict, the Brongniart family had established itself as a distinct bloc. Alexandre Brongniart had been able to place his son Alphonse and his two sons-in-law Victor Audoin and Jean-Baptiste Dumas within the Muséum. Unlike Cuvier, Brongniart had been able to exploit family politics to the full. Contemporary gossip ascribed to a decision made by Cuvier in the Conseil d'Etat Brongniart's withdrawal of support.[93] From 1824, the two Brongniarts, Audoin and Dumas, were involved in the publication of a new journal in natural history, the *Annales des Sciences naturelles*, which at least until 1830, tended to publish papers sympathetic to Geoffroy's approach. This practice was only halted by Audoin's sudden reorientation of his work in a direction more likely to find favour with Cuvier.[94]

By 1830, therefore, the scene was set for the great debate with Geoffroy. The scientific issues at stake have been described in great detail by Appel, Coleman and Piveteau, and it is upon their accounts that I rely here. For a long time before 1830, it had been apparent that the former collaboration between Cuvier and Geoffroy had not produced a unity of views between them. Cuvier's thought remained essentially physiological; for him, form and function were inseparable, and function was the dominant consideration. He focussed on the organism itself, as it actually, positively existed. His work tended to emphasise the idea of the necessary correlations between physiological systems. Some correlations of systems were obviously impossible; others were combinations necessary to the life of the organism as presently constituted, and therefore impossible to alter. In 1812, Cuvier put forward his idea that there were four basic *plans* or sets of possible correlations in the animal world, and rejected the idea that there could be any passage of species from one *plan* to another.

At this time, however, he was still willing to consider morphological relationships between species within the same *plan*, and in the same year published a paper on the morphology of the bones of the skulls of vertebrates.

Meanwhile, Geoffory in a series of papers published in 1807, was working on the idea that it was possible to establish a unity of plan which would apply to all vertebrates; in other words that there were relationships between groups of organisms which transcended the divisions between Cuvier's four *embranchements* (vertebrates, molluscs, insects, zoophytes). The principles for these homologies were set out in his *Philosophie anatomique*, and in 1820, Geoffroy began to argue that the vertebrate plan was also assimilable to insects and crustaceans. These ideas were in turn attacked by Cuvier in his 1825 article *Nature*, and in the introduction to the first volume of the *Histoire naturelle des Poissons*, which appeared in 1828. In 1830 two young naturalists, Meyranx and Laurencet, presented to the Academy of Sciences for comment their paper 'Quelques considérations sur l'organisation des mollusques', in which they pointed out that by bending the molluscan body a *plan* could be obtained which could be assimilated to that of the vertebrates. Cuvier combatted this apparent support for Geoffroy's contention that there existed a single unified plan for the whole animal kingdom in a paper presented to the Academy on 22 February 1830, and published in that year's *Annales des Sciences Naturelles*. In this 'Considérations sur les molluscs', Cuvier clearly set out the conflict between the physiological and morphological conceptions of animal organisation. Geoffroy in his turn replied with a paper presented to the Academy on 1 March, entitled, 'De la théorie des analogues'. In it he attempted to restrict the scope of the discussion away from the unity of composition of insects, molluscs and vertebrates, and only discussed the hyoid bone in vertebrates. Cuvier replied in a paper read on 22 March that the bone in question did not prove Geoffroy's case, since it varies between many classes of vertebrates. He also pointed out that the real question at stake between him and Geoffroy was whether the theory of analogues is universal, or whether analogues are limited, and if so, in virtue of what criteria. Two further papers, by Geoffroy on 29 March, and by Cuvier on

The Restoration and the crisis of patronage

5 April, continued the discussion of the hyoid bone. Geoffroy attacked Cuvier's desire to keep solely to observed facts in natural history, and approved the tendency in *Naturphilosophie* to rely also on *a priori* deduction, a tendency which, as we will see in the next chapter, had already aroused Cuvier's criticism on numerous occasions. After 5 April, both men agreed to cease the argument within the walls of the Académie des Sciences, and the discussion was continued in Cuvier's lessons to the Collège de France on the history of science, and in Geoffroy's *Principes de philosphie zoologique*. Neither man altered his position and Cuvier continued to oppose Geoffroy's attempts to reduce the different organisation apparent in the animal world to identity, and Geoffroy to see an underlying unity of organisation in that realm of nature.

It only needed the presentation of the paper by Laurencet and Meyranx to spark the explosion.[95] In the period before, two years stand out as especially important. In 1822, Delambre's death set in motion a significant change in the balance of forces within the Institut. Simultaneously, electoral victory by the right-wing opened a period of political reaction. Cuvier lost control of the Université, failed to save the Ecole normale from closure, and suffered a drop in both prestige and power. At the same time, the movement for *enseignement mutuel* suffered a decisive set-back. In 1827, Clémentine Cuvier died; with Frédéric Cuvier's failure to win election to the Institut, the resources of family politics were exhausted. Far less easy to chart, however, is the effect of these events on the way in which Cuvier viewed his own role in public life. As we have seen, Cuvier's identity in the public world cannot be separated from his identity as a man of science. He tried to use his public positions outside science to implement an ideal of science as a responsible, ordered activity, containing its own standards of procedure which could be endorsed by the state. He also did so in virtue of a cosmopolitan experience and education which marked him as different in outlook from most of his colleagues both in science and in public administration, and which he clearly regarded as conferring a superiority upon himself. Yet more intimately, he also maintained on at least one level a strong identification with the official rhetoric of science which he also endorsed as part of his official position as Permanent

Secretary. A man who habitually wore a Greek engraved stone representing 'Study' was hardly likely to be paying mere lip-service to the ideals he on occasion expounded.[96] He was not only, perhaps, seeking defence in rhetoric when he occasionally described himself to the Chamber of Deputies as far removed from political considerations because of his scientific labours.[97]

Increasingly, however, contemporaries came to regard science and public life as incompatible spheres of activity. Correspondingly delicate choices were involved for Cuvier in the question of which public presentation to bring out on any given occasion. There are also considerable signs that repeated public attacks on Cuvier in virtue of his scientific position, most notably in the debates on the *cumul*, caused some weakening of confidence. Clémentine's death also seems to have brought about a critical spiritual revaluation.[98] In another sense, the dominance of a purely professional and vocational code in the conduct of life may have been increasingly internally questioned. Socially, he would often de-emphasise his scientific interests and expertise. Lyell, for example, complained after their first few meetings of how difficult it was to induce Cuvier to talk on scientific matters, and it was only after their friendship had become secure that Cuvier was able to reveal to Lyell his working methods and his current projects.[99]

Yet each possible self-image shared one salient characteristic: its potential for frustration in the circumstances of Restoration France. As a Protestant, Cuvier, as we have seen, after a moment of euphoria regarded his political career as blocked at its outset; politically he could only survive by ostentatious displays of tolerance. As a man of science in politics he was in any case automatically regarded as anomalous by many of his contemporaries and at any moment his scientific standing could be called into question by the very public involvement he saw as necessary to maintain the status of science. It was the struggle for this status and the codification of the language and practice of science which were implicitly at stake in the conflict with Geoffroy and which were sharply called into question by Geoffroy's politicisation of scientific debate. As a political liberal in 1815, the

The Restoration and the crisis of patronage

increasing polarisation of politics after 1825 left Cuvier behind. His brand of social engineering for peaceful change within existing structures began to look like conservatism. As the political situation became more tense and hostility grew to the actions of the monarchy, nationalism and democracy became values endorsed by sections of the opposition. To a Protestant born and educated outside France with a strong personal commitment to the values of intellectual expertise, they would have made little appeal. Ultimately, Cuvier's public life was one of considerable frustration and uncertainty, rather than that untrammelled enjoyment of multifarious office which has been so often depicted. In one sense, his own life proved the mythology of science right: the only free activity which did not involve him in the genuine contradictions produced by combining science with politics *was* the contemplation of nature.[100] The myth of science as a pastoral world outside the social realm collapsed, as it was bound to do, with the increase of heterogeneity amongst the intellectual and political élite,[101] an increase of which the revolution of 1830 was only the most violent sign. The debate of that year between Cuvier and Geoffroy cannot be seen simply as yet another change round in the workings of patronage.[102] Nor is it enough to try to explain Cuvier's public behaviour simply as a product of crudely defined positions such as 'conservatism', or of psychological flaws which led him to be over-concerned with the retention of power at the expense of scientific 'progress'. That Cuvier was ambitious does not mean he was unprincipled; that he was constantly in the public eye does not mean that his confidence was always complete; that he was a man of science does not mean that his career was not shaped by both the reality of power and by mythologies which defined and circumscribed its use, and whose contradictions exercised a strong influence on forming his own highly ambiguous public reputation and presentation.

VI
Controversy, authority and the market: Lamarck, Gall and *Naturphilosophie*

d'un tempérament sanguin et nerveux, vif, passionné, il embrassait avec chaleur une résolution une fois prise.
(Duvernoy, 1833, p. 149.)

During Cuvier's tenure of the Permanent Secretaryship of the First Class of the Institut, and after 1815 of the Académie des sciences, science maintained and expanded the reading and listening audience which it had already acquired among the public of the *Ancien Régime*. Readership for scientific books on many levels was large and expanding. Public lecture courses such as those at the Muséum and at the private Lycée de Paris, attracted high attendance. The military exploits of the Revolution and Empire increased the numbers of young men undergoing medical training for service in the army and navy, and hence the numbers of those willing to undergo a general scientific training.[1] The foundation of the Imperial University in 1808 led, far more than the loosely controlled *Ecoles centrales* which it replaced, to a captive and expanding market for elementary and advanced scientific textbooks.[2] Science as a business venture appealing to a wide, interested but non-expert audience was at last becoming possible in France. It will be one of the aims of this chapter to evaluate the importance of this development, and especially to evaluate its importance to the changing nature of scientific controversy in the period of the Empire and the Restoration.

The problems raised by the growth of popular science were complex. It was not simply that science itself had become an article of consumption. It was also that from the closing years of the *Ancien Régime* a debate on the relationship of the public to culture had been built into the struggle for dominance between different kinds of scientific and political involvement.

Controversy, authority and the market

The belief, supported by Bernardin de St Pierre and others, that insight into the natural world was available to all, cut into the idea of an 'élite' science of experts such as the members of the Academy of Sciences.[3] Who was the real controller of what was to be defined as 'real' science, if all were capable of being 'producers' of science? This was a problem which, as we have seen in the case of Geoffroy St Hilaire, was to become extremely important in the scientific debates which immediately preceded the revolution of 1830.

Men like Cuvier, who earned a significant portion of their income from public lectures, and yet were also paid by the state to represent the practice and standards of the inner scientific community, were placed in a difficult position. They competed for audiences against the dispensers of animal magnetism or phrenology, and at the same time had to satisfy the demands of a specialised science using heavily codified and esoteric standards of practice. Although attempts to define what was an acceptable kind of scientific practice preoccupied Cuvier for most of his working life, and often involved him in attacks on the sciences or pseudo-sciences of public appeal, it is not surprising that he never achieved complete clarity or consistency in achieving this aim.

In reaction against the anti-élite movements of the early Revolution, Cuvier asserted again and again that public debate and controversy could only ruin the reputation of real science. At the same time, the Napoleonic state manifested a peculiar horror of public meetings and of public enthusiasm not directed towards the veneration of the Empire.[4] It was on both counts impossible to use public approval as a means of support in contexts depending on state validation. On the other hand, Cuvier himself used the wide public audience as a deliberate aid in his debates with scientific colleagues, particularly with Lamarck, and was preoccupied with the control of his presentation in the public press. Inconsistency was, in these circumstances, built into scientific debate.

So, therefore, were very sharply defined kinds of language in debate. What could be said in some circumstances could not be said in others. This last point is of vital importance, since so much criticism of the way Cuvier carried on controversy has been based on accusations of hypocrisy, or of unworthy personal hostility against those unable to defend themselves.[5]

Before we repeat such anachronistic mistakes we should find out what contemporaries thought *were* appropriate forums and audiences for different kinds of opinion, and to take account of their own confusions in actually using them.

Cuvier lived surrounded by controversy. It shaped his ideas, personal relations and public standing. Yet the reality of Cuvier the controversialist has been eclipsed, except for the case of his debate with Geoffroy, by the image of Cuvier the 'legislator of science'.[6] Partly, this has been done in virtue of an ideal of the scientific community which plays down the possibility of dissension within it.[7]

Yet that Cuvier was involved in other controversies besides those with Lamarck and Geoffroy most insisted upon by the historiography, and that involvement in such an uneasy field as natural science made him tone down or even conceal his real views, is rarely admitted. Cuvier's own views on many of the most important issues in natural history often took many years to reach a definitive, publicly upheld formulation. Particularly in the early stages of his career Cuvier the embattled controversialist was less evident than Cuvier the master of equivocation.

To substantiate these assertions, let us examine in more detail some aspects of Cuvier's work on one of the great issues of the life sciences under the Empire and Restoration, that of the mutability of species. The papers written by Cuvier between 1795 and 1800 represent an attempt to claim mastery over several different and controverted fields; firstly, over the reclassification of the heterogenous class of invertebrate animals called *vers* by Linneaus; second, to establish the basis of a new paleontology via the comparative anatomy of living species; and third, the attempt to find a valid basis for the classification of mammals, and indeed for the whole animal kingdom, and to feed the findings of this attempt into those of physiology.[8] In the 1790s, as Burckhardt had shown, ideas about the mutability of species were much in the air. They had few, if any, outright opponents if at the same time little concern had been shown with a systematic development of their implications.[9] By 1800, Cuvier had become a public opponent of mutability, and Lamarck had begun systematically to develop his

Controversy, authority and the market

transformist position;[10] but while Cuvier's taxonomic contributions before that date had shown remarkable clarity, his pronouncements on more general issues in natural history had been more equivocal. This is particularly true in the case of the papers which he wrote in collaboration with Geoffroy St Hilaire.[11] Later, Cuvier was to make an explicit connection between the use of the subordination of characters as a classificatory procedure, and the argument for fixity;[12] in 1795, his first use of the same classificatory procedure is accompanied by strong hints that species are merely handy abstractions for the naturalist, without real existence in nature.[13] The second paper which Cuvier and Geoffroy wrote in collaboration in 1795 was a test case for the application of the rules for the classification of mammals which they had established in their first joint paper, but even here, there was a strong concern to argue the case that 'nature makes no leaps', the very last position that Cuvier would argue by 1812.[14] The last collaborative paper, that on the classification of monkeys and orangutans, published in January 1798, puts forward an idea of species descent which is far from implying fixity, and has much more in common with Lamarck's idea of the descent of species as the result of 'degradation' over time:

Or, c'est une loi assez générale de la nature, que le nombre des espèces d'un genre est à peu-près en raison de la fécondité de chacune d'elle, soit que ce que nous appelons des espèces ne soient que les diverses dégénerations d'une même espèce ... soit que beaucoup d'entre-elles soient nées de l'accouplement des espèces voisines ...'[15]

The collaborative papers thus not only form a challenge to those who believe that Cuvier's views on the fixity of species were stable from the beginning of his career. Their existence also poses a series of other problems. It is now impossible to determine which sections of these papers were the responsibility of Cuvier and which of Geoffroy. It remains important that Cuvier was willing to put his signature to works which not only differed in tendency from his later work but which also differ markedly from work published immediately after Geoffroy's departure for Egypt in 1799, which marked the end of their collaboration. There are several suggestions which can be made towards solving these problems. The most obvious is that in collaborating with Geoffroy, who was not only closely linked with Haüy and Daubenton, but also with Lamarck, Cuvier was in some way neutralising an important element of opposition in the Muséum. By offering the young and inexperienced Geoffroy access to his taxonomical expertise he could in turn make it more difficult for him to enter into full collaboration with Lamarck.[16] Cuvier was detaching a potential member of the opposition. After 1799, Geoffroy's absence and Cuvier's own increasingly secure administrative and bureaucratic employment enabled him to do without such forms of protective covering, and to come forward with the strong statements in favour of species fixity of 1799 and 1802.[17] This hypothesis would not of course rule out the possibility that Cuvier may have had genuinely uncertain views on this issue, like many of his contemporaries. It would also not necessarily rule out that the adoption of an ambiguous point of view on mutability might have arisen from the extremely varied public response to Cuvier's 1796 paper on fossil elephants, his first statement of the reality of extinction.[18] The struggle for control of whole fields of classification which Cuvier was undertaking at the same time may well have induced him to limit controversy with his scientific rivals, already heated enough, to the sphere of taxonomy rather than extending to the general 'philosophical' ideas such as mutability also being debated at this time.

Another reason for this decision could well have been the simple fact that it was in the field of classification that it was easiest to make priority claims: to produce scientific 'goods' whose ownership was unmistakable.[19] There is no lack of evidence about the importance attached by Cuvier to the successful making of claims to priority. He wrote to Adriaan Camper, for example, that one of the advantages of membership of the Société philomatique was that 'Le bulletin est en effet un moyen très commode de fixer la date des découvertes et d'empêcher qu'elles ne soient prises par d'autres en attendant qu'on ait le temps de le publier en détail'.[20] The publication of the first three volumes of the *Leçons d'anatomie comparée* in 1800 was prompted by similar considerations, as Cuvier himself made clear.[21] His concern for priority, though it infringed hallowed ideas of knowledge as a free good, and turned it instead into personal property, was hardly unrealistic. The social organisation of science, the uncertainty of the 'internal' structures of thought in many key areas, the importance of publicity in the making of a career, all combined to make the cumulation of personal intellectual capital of the highest importance. As Lamarck himself recognised, 'It is not enough to make a discovery: one must propagate it and get it recognised'.[22]

Priority and property could lead to empire. Natural history possessed many confused areas of uncertain ownership. The mass of invertebrates lumped together by Linnaeus under the title of *vers* was one of these disputed territories. One of Cuvier's earliest papers, based on work in Normandy, staked an advance claim for their reclassification.[23] It was a paper important not only for its classificatory content, but also as one of the first statements of the relations between internal structure and classificatory position which were to establish Cuvier's name: but even after he had submitted both Bruguière's and Linnaeus' classifications based on external characteristics to intensive criticism, Cuvier was not left in undisputed possession of the field. The claim to reform the *vers* was a direct trespass on Lamarck's teaching at the Muséum, on the invertebrates. Initially, Cuvier and Lamarck each gave a coolly courteous reception to the work of his colleague. Lamarck's opening lecture for 1796 announced the intention of following the divisions of the animal kingdom introduced by the younger man.[24] The following year, and again in 1799, he suggested that Cuvier deserved the basic credit for having reformed invertebrate classification. Cuvier in his turn mentioned Lamarck as one of the naturalists to whom he was most indebted.[25]

With Geoffroy's departure in 1799, the situation changed. Lamarck proclaimed his adherence to species mutability in 1800. In 1801, the exchange of courtesies between those left behind to struggle in the classificatory field, began to grow distinctly muted. In 1801, reviewing Lamarck's *Système des animaux sans vertèbres* Cuvier only unwillingly admitted that he himself had not provided a complete classificatory system for the white-blooded animals, in so far as he had not dealt with the *genera* and the species. He then paid Lamarck a backhanded compliment, by hailing the book as a proof that none other than Lamarck was capable of occupying himself with what *remained to be done* to complete the methodological arrangement of this part of the animal kingdom.[26] After that, the competition for priority and empire between the two men became explicit. Lamarck's *Philosophie zoologique* of 1809 asserted that his own arrangement of the *vers* had originated in 1794, a year before Cuvier's who, he alleged, had merely consolidated Lamarck's own discoveries.[27] By 1822, when Cuvier wrote his 'autobiography', the issue still rankled so much that Cuvier went so far as to accuse Lamarck of plagiarism.[28] The picture drawn by Lamarck's most recent biographer of each man calmly accepting the other's contributions to a common field of interest, may well require modification.[29]

The ambiguity of the expression of Cuvier's ideas on the issue of species mutability in his early years, and the progress of his territorial conflict with Lamarck, show how the expression of ideas in science was profoundly influenced by their polemical setting. Cuvier took a long time to emerge as the unambiguous champion of species fixity. Even in 1800 he was able to praise Lacepède's highly mutationist work.[30] All this hardly fits the image of Cuvier 'legislating' with undispute authority over a distinct 'line' in natural history. Far more, it seems to suggest a picture of Cuvier in these early years keeping a wavering course between the need to establish himself by the piling up of convincing priority claims and the need to neutralise potentially hostile forces, such as Lamarck, or conciliate important early patrons such as Lacepède. It was only after he gained the Permanent Secretaryship in 1803 that Cuvier achieved a unique position of strength which enabled him to some extent to consolidate his authority. In this role, Cuvier became the official mouthpiece of the scientific community in Paris. It was in this role that he was to encounter two other major controversies of his career apart from those with Lamarck, that with phrenology in the person of Franz-Joseph Gall, and that with German *Naturphilosophie*. It was here in fact that his frequent pronouncements on the nature and direction of 'good' science were to earn him, if anywhere, the title of 'legislator of science'.

The appointment was all the more valuable because of the

real limitations on Cuvier's power in other directions. He possessed, for example, little influence over research directions in agriculture, in pharmacy or in any of the applied sciences. The work done in the provincial agricultural and scientific societies owed little to him, as did the work undertaken under the aegis of the army and navy. Nor did Cuvier's institutional affiliations help him to enforce his ideas. No more than he could prevent the infiltration of his family by extremist political ideas, could he prevent the infiltration of the Muséum by scientific tendencies which he deplored. The Muséum, after all, contained not only Lamarck and Geoffroy as his colleagues, but also, as its librarian and editor of its *Annales*, J. P. F. Deleuze, an obdurate and lifelong proponent of 'animal magnetism', the successor of mesmerism, who managed to carry with him into magnetic circles Cuvier's own assistant Duméril.[31]

The difficulties of extending personal control for Cuvier were increased by the tendency of individuals within institutions to divide into tiny, hostile factions, shifting according to the pressures of the development of ideas and the patterns of patronage. Within the Muséum, for example, Lamarck was set against Desfontaines and De Jussieu, who had prevented him using the botanical collections after 1793; Cuvier criticised Lamarck and Faujas de St Fond, but was aided by Lacepède, de Jussieu, and initially by Geoffroy and even Lamarck; Cuvier's friend De Candolle tried hard to become Lamarck's pupil; and so on.[32] No firm authority could be founded on such shifting ground.

It is therefore not surprising that Cuvier tried hard and consistently to elevate the Institut into a forum which had the obligation to set the norms of science. The Institut was Cuvier's most secure institutional base, the only one where he held unlimited lifelong authority, shared only with his counterpart for the physical and mathematical sciences, the astronomer Delambre.[33] Only the Permanent Secretaryships gave the right to judge the work of other *savants* in an ostensibly neutral way in front of the rest of the community of science. As part of his regular duties, the Permanent Secretary prepared annual reports on the work of the preceding twelve months in the sciences within his purview, as well as in special long-term analyses, such as the report which Cuvier presented to Napoleon in 1808 on the progress of scientific work since 1789.[34] The funeral *éloges* on departed members which it was his duty to prepare, and to read at the four yearly public sessions of the Institut offered many opportunities for summing up the history of a speciality, and for outlining a research programme for the dead man's successors.[35] Although the composition of the commissions appointed to report to the body of the sections on specific pieces of research submitted for the Institut's judgement was left to the relevant section, as Secretary, Cuvier had no difficulty in appointing himself to the committees which were reporting on works of special interest to him.[36] It was through these means that Cuvier used his position in the Institut to define what he considered to be a standard of acceptable science and hence also to define what the direction of that science should be. Moreover, within the Institut, this could be done in ways which respected the privacy, and hence the expert status, of science. Both early and late in his career Cuvier was concerned to protect the meetings of the Institut from public participation.[37] Playing to the gallery, he felt, would mean that scientific issues would be decided by public pressure rather than on their merits. That this was a justifiable fear we have already seen in the case of the Geoffroy debate. Such participation would also have destroyed the unique feature of the Institut as a forum for scientific debate, which was its ethic of impartiality. Not persons but ideas were the subject of debate. Demands for the implementation of research programmes could stand out with especial strength because they were made impersonally. The Institut, in other words, represented all the benefits for science of escape from its public audience.

We need now to proceed to examine how Cuvier actually used the power at his disposal after 1803. The test case provided by the historiography is Cuvier's treatment of Lamarck. It has often been held that Lamarck was reduced to obscurity in his own lifetime by Cuvier's combination of public neglect and private mockery. In spite of some challenge, this view reappears intact even in recent works.[38] Cuvier's alleged stifling of Lamarck has been adduced as an example of his willingness to slow down scientific progress and to compel

Controversy, authority and the market   127

French science to mount a 'mistaken' opposition to transformism[39] As we have seen, such accusations were already common currency under the Restoration, but an examination of what actually happened does not in fact support the view that Cuvier unrestrictedly used his power as Permanent Secretary to stifle Lamarck, or indeed that Lamarck was stifled at all. In his public lectures at the Muséum, reprinted at the same time, he repeatedly attacked Cuvier's large-scale classificatory works.[40]

Cuvier himself showed little restraint in subjecting his colleague to public attack in return. In his open lectures at the Athénée (Lycée) de Paris, a contemporary recorded in 1805, Cuvier ridiculed Lamarck's new work on organised beings: '... the formation of different organs by habits was joked about. And whatever tenderness the amiable and learned materialist who is the author of it merits ... a Cuvier can take the liberty of joking when it comes to animals'.[41] All this hardly constitutes a campaign of public silence on the one side and a consignment to oblivion on the other. Cuvier did campaign against Lamarck, but very publicly indeed. The public lecture was clearly regarded by both men as a fit forum for dismantling the other's work. Conversely, the 'private' life of science as represented in Cuvier's 1808 report, paid little attention to the question of their rivalry.[42] Nor was Lamarck the outcast from official life that he has been sometimes represented as being, in contrast to Cuvier. His books, for example, regularly received extensive, respectful, if not wholly convinced reviews in the pages of the official *Moniteur universel*[43]. For several years the *Moniteur* also gave space to Lamarck's metereological controversies with Lalande.[44] De Candolle, who produced the new edition of Lamarck's *Flore française* of 1788, made it clear that Lamarck was not only able to gain substantial sums from the sale of the *Flore*, but was also easily able to gain access to Napoleon himself.[45] If Lamarck had difficulty finding pupils, this was very often his own fault, as his collaborator Candolle again makes clear.[46] No picture emerges of Cuvier using some mysterious authority to silence Lamarck. In the Institut, where he could most effectively have silenced the older man, he refrained from doing so: the ethic of neutrality in the 'private' forum of science was stronger than his undoubted hostility.

If the case of Lamarck is a study in what Cuvier did *not* do with his power as Permanent Secretary, we now need to look at his positive aspirations in that role. It was certainly his view that the Institut, with himself as its mouthpiece, not only could, but should give a decisive lead to contemporary science.[47] What kind of science did he favour? In his own reports on specific pieces of research submitted to the Institut, he gradually made his ideas plain. One of the most important of these reports was published in 1807, and encapsulated most of Cuvier's *desiderata* for the future direction of the observational natural sciences such as geology and natural history.[48] First came the demand for rigorous attention to 'faits et observations' and for an equally rigorous avoidance of that 'recherche des causes', or final causes, which had for so long degraded the status of such sciences. For Cuvier, science could only be pursued as a respectable intellectual enterprise at the level of secondary causes.[49] Otherwise, science was nothing but '... un tissu d'hypothèses et de conjectures, tellement vaines et qui se sont tellement combattues les unes et les autres, qu'il est devenue presqu'impossible de prononcer son nom sans exciter le rire'.[50] In other words, the establishment of a correct, fruitful methodology for a science, connecting it with objectives 'reél et capable d'être atteint',[51] was inextricable from the question of its attaining respectable public status. These two objectives were also linked with a strong attack on controversy as a means of arriving at the truth. In particular, the Institut itself should not encourage such argument, but regard its task as that of encouraging 'ceux qui constatent des faits positifs, et garder un silence absolu sur les systèmes qui succèdent'.[52] For Cuvier, the necessity for the observational sciences of avoiding controversy as a means of gaining truth was increased by their uncertain epistemological status vis-a-vis the more prestigious mathematically based sciences:

Placés entre les sciences mathématiques et les sciences morales, elles commencent où les phénomènes ne sont plus susceptibles d'être mesurés avec précision, ni les résultats d'être calculés avec exactitude; elles finissent, lorsqu'il n'y a plus à considérer que les opérations de l'esprit et leur influence sur la volonté ... Une fois sortis des phénomènes du choc nous n'avons plus d'idée nette des rapports de cause et d'effet. Tout se réduit à recueillir des faits particuliers, et à chercher des propositions générales qui en embrassent le plus grande nombre possible ... il s'en faut encore beaucoup qu'elles aient été ramenees aux lois du choc, qui seules pourroient les changer en véritables explications.[53]

It was in virtue of ideas like these that Cuvier as Permanent Secretary entered into his debate with Franz-Joseph Gall, the phrenologist. Cuvier's interest in Gall's system began many years before his famous report to the Institut of 1808. His German contacts placed him in a peculiarly advantageous position to gather information on the movement. He may well have written to Gall himself, although no trace of this letter survives.[54] By 1801, he was certainly in contact with Gall's pupils, including the famous Berlin *salonnière* Fanny von Arnstein.[55] In 1802, he was writing to his friend Charles de Villers in joking terms of the exposition of Gall's system which he had read in a German journal.[56] Villers responded with a far longer and more serious exposition of phrenology, which achieved a wide circulation in both French and German.[57] Cuvier was undoubtedly in basic agreement at this point with Viller's comments on the new system. Like most writing on Gall before Cuvier's 1808 report, Villers' work concentrated on a criticism of Gall's psychology, on the impossibility of obtaining agreement about the definition of his moral and intellectual 'qualities' and on the weakness of their alleged connection both with the cerebral anatomy and the anecdotal evidence which Gall produced in its support. However, he easily absolved Gall from tendencies towards materialism which could be deduced from his linkage of moral tendencies with innate physical disposition.

In many of these comments, Cuvier and Villers were not exceptional. Cuvier's friend and pupil, the doctor Moreau de la Sarthe, for example, made very similar observations to establish that Gall's anatomical work had failed to establish the brain as a multiple organ whose parts had distinct functions; the link which Gall emphasised between the anatomy of the brain and his version of faculty psychology was therefore not proven.[58] Lamarck also differed from Gall on precisely this point.[59]

Cuvier's report of 1808 changed the nature of this debate in two main ways.[60] It refocused attention on Gall's anatomy at the expense of his psychology, which was expressly excluded from consideration. In correspondence, both with Gall himself and with others, which grew out of the 1808 report to the Institut, he also opened discussion on the relationship between Gall's phrenological teaching and its public audience. Did the immense public interest aroused by Gall mean that in fact his system as a whole, whatever might be the merits of its individual discoveries, was merely a pseudo-science? It is as well to insist that Cuvier's hostility to Gall was not motivated by fears that his doctrines were the stalking horses of materialism. This issue in fact is never raised in Cuvier's surviving written reactions to phrenology. What bothered Cuvier far more was the possible effect of such pseudo-sciences on the status of the natural sciences as a whole.

However, there may well have been an implicit struggle between Cuvier and Gall for the control of direction in research into the anatomy of the skull and brain. Both men had worked on the problem of establishing the trajectory of the cranial nerves.[61] Cuvier's solution to the problem differed markedly from Gall's. Each man could see the other as a rival claimant to disputed territory.[62] More basically, Gall's work on the brain attempted to pull anatomical interest in a different direction from the morphological studies initiated by Cuvier's work on the bones of the skull.[63]

On the other hand, the report which Cuvier produced on Gall's anatomy was not wholly unfavourable. The criticisms it contained, on points of anatomical procedure, and principally of the idea that one can treat the brain as a collection of separate organs, were in themselves no more damning than those he was later to address to the first neurological researches of his protégé Pierre Flourens, which contained criticisms of procedure, of terminology and of incompleteness.[64] Cuvier's real crime in Gall's eyes was to have explicitly dissociated consideration of his anatomical work from that of his psychology, and to have stated that the latter lay outside the competence of the First Class of the Institut. The implication that anatomy and psychology could be dissociated in his system, though not, as we have seen, a very unusual one

Controversy, authority and the market 131

in contemporary critiques of Gall, was viewed by him as a judgement against the status of his theory as real science. In turn, the report strengthened further attacks on Gall. Cuvier's friend Maine de Biran, for example, produced a lengthy résumé of Gall's work very shortly after the publication of the report to the Institut.[65] In many ways, it went further in its criticisms of Gall than Cuvier himself had done. Both anatomy and psychology, he pointed out, were undermined as valid, autonomous bodies of thought by the effort to bring them together.[66] This was a point very much after Cuvier's own heart, but one which he himself did not explicitly make.

Gall's reaction to Cuvier was violent. He quickly published a massive 274-page rebuttal of the 1808 report, and wrote Cuvier at least two lengthy and agitated letters in quick succession.[67] Some of Gall's protests in both letters and book were purely anatomical in character, like his assertion that Cuvier had radically misinterpreted his work on the nature of the medullary matter. The rest of Gall's protests were tributes to the very power of the concept of 'real science' that Cuvier defended. It was mistaken, he protested, to assert (as in fact Cuvier's report had not) that his system involved speculation on moral dispositions, and the erection of casual links between moral and physical characteristics. In Gall's denials, and in his reiteration that he too was only interested in 'facts', we see him trying to meet Cuvier's previous definitions of a real science as distinguished from a pseudo-science.[68] Gall's printed reply to Cuvier's report veered sharply between an insistence that his system was concerned only with a purely factual study of the operation of the nervous system, and a strong emphasis on a view of the brain as a collection of organs whose function was yet susceptible to a 'philosophical' analysis.[69] Gall in fact could never be content either with the 'factual' cerebral anatomy which fitted Cuvier's definition of good science, or with the appeal to public interest which lay in the 'philosophical' science of his system. It was above all the relation of phrenology to the public which alienated Cuvier as much as or more than the illegitimacy of Gall's attempts to draw moral consequences from the anatomy of the brain.

For Cuvier, Gall's relation with the public defined him immediately as a charlatan, and hence as someone who could draw the natural sciences as a whole into disrepute. The account of his conflict with Gall in the 'autobiography' of 1822, written while phrenology was still a powerful force in the popular science of Paris, was conceived almost entirely in these terms:

Gall vint à Paris; il présenta à l'Académie [sic] ses découvertes sur le cerveau. Mais il reserva sa craniologie pour le vulgaire; mon rapport sur son mémoire a été un assez grand travail; malgré la manière honorable dont je parlai de lui, il crut, à la manière des charlatans, devoir répondre un gros volume à quelques restrictions que j'apportais à ses propositions. Il espérait que je répliqueras et que nous occupérions ainsi le public, mais je me gardai bien de me donner dans le piège.[70]

Public debate, in other words, could only be a trap degrading to real science. It was a view which was likely to find wide acceptance in the inner community of science in Paris, because it implicitly strengthened the power and prestige of the Institut – and hence, of course, those of its Permanent Secretary. Because of the attacks in the period of the early Revolution on the scientific élite in the name of democratic intellect, which had culminated in the closure of the Academy of Sciences in 1793, Cuvier's portrayals of the 'crowd' as a threat to scientific excellence were likely to seem convincing.[71] It was this historic insecurity, rather than any incipient 'professionalisation' of science, which made Cuvier connect good science, in this context, with rigorous abstention from the public arena. There was also the point that when knowledge was property, too wide a diffusion of this precious commodity might reduce its price. As Cuvier wrote to his friend in Tübingen, Karl-Friedrich Keilmeyer, in 1808, on the subject of his conflict with Gall:

dans ce pays-ci la première règle de conduite pour un savant c'est de ne jamais parler de ce qui est livré au grand public et aux journaux; en un mot des objets de la curiosité populaire. Ce serait se traîner dans la boue et se livrer aux bêtes.[72]

Nor was Cuvier alone in this point of view. Maine de Biran also heavily censured Gall for 'popularising' anatomical research, and 'dazzling and leading astray' an ignorant public.[73] One of the easiest ways for an insecure élite, like the knowledge élite of Napoleonic France, to ensure its own unique status is to

Controversy, authority and the market 133

exclude others, that is 'the public', from participation.

In spite of all his efforts, Cuvier's report had little influence on the international spread of Gall's teachings, or on his continued acceptance in Parisian society, in many areas of the medical profession, and indeed in at least one of the public forums used by Cuvier himself, that of the public lectures of the Athénée de Paris, where Gall lectured until the end of his life. Given this continued resistance, it is not surprising that fulminations against Gall's system form one of the major themes of Cuvier's international correspondence.[74] Nor was this all. In spite of his own contrary pronouncements, Cuvier did not abstain from mobilising publicity on his own behalf in the fight against Gall. Besides ensuring the frequent reprinting of his report in full, he also ensured that many shortened versions of it appeared in the popular literary journals. Gall himself, turning the tables on Cuvier, commented on this practice with much asperity.[75] Even in a case which looks as though the exercise of Cuvier's authority must rest entirely on the Institut, the existence of the public realm for science could produce peculiar ambiguities in Cuvier's use of the concepts of the privacy of science and its necessary remoteness from the public field.

It is tempting to speculate that Cuvier's encouragement of the neurological experiments of his protégé Flourens may have been motivated as much by the need to mount a new onslaught on Gall, as by his encouragement of the new physiology of François Magendie.[76] Flourens' 1822 experiments on the functions of the cerebellum, although it cited Gall's latest work on the spinal cord and medulla, was certainly seen by Gall himself as a challenge, and led to the production of counter-experiments.[77] Flourens and Gall in fact put forward different programmes for the study of the brain and nervous system, based on incompatible assumptions. Flourens' *questionnaire* was not posed by Gall's, but came from a re-examination of Hallerian concepts of irritability and sensibility, and the wish to find experimentally valid ways of distinguishing sensation from muscular irritation. His ablation experiments on birds tried to establish distinctions between volition, located in the cerebral lobes, and muscular contraction and co-ordination, located in the spinal cord, the medulla and the nerve trunks. But although Flourens thought he had succeeded in localising different functions in different parts of the nervous system, he still considered the cerebral hemisphere a unitary organ.[78] The major impetus for Flourens' work came from Cuvier. It was Cuvier who established the subjects for the Montyon prize offered by the Academy of Sciences for functional descriptions of the parts of the brain, which Flourens won two years in succession, in 1824 and 1825.

In 1828, Flourens was elected to the Academy of Sciences, and became Cuvier's *suppléant* at the Collège de France. In 1832, he succeeded both to Cuvier's chair there, and to his position as Permanent Secretary. There are few clearer cases of Cuvier's use of his powers of patronage especially those located within the Academy of Sciences, to foster a particular view not only of physiology, but of the work of Gall.[79] Cuvier's support of Flourens was exhibited at the same time as he took active measures to prevent the spread of Gall's teachings. Gall had already failed in his 1821 attempt to gain election to the Academy of Sciences, and thus win official endorsement of his status as a true scientist by the inner scientific community. The only vote cast for him had belonged to Cuvier's rival Geoffroy.[80] In 1823, Cuvier used his influence in the administration of the Université de France to ban the teaching of phrenology within the medical faculty of Paris by Gall's follower Fossati. The ban was only lifted after Fossati had agreed to reclassify his course as one in 'philosophy' rather than in mediciné, in other words, until he had admitted that phrenology was a speculative doctrine outside the realm of positive science.[81]

Cuvier's campaign against Gall was so prolonged that it is worth studying as a compendium of the ways in which controversy was conducted and authority maintained. It is noteworthy, first of all, that Cuvier rarely attacked the quality of Gall's anatomical work.[82] As has been seen, Cuvier was certainly not alone in his criticisms of Gall's system. Cuvier's strongest criticisms of Gall were expressed in his private correspondence, and centred on the idea that Gall was a charlatan and that the public presentation of his work compromised the status of natural science. A clear and conscious distinction seems to have been drawn between what

Cuvier felt it was permissible for him to say in his capacity as Permanent Secretary, and what it was permissible to say as a private person in private communications.

For all Cuvier's strictures, and for all his success in mounting alternative research programmes to those of Gall, the basic problem still remained unsolved and indeed incapable of solution. How far did certain kinds of public reception of a supposed knowledge undermine or influence its very status as knowledge? *Naturphilosphie*, no less than phrenology, faced Cuvier with the same set of problems. Cuvier's first official contacts with this body of belief came in 1801 when, as temporary secretary to the First Class, he composed a report on experiments performed by the German chemist Ritter, who had worked on the decomposition of water into its constituent gases by the passage of an electric current.[83] In setting up such experiments, Ritter was hoping to support the philosopher Schelling's contention that electricity was the principle of all life in nature.[84] Ritter was to go on to try to demonstrate electrical properties, especially polarities, in many different forms of nature. Most notably, he asserted that sight, hearing, taste and touch were nothing more than individual manifestations of the primeval sensibility of man, his electrical sense. Ritter's experiments were in fact strongly linked to the tendency of *Naturphilosophie* to seek a limited number of basic phenomena in nature, and to see such phenomena in terms of the bipolarities which, as the philosopher Schelling insisted, governed not only natural phenomena, but also the social and moral experience of man. It was therefore engaged in that very search for prime causes which Cuvier excluded from the proper province of science.[85]

Cuvier's aversion to *Naturphilosophie* was already well established by the period of his stay in Normandy. It was also fed by his friendship with Karl-Friedrich Kielmeyer. By 1805, Cuvier made his opposition to the movement very clear: in publishing the *Leçons d'anatomie comparée* he hoped that

la facilité de méditer sur des faits positifs, et celle d'en découvrir de nouveaux en partant de ceux qui sont connus, détourneront les bons esprits de cette méthode bizarre de philosopher, qui consiste à vouloir tout créér par le raisonnement, à produire *a priori*, et à faire sortir tout armée de son cerveau une science qui ne peut nous arriver que par les sens extérieurs, puisqu'elle ne peut avoir de réalité que dans l'expérience, méthode qui n'a mené jusqu'à présent ses sécateurs qu'à des résultats inutiles lorsqu'ils n'a pas été absurdes.[86]

All this found a sympathetic hearer in Kielmeyer, and it was undoubtedly upon Kielmeyer's comments to Cuvier that the section of the large-scale report of 1808 dealing with *Naturphilosophie* was written.[87]

Cuvier not only reprehended the tendency of the movement to envisage nature in an experimentally unverifiable way, as a living organism, an active force, a unified whole, the product of endlessly interacting polarities; Schelling had argued that in order that the individual products of nature can exist as enduring objects at all, the perpetually active nature-force must act as a perpetual polarity, an obstruction checking force. Nature for him was a unity of mutually conflicting forces, and this conflict explains the progress observable from the highest to the lowest forms. It was such metaphysical statements whose invasion into scientific discourse and practice Cuvier viewed as potentially compromising to the reputation of the natural sciences. Such movements, he thought, could only lead to a

mépris des sciences parmi les hommes puissans, dont la protection est pourtant indispensable pour les sciences, au moins pour les sciences naturelles. Vous ne vous figurez pas à quel point on a excité des préjugés dans certaines têtes très influents, contre ses systèmes qui dominent aujourd'hui chez vous et que l'on a cherché à représenter comme y occupant tous les esprits sans exception ... Eh bien, mon ami, avec un Prince qui s'occupe des sciences et commande depuis le Vistule jusqu'au Tage, ces choses-là influent sinon sur le sort des nations, du moins sur beaucoup de mesures qui peuvent rendre une foule de particuliers malheureux.[88]

The point which most impressed Cuvier after an extensive reading of authors such as Schelling, Troxler, Steffens, Kieser and Oken, was the poor logical quality of *Naturphilosophie*[89] Most of all, he disliked 'cette prétention de déduire *a priori* les faits réels des principes abstraites'.[90] In particular Cuvier was attacking here such notions as Oken's postulate of the primal organisation of constitutive animalicules which, according to him, formed the constituent parts of all living beings. These original materials were not created but developed. These ideas

Controversy, authority and the market 137

of permanent being and becoming, unregulated by the precise condition of life altering every organism, were particularly disliked by Cuvier. He was not alone in his hostility, for the Institut itself also adopted a harsh line towards *Naturphilosophie* in chemistry and physics. Further experiments by Ritter for example, reported upon by Haüy, failed to replicate themselves. This was unfortunate, since those investigations on the swing of the pendulum were meant to demonstrate yet again the unending operation of polarities in nature. Again, experiments by the Budapest chemist Winterl also failed to replicate in 1809 when performed in Paris by Berthollet. The work of the two men was closely associated, for Ritter had supplied the preface to the 1803 German summary of Winterl's exposition of his chemical beliefs.[91] In it he attacked the treatment given to Winterl by the Institut. Cuvier, after lamenting what he saw as the waste of Ritter's fine qualities as a physical scientist, could hardly contain his fury at this attack.[92] Winterl, who died in 1809 shortly after receiving Cuvier's curt notification of the failure of his chemical system to satisfy its critics in the Institut, had evolved a dualistic chemical system which enjoyed a wide popularity in Germany and the Austrian Empire.[93] He claimed in his 1800 *Prolusiones* to have discovered basic substances simpler than Lavoisier's chemical elements. It was these elements whose existence were so difficult to demonstrate in Paris. Science as practised in some quarters in Germany and science as it was understood in Paris, were two incompatible systems. In his lengthy report on the state of science, published in 1810, Cuvier expatiated at length upon the case of Winterl. After remarking that his system must ultimately be set aside because its philosophical basis made it incapable of experimental verification, he went on to point out the importance of the experimental method in any science worthy of the name:

L'expérience seule, l'expérience précise, faite avec poids, mesure, calcul et comparaison de tous les substances employés et de toutes les substances obtenues, voilà aujourd'hui la seule voie légitime de raisonnement, de démonstration.[94]

In the case of *Naturphilosophie*, Cuvier appeared to have achieved a coherent, consistent and strong case, but we must now conclude by asking questions about the net effect and consequences of all these exertions of authority both within and without the Academy of Sciences.

Cuvier was hardly a dominant 'legislator' figure. Even within the terms of his position as Permanent Secretary, for example, there were other synoptic descriptions than his of the years work in the scientific community, such as that published annually in the *Journal de Physique* by his old enemy De Lamethérie. Nor could he stop the growth of many pseudosciences which relied on public interest and public consumption for their existence. While it is clear that as for example in the case of Flourens, Cuvier possessed great control over research directions, it is also true that in the case of colleagues outside the direct sphere of his patronage, such as Lamarck, his influence was likely to be limited.[95] Nor could he prevent the formation of hostile blocs inside the Institut itself.

However, the attainment of the post of Permanent Secretary does seem to have had an important influence on Cuvier's own work. It enabled him to abandon the inconsistency of some of his earlier work, and to make himself into the champion of a certain kind of science: 'positive', factual, drawing its materials from the world immediately accessible to the senses, and above all anchored in the world of secondary causes. But if the Institut gave Cuvier a forum uniquely suitable in some respects for the mounting of propaganda for a certain kind of science, it is also obvious that Cuvier considered the Institut an unsuitable forum for many kinds of utterances. It was only in the public forums such as the Athenée de Paris or the Collège de France, both of whose courses were open to all who could pay the modest attendance fees, that he tended to mount the stronger attacks upon personalities and ideas.[96]

This conclusion, if correct, sits very oddly with the repeated assertions that Cuvier conducted his most deadly scientific conflicts by using significant silence, or private conversation. The isolation of such different types of utterances may help the historians to know what to expect from different sources; for example, not to take a relatively sketchy or charitable viewpoint expressed in one of the yearly reports to the Institut as the last word on Cuvier's real views. Some of the rules of controversy were thus fairly sharply defined. Where the ambiguity came in was whenever the *savant* had to appeal to a public wider than that of his peers. Cuvier, as we have seen, in his explicit statements consistently viewed the exclusion of an appeal to the public as one of the marks of real science, and an openness to a wide public as the sign of a pseudo-science. Yet Cuvier himself used appeal to a wide public as one of his main controversial weapons, and showed great preoccupation in the case of Gall with the reprinting and dissemination of the judgement on Gall undertaken in the name of élite science. What these ambiguities mean is that reputation in science was a far more shifting thing than Cuvier could admit. It was only partly formed by the judgement of one's peers; the state, the public, and hence the market, all contributed. The view of Cuvier as a 'legislator' of science is an image generated by the ideology of the inner community of science. It fulfils the function of removing from view the extent to which the pressures of controversy and of the market shaped Cuvier's work; it also thus hides the extent of the insecurity of the evaluation of reputation which beset the scientific community of Cuvier's age, and which was itself one of the strongest pressures for the removal of 'the public' from its ideology.

The conflicts in which Cuvier became involved as a man of science have many features in common with the political conflicts described in the last chapter. The first, most striking, similarity is their frequency. Cuvier's whole life was lived in an atmosphere of continued controversy. In this he was not unique; the same happened to Lamarck, and to a lesser extent to Geoffroy, and not simply in virtue of their conflicts with Cuvier. Controversy itself was simply an inescapable feature of public life throughout this period. The lack of a single universally accepted synthesis in natural science made the growth of radically incompatible research programmes almost inevitable. The rise of a public for science, and the insecurity of career patterns within the scientific community made it very likely that men of science would use public controversy as a means of gaining advantage in the chase for scarce renumerated positions. On a broader front, the instability of the ruling élite of which the *savants* formed a part – instability in powers and in actual public competence from one régime to another – made every man in public life liable to violent assaults on his authority from every conceivable direction. All these factors taken together help to explain Cuvier's difficult but intense relationship with the public. The public presented a threat to the true life of science, just as did the masses to the efforts of the true élite to build a strong state; on the other hand, without the public Cuvier could not have made his career in science in the way he did. As Cuvier's public position became ever more controverted under the Restoration, he turned increasingly in his scientific life against the notion of public participation in the life of science. It was Geoffroy's moral – if not intellectual – victory to have broken down these carefully constructed barriers in 1830 and to have introduced the strains, tensions and rhetoric of public life into the hitherto jealously guarded neutrality of the Institut.

VII
Geology, history and the shaping of a self-image

Ces idées m'ont poursuivis, je dirois presque tourmenté
(Cuvier, 1812, p. 112.)

In the *Discours Préliminaire*, Cuvier was to employ an enormously wide range of methods of claim-staking, which ranged from a romantic, emotional rhetoric of self-discovery, to the most carefully used ambiguity over the controverted religious issues attached to geological enquiry, to wider-ranging critiques of the work of most previous authors in the field, to the claim that Cuvier had established the epistemological independence of geology. Such a wide-ranging work clearly cannot achieve a full discussion within a description of intellectual tactics. For that reason, it will be as well to signal here those aspects of the *Discours* which will not be discussed. While discussion of Cuvier's religious opinions is inescapable in this context, no attention will be paid to the later history of the *Discours* and its use as ammunition, after 1812, and especially in the Restoration, for warring religious opinions. Cuvier's other palaeontological work and its relation to the later editions of this work, will also not be discussed; nor will we enter into the topic of how the *Discours* influenced Cuvier's reputation outside France. But the breadth of the issues contained in the *Discours* is in any case enormous.

The *Discours préliminaire* was originally published at the head of the *Recherches sur les ossemens fossiles des quadrupèdes* and reissued separately under the title of *Discours préliminaire sur les révolutions du globe*. During Cuvier's lifetime, this work went into six editions in French, was translated into all the major European languages, and was continually expanded, though not radically revised, by its author.[1] Its reception in Britain in a translation by James Kerr and with annotations by the Wernerian geologist Robert Jameson which soon doubled or tripled its original length, was particularly enthusiastic, and it was fed into many of the debates on scriptural geology which mark the first half of the nineteenth century in Britain.[2]

The *Preliminary Discourse* was triumphantly successful in crossing the boundary which Cuvier himself had insisted upon in other contexts, between 'real science' and works of popularisation. It represents Cuvier's only attempt to write in a general way about the geological issues raised by his work on the reconstruction of fossil species. It discusses the anatomical principles by which reconstructions are guided. It attempts to explain the causes of extinction by pointing out that geological evidence about the strata in which fossils were found suggests that geological cataclysms or 'revolutions' might have wiped out entire populations of animals, or at the very least forced them to migrate to other parts of the globe. A long historical section attempts to fix the date of the last such geological cataclysm by reference to the legends of the Flood common throughout the near east, including the Hebrew story recorded in the Book of Genesis. It therefore occupies a special place in Cuvier's work as the only such general essay to venture outside the fields of physiology, anatomy and taxonomy, to achieve a Humboldtian breadth of enquiry.

Historians of science have shown an interest in the *Preliminary Discourse* scarcely inferior to that displayed by Cuvier's contemporaries. In particular, this work has been taken as the *locus classicus* for discussion of Cuvier's views on religious issues. Presenting Cuvier as a lukewarm hypocrite in religious matters, many commentators have used the *Preliminary Discourse* to argue that Cuvier supported the literal sense of Biblical accounts of the Flood, and the shortened timescale for the history of the earth which such a belief is also held to imply. Cuvier did so, it is argued, partly in order to join the increasing tide of official encouragement of religious orthodoxy in the years after 1802, and hence strengthen his hold on his administrative positions; and partly because a short time-span for the history of the earth would, if proved, offer a decisive blow to Lamarck's views on the transformation of species, a slow process consuming many aeons.[3]

Geology, history and the shaping of a self-image 143

However, the case against Cuvier on the score of religious hypocrisy has rarely if ever been accompanied by an attempt to discover just what his religious ideas really were. If we can discover that Cuvier's real ideas in this area differed from those he is asserted to have had, then the neat connection with the attack on Lamarck also breaks down, and we are left with the task of discovering the real areas of agreement and disagreement between the two men. Finally, exclusive concern with such questions has obscured the other purposes which may have been in Cuvier's mind when he wrote the *Preliminary Discourse*. I shall argue here that in fact this work formed a vital element in the development of Cuvier's self-presentation as a *savant*. It was so because it detached both science and the *savant* himself from the concerns of scriptural geology and linked them to an intimate concern with the problem of time, and the psychology of scientific discovery.

Let us take first the question of Cuvier's own religious views. Recent work has made it clear that the term scripture geology described no coherent body of thought in this period of France.[4] In other words, even if Cuvier had wished to be a Biblical geologist, we would still be faced with the task of describing the precise ways in which his religious beliefs entered his geological thinking, and hence of discovering what those beliefs really were. In fact, the evidence points strongly to the conclusion that Cuvier was unlikely to have wanted to be any sort of apologist for the Mosaic account of notable geological events such as the Flood. In the early years of the Empire, in fact, Cuvier had a reputation for religious irreverence upon which contemporaries such as the Italian visitor Marzari Pencati, were quick to seize.[5] Contemporary testimony from the end of his life gives very much the same impression. His friend, relative, compatriot and collaborator, Georges Duvernoy, was forced to admit in his admiring study of Cuvier's achievements that it had not been Christ but scientific labour which had formed his *ancre du salut*.[6] It is also noticeable that none of the numerous accounts of Cuvier's death-bed contains any reference to religious matters made by the dying man.[7] However, the most striking and detailed testimony on this point comes from Mark Wilks, Pastor to the English community in Paris, who was a close friend of Cuvier's daughter, Clémentine, and the author of one of the many emotional commemorations of her piety and good works which appeared after her early death in 1827.[8] Wilks' account is interesting because of its detailed evocation of the divided religious atmosphere of the Cuvier household. Clémentine, he relates, became a member of a group of young women who met regularly in the Cuvier home to pray for '... the conversion of their relatives ... and one can easily imagine what were the hallowed breathings of her soul, in those solemn seasons set apart to plead with God for the conversion of her illustrious parent'.[9] In Cuvier's household, in fact, the deism of the Enlightenment confronted across the generations the emotional Christianity of the Restoration. Wilks elaborated the point with a wealth of theological detail:

What Baron Cuvier's precise sentiments were on the subject of revealed religion does not appear from anything I have read. Whether he contented himself with those ministrations which he performed with such ability at the altar of natural religion, and thus added one more to the highly systematic minds who are content with worshipping God the Creator, without doing homage to God the Saviour and the Sanctifier; or whether he paid a sincere homage to the Redeemer of the World, I pretend not to determine. Certain, however, it is, that in his last moments ... there were no expressions of a faith first looking for comfort and peace to the cross of Christ, then penetrating the veil, and ranging through the regions of immortality ... but oh how different was the case of his sainted, seraphed daughter: she also yearned for glory, but it was for the glory to be revealed in heaven; for honour, but it was for that honour which cometh from above ... Contrast the silence and reserve of philosophy with the full and joyful testimony of faith.[10]

It is also noticeable that Clémentine is described as praying for Cuvier's conversion, and important to note that this is highly unlikely to mean conversion to Catholicism. Cuvier's children by his marriage to Madame Duvaucel were brought up as Protestant, unlike those from her first marriage, who remained nominally Catholic.[11] The inference can therefore only be that Clémentine was praying for Cuvier's conversion at least to some form of revealed religion, if not to religion altogether. It is also possible to point to many passages in his writings where nature appears not as an image of the benevolent intentions of God, but rather of the worst

Geology, history and the shaping of a self-image 145

characteristics of human society. In 1800 for example, Cuvier pointed out that the study of animal life must often strike the observer 'with those bizarre assortments of benefits and evils which so often appear to question the dispositions of Providence'.[12] Amongst the animals, he continued, we are faced with

> the same spectacle as in the world of men; in spite of what the moralists say, the animals are hardly less wicked or less unhappy than we are ourselves. The arrogance of the strong, the servility of the weak, low rapacity, ephemeral pleasure purchased by great effort, death preceded by long suffering, all belong to the animals as much as they do to men.

These are hardly the words of a man possessed by a deep inner conviction that the natural world is organised by God as an image of his benevolent order.

However, we have still to explain Cuvier's prominence in Protestant organisations if, as seems likely, his personal belief consisted of a minimal deism, replaced on some occasions by a darker vision of the nature of the organised world. Cuvier was elected to the committee appointing the Consistory of Paris in 1803, and under the Restoration became Grand-Master of the Faculties of Protestant theology within the University of France, and Director of the non-Catholic religions. As we have seen, his family, in the persons of the Napoleonic General Walther, his uncle, and Walther's son-in-law, the banker Bartholdi, penetrated into the Parisian Protestant élite. He was widely respected as an effective spokesman for Protestant interests even under the Empire,[14] but on the other hand, it is also clear that while Cuvier was an efficient administrator in the sense of safeguarding Protestant interests in the erection of new schools and temples, in improving their financing, in modernising the training of pastors, and in mediating the internal disputes to which the Protestant communities were particularly prone, he also manifested very little concern with the spirituality of Protestantism. He took little part in the missionary work and social endeavour which was then becoming a characteristic feature of Protestant life in France.[15] Cuvier may well, in fact, have tended, after the Revolution to see Protestantism as a series of opportunities rather than as a body of belief.

The Revolution's consecration of religious toleration opened many opportunities for Protestants which had not previously existed, although this was an advantage whose value rapidly declined during the Catholic reaction in the Restoration. However, it is clear that Cuvier regarded the Protestant faiths as possessing peculiar advantages for the encouragement of a scientific mentality. Protestant thought in his lifetime produced increasingly radical versions of the theory of the *libre examen* of scripture. The religious revival noticeable throughout the Protestant world became linked with the contemporary liberal emphasis on individualism. Inner religious convictions of the individual were reaffirmed and sharply opposed to an image of the Catholic Church above all as a religion of authority. The idea that scripture should be open to free interpretation by individuals, as distinct from the Protestant churches as such, as the eighteenth century had argued, was first formulated by Benjamin Constant in 1816. The idea was taken up by Guizot in his 1826 lecture course at the Ecole normale on the history of European civilisation. It thus had every chance of penetrating rapidly into Cuvier's own circle. This was especially true because other writers, such as Samuel Vincent, also saw the *libre examen* as a means of ensuring a more efficient diffusion of Christian morality from the higher social classes to the lower; as, in other words, another form of that very social control which Cuvier had so stressed as part of the functions of education, as we saw in Chapter IV. Cuvier also stressed the advantages to science of the habit of the *libre examen*. Under the Empire, Cuvier had little hesitation in ascribing the achievement of such Swiss scientists as Bonnet and Saussure to the liberty of thought in Protestant states.[16] Nor was he afraid to draw the corollary that the Catholic Church tended to discourage the free enquiry which alone could advance scientific learning. Speaking of the botanist Ventenat, for example, who was a former member of a religious order, he remarked pointedly that his enquiries had only begun to bear fruit after he had left the religious life.[17] From these incidents, it is difficult to portray Cuvier as a time-serving supporter of the Catholic reaction under the Empire, any more than he can really be portrayed as a man whose religious views were likely to impel him strongly to support a

Geology, history and the shaping of a self-image 147

literal Biblical account of the Deluge.

Thus attempts to explain the content of the *Preliminary Discourse* along these lines must fail, simply because Cuvier did not in fact hold the religious views which have been ascribed to him, and did not noticeably tailor his public utterances to supporting the religious revival of the Empire or indeed of the Restoration.

I will argue that our preoccupation with Cuvier's relations to questions of Biblical geology has obscured the real importance of this work. In fact, it can be argued that Cuvier was attempting in this work to reorientate the sciences of geology and palaeontology away from reference points provided by speculation on Biblical geology and theological issues generally, and towards its integration with a new understanding of time and history. The first stage in this enterprise was the argument that geology and palaeontology existed in their own right as sciences, that epistemological autonomy was an inherent part of their constitution as sciences, and that this autonomy must especially exclude religious speculation. Cuvier's condemnation of, for example, Joseph Priestley's involvement in religious controversy is well known. The search for truth in religious affairs, he argued, was essentially futile, because inherently beyond human reason.[18] Cuvier strongly believed that religious thought and scientific enquiry could contribute little to one another and might even be mutually harmful. This was also very much the basis of his complaint against *Naturphilosophie*, that it refused to science the kinds of reasoning and proof which it needed to establish its claim to be a distinct autonomous area of enquiry. Cuvier then passed specifically to the case of the harmful impact of theological and scriptural speculation on the growth of geological science, in a report read to the Institut in 1807. So important did the topic seem to him that he devoted all but five pages of his report to the problem, and spent very little time on detailed consideration of the book he had been asked to review. André's *Theory of the Present Surface of the Earth*.[19] He emphasised the way in which speculation on the Biblical Deluge had distorted the direction of geological research. Problems such as the causes of the appearance of marine fossils in formations now far removed from the oceans, or of tropical species in zones now arctic, had all been referred to a single universal Deluge. The problem of the cause of the Deluge had, in its turn, come to dominate the direction of geological enquiry, but Cuvier continued, geologists had forgotten that the Deluge was described in Genesis as nothing more nor less than a miracle, a direct act of the will of the Creator; it was thus a fruitless enterprise to search for its secondary causes.[20] With this neat, though not entirely foolproof logical subterfuge Cuvier sought to place Biblical geology once and for all outside the domain of legitimate scientific enquiry. He proceeded to point out that even the habit of some other geologists of regarding the Biblical Deluge as merely the last of a series of cataclysmic changes to the earth's crust, had done just as much harm as had accepting the Biblical account as a literal rendering of a unique event. Once the Flood had been demoted to merely another cataclysm, he pointed out, there was no possible way of restricting the growth of unverified hypotheses in geology.[21] The consequent multiplication of geological systems insecurely anchored either to empirical verification, or even to the doubtful authority of a literal rendering of scripture, had led the whole field of enquiry into disrepute. Such violent and fruitless controversy had broken out amongst the rival systems, that it had, according to Cuvier, become almost impossible to speak of geology without exciting irreverent laughter in one's audience.[22]

The general tendency of Cuvier's remarks is clear. Whether or not the Biblical story of the Flood is true or not should be irrelevant to any geology worthy of the name. The removal of the Flood as a causal agent in the shaping of the current surface of the earth was a prerequisite for the establishment of geology as a respectable and autonomous science. It is therefore not surprising that in the *Preliminary Discourse* Cuvier avoids making any explicit identification between the last 'revolution' undergone by the surface of the earth with the Biblical deluge, or that he treats the Mosaic account of the Flood as simply one among many of the traditional accounts of a great flood to be found amongst many other near-eastern peoples other than the Jews.[23]

Here we are at the heart of the objectives of the *Preliminary Discourse:* the jettisoning of a theological point of reference for geology is accompanied by an acceptance of historical relativity, in the downgrading of the Bible story of the Flood to the position of yet another near-eastern legend. However Cuvier's purposes in introducing a relativistic view of human history into a work concerned with the popularisation of geology, were complex and should be analysed in turn. First came the problem of how geology, and his own geology in particular, should be legitimised. Having refused the traditional anchor of scripture, and being unable to rely on a long tradition of fieldwork, Cuvier was forced to try to raise the status of the infant science by demanding its epistemological autonomy and at the same time by calling down the protection of other more established scientific disciplines, such as mathematics. This enterprise was all the more necessary, given the extent to which geology was also under attack from certain sections of theological opinion. The reviving fundamentalist Catholicism of the Empire, which received enormous stimulation from the success of Chateaubriand's *Génie du Christianisme* (1802). In particular, Chateaubriand had argued against the impiety of geologists and palaeontologists who sought to argue for the great antiquity of the world from the deposition of geological strata and the existence of fossils. He attempted to argue, instead, that fossils had been put into rocks by God at the creation of the world, in order to lend it a comforting air of antiquity for the first members of the human race. Such arguments were more common in the Empire than they had been under the Enlightenment, and in this France was not unique. English geologists also found themselves forced to vindicate their science from accusations of impiety, as the very titles of some of Cuvier's correspondent Buckland's works would seem to suggest.[24]

The *Preliminary Discourse* opens with a fulsome dedication to the great mathematician Laplace. The existence of this dedication has often been taken to mean that in the *Discourse* Cuvier was concerned above all with raising the status of geology and palaeontology to the position of prestige occupied by the mathematical sciences of which Laplace was the supreme contemporary exponent. Yet Cuvier did not invoke the figure of Laplace to make substantive claims that the geological sciences could ever hope to establish proofs of a geometrical order of certainty, a goal which he explicitly stated in the *Discourse* as very distant, almost unattainable; what Cuvier is more concerned to do is to make bold claims for geology as a science, and to do so in a very general way, by asserting that geology has the same command over the laws of time, as that which the work of Laplace had enabled mathematics to achieve over the laws of space.[25] In other words, geology and palaeontology, in order to achieve validation as independent respectable sciences, had to come to terms with the laws of time. As he wrote in the *Discourse:* 'One of the results of good geology which is at the same time the best proved and the least expected is that it links natural and civil history together in an uninterrupted chain.'[26] Not only were the history of man and the history of nature inseparable in a substantive sense, but it was also through geology that man could attain a psychological enlargement once reserved for the operation of religion, a sense of universal history which would allow him to overcome the limitations of his own conditions of life, and to break the bounds of ordinary human perception of the world. Man, Cuvier exulted, 'whose span on this earth is so short, will have the glory of reconstructing the history of thousands of centuries which passed before his appearance, and thousands of beings which the human race has never seen!'[27] The object of interest has shifted from the divine plan of nature to the process of man's unaided discovery of the history of life. It is likely that Cuvier was influenced in this radical reworking of the epistemological relation between geology and history by the contemporaneous rise of history itself as a self-conscious relativistic and critical discipline. In the first paper he read before the Institut, he took the opportunity of remarking how closely allied were the critical techniques of the naturalist and of the historian.[28]

This was the era in which not only classical texts but the Bible itself were subjected to analysis not as the revealed word of God but as documents produced by particular societies at particular times.[29] The growth of a body of critical techniques likewise forced attention not only on the *content* of history but also on the *processes* of human cogitation and intuition by which the content of history was established.

At the same time, an increasingly precise relativism entered

Geology, history and the shaping of a self-image 151

historical knowledge through the opening up of ancient Oriental languages by such scholars as Sir William Jones. There is ample evidence that Cuvier was highly aware of these movements. He maintained a friendship with the younger Champollion.[30] He assisted with the French translation of the proceedings of the Asiatic Society of Calcutta in which Jones had made his communications on the ancient literature of India, and himself became a member of the Society.[31]

The power of this new scheme, where human and natural history mingled, and excluded the divine, is reflected in Cuvier's own habit, a very common one at the time, of calling himself not a 'natural' historian but simply an 'historian', or even an 'antiquary'. With uncommon bravura Cuvier utilised the clichéd equivalence between natural history and archaeology to present a new image of the naturalist as an explorer not only of the order of animated nature, but also of new worlds of time: this self-portrayal prefaces the *Preliminary Discourse*, is probably its best known passage, and certainly one of the best-known that Cuvier ever wrote. It accords an absolute and emotional primacy to the act of discovery and the processes of the acquisition of knowledge:

I travel a road where man has hitherto taken but few and uncertain steps; I am trying to make known the neglected monuments of the history of the earth. I am an antiquary of a new kind. I have had to learn how to decipher and to restore these monuments, how to recognise and reassemble their scattered and mutilated fragments in their original order, how to reconstruct the vanished beings to which these fragments belong; to reproduce them in their true character and proportion; and finally to compare them to those still living today on the surface of the earth. These skills were almost unknown. Their exercise pre-supposed a wholly new science, that of the laws of the co-existence of forms in organised beings ... but in the end, the whole animal kingdom has been explained by new laws, simply as a result of the examination of a small part of the theory of the earth.[32]

The final disclaimer should deceive no one. Few more total claims exist in the history of science than those of the opening pages of the *Discourse*.[33] Not only does Cuvier claim intellectual novelty, and a complete intellectual hegemony over a new field of natural science, that of palaeontology, but the style and language of these claims imply an emotional dedication and energy which orientates the deepest drives of the personality towards the task of recovery and reconstruction. It is this drive which makes this passage one of the most powerful and the most revealing that Cuvier ever wrote in its unusual combination of emotional urgency and intellectual control. It is also this drive which underpins the claims to intellectual control of the whole field which also appear in this passage. Cuvier seems to have liberated geology from the control of natural theology only to claim unlimited power over it for himself, and to have done so not only in virtue of intellectual claims but also of emotional ones. The naturalist himself is dominant: it is he who creates this new world of the past. Ideas, however distant, of a providential order placed there *to be discovered* have been rejected in favour of a rhetoric which places a total emphasis on the human *process* of discovery, almost of creation; which furthermore links this process indissolubly with the exploration of the history of life, and with the operation of the laws of comparative anatomy. Personality, history, time, and the new sciences of geology and palaeontology are linked like chainmail.

Of course, the *Preliminary Discourse* is a work which grew out of a prolonged conflict, out of controversial cut and thrust over specific scientific issues between Cuvier and his opponents. In particular, his reconstructions of extinct species had come under strong attack in many instances from his colleague at the Muséum, Barthélemy Faujas de St Fond.[34] An even greater input came from Cuvier's conflict with Lamarck, whose views on the origins of the globe and of the history of life are violently and openly attacked in the pages of the *Discourse*. In particular, his belief that life had arisen from the development of tiny animalcules present in the original fluid from which the earth had been formed, came under sharp fire from Cuvier.[35] In fact the programme of the *Discourse* was as old as the conflict between the two men on the fixity of species, and the proofs of extinction of species caused, in Cuvier's view, by violent geological change or 'catastrophes'. His 1801 publication, the *Extrait d'un ouvrage sur les espèces des quadrupèdes dont on a trouvé les ossemens à l'intérieure de la terre* already contains the major ideas and even some of the very phrases of the *Discourse* of 1812.[36] In both works, Cuvier was preoccupied by the thesis that it was the fossils of the large quadrupeds, in which he specialised, rather than the fossil molluscs investigated by Lamarck, which provided the real key to changes in the earth's crust. Since Cuvier, like Werner, tended to view these changes primarily as alterations in water level which would have destroyed large numbers of land animals, while having little influence on the life of marine species, his case did tend to be somewhat self-confirming. This did not prevent Cuvier arguing at great length against Lamarck's comments that many fossil marine shells differed little if at all from their present-day analogues, and therefore gave no evidence either for extinction or for geological catastrophies.[37] As the work of Lamarck and Faujas showed Cuvier was not, in fact, the only antiquary of a new kind at work; he had therefore to justify his specialisation in land animal fossils as providing superior markers both in time (as stratigraphic indicators) and in space (as marking the outer limits of submerged land masses). In 1807, Cuvier, in the company of his colleague at the Muséum, Alexandre Brongniart, undertook extensive fieldwork in the Paris region to prove these very points.[38] They aimed to map the strata of the Paris region, and correlate them with the fossil species which they contained. They distinguished seven major formations above a basic layer of chalk, with a constant order of superimposition of individual strata over distances of up to 120 kilometres, as defined by the order of species found therein. Fossils, they demonstrated, could be used not merely to show the coherence of whole formations, but also to identify in much greater detail the individual strata in a formation. To his own satisfaction at least, Cuvier had 'proved' his point about the heuristic superiority of the study of fossil quadrupeds over the study of fossil marine creatures as 'markers'.

Cuvier's claims for the stratigraphical importance of fossils of course rested in their turn on his argument for the reality of the extinction of species. In spite of Cuvier's attempts to demonstrate by means of comparative anatomy that extinction was a reality, many of his colleagues continued to support Lamarck's contrary views. Faujas de St Fond's 1803 *Geological Essay or Memoirs on the Natural History of the Globe* fully supported Larmarck's case that molluscs revealed none of the phenomena which Cuvier inferred from the fossil quadrupeds.[39] Over 56 species of fossil mollusc, he pointed out, had living analogues. This was not simply a conflict caused by the use of different kinds of evidence; it was also a conflict between a traditional speciality in natural history, that of conchology, and a new one, that of palaeontology.

However, the *Preliminary Discourse* can teach us more about the controversy between Cuvier and Lamarck than this. For a start, it is not possible to view their differences simply as a succession of assertions and rebuttals, or in other words as a dialogue. One of the most striking features of the so-called controversy between Cuvier and Lamarck was the extent to which they talked past each other. The extent of their non-engagement as it is revealed in the *Discourse* is surely partly a result of the claims to hegemony which form its basis. Cuvier could not admit a full discussion of the ideas of others into the work without damaging the claims to complete control of his field so forcibly implied in his depiction of the *antiquaire d'un espèce nouvelle*. Cuvier, for example, never supplied a positive alternative to Lamarck's speculations about the origins of species. He certainly did not subscribe to the idea of special creations after each catastrophe to replenish the world with species. Direct divine intervention in nature, as we have seen, was not regarded by him as scientifically tenable. He did suppose that migration might have populated various areas with new species, but otherwise, a limited subscription to Charles Bonnet's theory of the preformation of germs was the nearest he came to direct tackling of the problem of the origin of species.[40] Even earlier, the two men were not producing arguments which could logically achieve rebuttal one by the other. The discussion of the stability of species begun in 1795, for example, reached new heights when Geoffroy St Hilaire brought back to France the mummified bodies of animals which had been living at the time of the pyramids. A commission of the professors of the Muséum, which included Lamarck, and was chaired by Cuvier, put forward the view that since these animals showed no difference from their modern counterparts, they provided proof for the fixity of species over time.[41] Although Lamarck signed this report, he very shortly afterwards, in the context of his own studies of fossil shells of the Paris basin, published a lengthy attack on Cuvier's view.

Geology, history and the shaping of a self-image 155

Given the short span of human history, he declared, man can have no knowledge of the amount of time needed for changes in species to take place. The fact that such changes have not occurred over a span of three thousand years thus proves nothing. He went on to attack Cuvier's own discipline of quadruped palaeontology as chaotic and speculative, far removed from the precision possible in the identification of shells.[42] But the real point about the interchange between the two men was that logically neither argument proved anything at all about the mutability of species. In fact the demands of controversy, and investments in claims for independence and hegemony for different research fields, had prevented the construction of truly interlocking arguments. Who was to say, after all, how much time *was* required for species to become modified? Even the further demand, which Cuvier made of Lamarck in the *Discourse* itself, that Lamarck produce an example of an actual transitional species was invalidated as a true test by the extremely fragmented state of the fossil record at this period.[43] In the case of both Lamarck and Cuvier, in fact, their investments in certain points of view had passed far beyond the capacity of the available evidence to offer clear and convincing proof of either of their positions. Cuvier and Lamarck were prevented from taking the simplest way out, that of agreeing to suspend judgement, by the need to safeguard competing areas of influence within science. Cuvier had built up a programme which attempted both to define geology as an autonomous, respectable science, and to link it with the new and controversial science of palaeontological reconstruction, for which he made large claims as a key which would unlock many of the problems of the order of nature. Since his own experience was overwhelmingly with the reconstruction of large quadruped land animals, he awarded these a supreme heuristic importance.

In order to establish his own form of palaeontology as the supreme one, Cuvier had not only to delineate the field carefully in terms of methodology, subject matter, and heuristic importance for neighbouring areas of enquiry; he had also to dignify it. To do this he turned to history.

Discussion of Cuvier's view of the union of history and nature cannot escape the influential interpretation of

Michel Foucault. Foucault, in *Words and Things*, sees Cuvier's work as marking the end of 'history' as it had been understood by the classical age of the eighteenth century, 'a meticulous examination of things themselves', transcribed into 'smooth neutralised and faithful words'. Cuvier, he writes,

> by substituting anatomy for classification, organism for structure, internal subordination for visible character, the series for tabulation, was to make possible the precipitation into the old flat world of animals and plants, engraved in black on white, a whole profound mass of time to which men were to give the renewed name of 'history'.[44]

Foucault is surely right to point out how the renewal of history is one of the central parts of the radicality of Cuvier's achievement. It was in the *Discourse* that this feature of his work was most strongly set out. His view of the history of the earth as punctuated by violent events which set whole species in peril calls into question the central predicate of natural theology; that the earth is a locus for beings, and that there is a beneficial adaptation between those beings and their environment which is providentially ordained.[45] In this way he also escaped all the problems involved trying to reconcile providentialism with extinction. This was a point which the French Catholic tradition certainly found difficult, as Chateaubriand pointed out in Part I, book V, § V & X of the *Génie*, and which even Cuvier's English commentator Jameson found difficult to accept in spite of the others, such as Paley and Lyell, who did not seem to allow it to bother them.[45]

In every successive edition of the *Discourse* Cuvier pointed out, on the contrary, that

> Life on this earth has often been troubled by terrible events, calamities which in the beginning perhaps stirred the earth's crust to a great depth, but which have since been less terrible and had less far-reaching consequences. Living beings without number have been the victims of these upheavals; some have been wiped out by floods, others died of thirst when the bed of the sea has suddenly been raised; their entire species have vanished for ever, leaving traces hardly recognisable even by the naturalist ... but what is even more surprising is that life itself has not always existed on the globe, and that it is easy for the observer to recognise the precise point where it has first left traces.[46]

Cuvier makes also, no face-saving remarks about the Biblical

Geology, history and the shaping of a self-image 157

story of the creation being open to the interpretation that aeons, rather than days, could have passed between the creation of the world and the creation of life. This was an option that was perfectly open to him in the contemporary state of Biblical exegesis. The absence of such a reference, taken with the picture of upheaval and death as the essence of the history of the world, leaves us with a picture of Cuvier as far removed from any endorsement of a steady-state theory of the history of the earth, which Martin Rudwick has seen as the concomitant of deism.[47]

The precise nature of the geological catastophes which play such a large role in the *Discours* has attracted much controversy. Recent studies have attempted to sustain the case that Cuvier in fact considered some of the causes of these upheavals to have been 'the same factors as are observable today, but acting with a greater energy', but this interpretation receives only momentary and tentative confirmation from Cuvier himself.[48] In many other places, Cuvier's 'revolutions' are presented as violent and overwhelming. Mammoths are overwhelmed with ice so quickly that their meal of spring flowers is preserved intact for their nineteenth-century discoverers; sea beds rise and overwhelm whole continents. The nearest that Cuvier came to considering the matter at length, endorses a very sudden and violent operation of these so-called current causes:

> I agree with MM Deluc and Dolomieu, that if there is one certainty in geology, it is that the surface of the earth has undergone a great and sudden change, which cannot be dated to less than five or six thousand years ago; this revolution overwhelmed and submerged the lands inhabited by men and by species of animals which are best known today; it exposed the sea bed and out of it made the lands inhabited today; and that after this change, the small numbers of surviving individuals repopulated the lands newly raised from the waters, and that consequently it is only since that epoch, that societies have regained their progress, that they have evolved institutions, erected monuments, gathered facts and developed systems of thought.[49]

On the simplest level, this passage also elucidates what Cuvier meant by saying that natural and civil history were linked by an unbreakable bond.[50] It is not really correct to argue, as Francis Haber does, that Cuvier thought the Deluge was a dividing line between man's history and the history of the earth.[51] Even the Biblical geologist which Haber makes Cuvier out to be could hardly have believed this, since after all, in the Bible account, the Flood overwhelms a developed, if sinful, urban civilisation. In any case, as we have seen, Cuvier thought of the Biblical Flood as simply one story amongst others of a great inundation.[52]

What then are we to make of the famous statement that the 'thread of operations is broken' between the antediluvial world and contemporary nature?[53] A possible explanation of the appearance of this phrase is to treat it as a genuine inconsistency caused by the insecurity and vagueness of Cuvier's idea of the nature of his geological 'revolutions'. Another explanation could be that this phrase referred to the need of finding a new thread to understand the operation of the unknown world which had vanished at the advent of the last geological upheaval. New eras of the world's past had to be constructed, and its development mapped out into distinct phases similar to those provided by the succession of the dynasties in human history. This could best be done by the careful linking of fossil species with the strata in which they occurred, and it was this task which Cuvier saw as the real object of his work.[54] By 1812, he had mapped out a general theory of the succession of life. It seemed clear that oviparous quadrupeds had appeared earlier than viviparous quadrupeds, which were contemporary with the fishes to be found in the secondary strata. Terrestrial creatures had appeared much later than the aquatic species; Cuvier went on refining this scheme until the end of his career.

In conclusion, it should now be clear that the *Preliminary Discourse* employs exceptionally complex strategies in support of Cuvier's claims to define and dominate the newly-defined field of geology. The intense controversies which informed Cuvier's scientific career until this date undoubtedly went for much in determining the strategies employed both in the *Discourse* and the timing of its publication. Cuvier in its pages at one blow altered the epistemological relationships between several different areas of knowledge. He separated geology from theology, and, in opposition, made it deeply dependent on the emerging techniques of historical criticism. His rhetorical creation of the romantic figure of the

Geology, history and the shaping of a self-image 159

palaeontologist, the *antiquaire d'une espèce nouvelle*, seemed to allow him to justify these claims to reorganise whole fields of knowledge. After all, a new type of man, in a different relation to the process of the understanding and recreation of nature, was bound to be able to reorder the whole traditional series of relationships between various areas of thought.[55] In doing this, of course, Cuvier was much aided by the contemporary confusion in theological exegesis of the Biblical stories of the Flood and the Creation. This was exactly the same technique which Cuvier had used in order to demonstrate his claims to mastery over the field of natural history as newly defined by him, by reordering the relationships between such formerly separate areas of expertise as physiology and comparative anatomy in the construction of a new order of nature.

But the very magnitude of the claims contained in the *Discours* impeded the presentation of logically coherent ideas. Just as Cuvier and Lamarck, under the pressure of controversy, did not really engage directly with each other, so Cuvier, under the pressure of an immense reorganisation of the structure of natural knowledge, produced a series of ideas which were not coherent with each other at all levels. There is little connection in the *Discours*, for example between the succession of the forms of life as sketched by Cuvier, and the means which he employed to classify and reconstruct the fossil specimens which formed the subject matter of the remainder of the *Recherches sur les ossemens fossiles des quadrupèdes*. Cuvier's theory of the earth in no way implies his palaeontological practice. Cuvier never really made it clear how he conceived the geological 'catastrophes' which marked each of the successive stages of life with a distinctive fossil population. In hesitating between inundatory theories, and those of drastic climatic changes perhaps caused by changes in the earth's tilt, Cuvier also showed that, in fact, his new sort of geology was not interested in the search for causes of effects such as extinction which Cuvier had already proved to his own satisfaction by other means. This approach, though leaving many ends untied in the presentation of a history of the forms of life, at least certainly satisfied the major criteria of the new geology: to abandon the search for prime cases and to concentrate on the registering of evident changes. In fact, of course, Cuvier's decision to validate geology by the use of history rather than by linking it to theological justification also involved him in an intellectual project which was not as value-free as he liked to make out.

All in all, the *Discours* is a profoundly paradoxical work, and is so because it contains so many different strategies which each exerted a different pull on the structure of the scientific ideas presented to the reader. Cuvier's ideal of factual positive geology coexists with, and is sustained by, the Romantic self-exploration of the *antiquaire d'une espèce nouvelle*.[56] This refocusing of the science away from its potential usefulness to theology and on to its opening up, for the human observer, of mastery over new worlds of time and perception, is the vehicle for Cuvier's strategies of intellectual control. Criticise the imperial age as he might, Cuvier had yet deeply absorbed its techniques of propaganda and rhetoric as the orchestration of territorial acquisition.

VIII
Families, friends and institutions: the Paris Museum of Natural History

Ces jardins seront un Elisée dont l'ami de la Nature n'approchera qu'avec respect
(Fourcroy, at the funeral of Daubenton in the Jardin des plantes, 1800.)

Georges Cuvier entered the staff of the Muséum in 1795, and remained connected with the institution until his death.[1] A full consideration of the impact of this, his longest institutional allegiance, is lacking in the literature devoted to his career.[2] Overwhelmingly, it has been assumed that the history of his collections of specimens in comparative anatomy is equivalent to the story of Cuvier's achievements and struggles in the Muséum.[3] In this chapter, the Muséum will be seen not simply as an institution containing collections relating to the work of its professors but also as a physical setting, as the locus for a distinct community, as a teaching institution and, in respect to its gardens and menagerie, as a place of public resort and entertainment. All these aspects of the life *of* the Muséum, and of life *in* the Muséum must be taken into account before we can evaluate its impact on Cuvier's work.

The Muséum which Cuvier entered was already profoundly different from the old Jardin du roi in which Buffon had played a dominant role as Intendant until his death in 1788.[4] Relatively little concerned with its teaching functions, then confined to botany and anatomy, his reign was marked by a large-scale extension of the physical area of the Jardin. In spite of his concern for the collections of the various *Cabinets* or collections of the Jardin in botany, mineralogy, zoology and anatomy, these remained small in relation to the size they were to assume after the Revolution. In the government of the Jardin, his authority was paramount, and the professors, demonstrators and subordinate holders of posts were of markedly unequal authority and salary. On Buffon's death, all this began to change. His succession by two Intendants of markedly inferior scientific reputation and personal authority, Flahaut de la Billarderie and the writer Bernardin de St Pierre, meant that the Jardin became increasingly dominated in practice by Buffon's aged collaborator Louis-Jean-Marie Daubenton, and by his protégé André Thouin, head gardener of the Jardin, and Buffon's former man of affairs. In the atmosphere of hostility which surrounded all the scientific institutions of the *Ancien Régime* between 1789 and 1793, it was these men whose work allowed the Jardin to escape the fate of the Academy of Sciences, and remain in being in augmented and improved form. They did not do this by seeking to recreate the Jardin as it was in the days of Buffon. Even if, in the atmosphere of the 1790s this had been feasible, it would not have seemed an attractive prospect for men like Daubenton, who welcomed the chance to throw off the dictatorial authority exercised by Buffon, and change the Jardin into a place where teaching and research occupied an equal place with the care of collections. The fact that the great naturalist had run the Jardin not only as his private domain, but also in many respects as a private business venture from which he extracted considerable personal profit, accentuated the desire to remodel the Jardin.[5] In the case of Daubenton, this desire was probably even further increased by resentment against Buffon's reaping of credit for his labours on their collaborative work, the *Histoire naturelle*.[6]

As a result of Daubenton's efforts, supported in the National Assembly and the Convention by the Deputies Joseph Lakanal and Antoine Thibaudeau, the National Museum of Natural History was resurrected from the old Jardin du roi, with a new constitution, new finances, an augmented range of duties, and a role as a public and national institution, rather than as a royal institution only accessible to the public as a matter of favour. The new constitution abolished the office of Intendant, and replaced it by a governing body composed of the holders of full chairs, now increased in number from three to twelve. Each member of this assembly of Professors had equal rights and salary, including the right to free accommodation in the buildings of the Muséum complex and an equal vote in the

Families, friends and institutions

annual election of a President from amongst their own number. The President was directly responsible to the Minister of the Interior, who controlled the Muséum's finances. The Muséum thus emerged as internally democratic and self-governing, and remained so throughout the Revolution, the Empire and the Restoration.

Until 1802, the Assembly of the Professors was empowered to appoint new members to the staff of the Muséum without outside interference. After that date, it had to present candidates for vacant posts to the Minister for approval, with the concurrence of the Academy of Sciences, which could introduce an alternative candidate; in practice, however, since most members of the Assembly of Professors were also members of the Academy, the candidate presented by the Muséum was almost certain to be elected.[7] These features of its new constitution did much to give the Muséum its peculiar character of a close-knit, if not always amicable community. The majority of its staff at the time of the presentation and ratification of its new constitution (1793-4) continued in their posts from the days of Buffon.[8] Frequently, they intermarried: most of them actually lived inside the grounds of the Muséum.[9] The physical isolation of the Muséum from the centre of Paris in the early days of the Empire contributed to the preservation of these tightly-knit groups who naturally gave preference in appointments to family members, friends and protégés.[10] Outsiders, like Cuvier, who nonetheless became members of the Muséum staff, in order to maintain their own positions, were forced to build up their own family and patronage groups. Such a situation intensified any divisions amongst the staff on the grounds of scientific outlook, by providing them with the aspect of quarrels between family and patronage groups. In the Restoration, this propensity to conflict was increased by the decline of cultural authority – experienced by such figures as Cuvier, as we have seen in a previous chapter.[11]

The new functions of the Muséum increased its tendency to mirror in an intense way the conflicts which marked the rest of the world of natural science. Before the 1790s the Jardin had been very much just that, an institution dominated by its origins and continuing function as the royal garden for medicinal herbs. Botanical teaching still provided its best known public function. The constitution of 1793, on the other hand, specified that the Muséum was to provide teaching over the whole range of the non-mathematical sciences. It brought to prominence the teaching in anatomy, human and comparative, which had also existed before 1793, and it instituted new chairs in chemistry, geology, the whole range of zoology, and mineralogy. It retained its botanical teaching and instituted a new chair of plant cultivation for André Thouin. Special gardens began to appear, devoted to rare and tropical plants, and to plants important in agriculture, where new breeds were developed and acclimatised. It introduced for the first time a menagerie of living animals. This menagerie was to become at once the greatest public attraction in the Muséum.[12]

For these collections the Muséum was the direct beneficiary of the Terror and the Revolutionary and Napoleonic wars. The menagerie was founded with animals formerly belonging to the royal collection at Versailles. The mineralogical cabinet was augmented with the collection of the Princes du Condé, and its library and specimen collections filled with the confiscated property of other *émigré* nobles.[13] Between 1794 and 1795, André Thouin and Barthélemy Faujas de St Fond toured Europe in the wake of the Revolutionary armies, stripping bare the conquered territories of Germany, the Netherlands and Italy of their rich collections of scientific specimens, books and instruments.[14] The most important of such collections to arrive in Paris was that of the Stadtholder of Holland which, besides a large number of zoological specimens contained live animals including two elephants which eventually arrived safely in Paris and which, on their deaths in 1802 and 1804, were to form the subject of one of Cuvier's most intensive anatomical investigations.[15] This tradition was carried on throughout the Empire. The ultimately disastrous French invasion of Spain and Portugal in 1808 was closely followed by the mission of Geoffroy St Hilaire whose objectives resembled strongly those of Thouin and St Fond.[16] In the same way, Geoffroy had followed the French army into Egypt in 1799. More than any other previously existing institution of science in Paris, the Muséum was a true beneficiary of the Revolution. But if the ideology, so powerful for the Jacobins,

Families, friends and institutions

that the display of the beauties of nature in such privileged spots as the Muséum, was an essential part of human existence because it contributed to human virtue, helped to ensure its survival, this does not mean that the events of the Terror had no impact on the life of the institution. The Terror and the emigration augmented the collections with the property of the conquered, the exiled and the guillotined; but it also struck hard at those in the Muséum who had found the *Ancien Régime* and the monarchy of Buffon more tolerable than had Daubenton. Antoine Petit, who held the chair of human anatomy, withdrew from Paris during the Terror, and died in 1794 at his estate near Orleans.[17] Lacepède was forced to do the same, although he was able to return to Paris in 1794, to take up the new chair of the zoology of reptiles and fish created for him at the Muséum. The future holder of the chair of mineralogy, the Abbé René-Just Haüy, who succeeded Dolomieu in 1802, was arrested in 1792 as a non-juring priest, and narrowly escaped the prison massacres of September. Cuvier's collaborator Latreille, who was appointed an acting *aide-naturaliste* in the Muséum in 1797, himself narrowly escaped deportation for the same reason.[18] The staff of the Muséum thus contained many men whose lives had been deeply marked by the Terror.

The Terror also, as we have seen in an earlier chapter, deeply disrupted the normal operation of patronage.[19] It allowed the appointment of newcomers such as Geoffroy St Hilaire, whose extreme youth, often commented upon in the contemporary press, was only paralleled by his ignorance of the subject matter of his chair.[20] It was the Terror's reversal of patronage which, as we have seen, made possible the final stages of Cuvier's own campaign for admittance to the staff of the Muséum. In addition the Muséum possessed, in the person of Antoine Fourcroy, chemist and from 1784 Professor of Chemistry at the Muséum, Jacobin and member of the Convention from 1793, the living embodiment of the threat posed by the Terror to the normal operations of patronage. The rumour that he had betrayed his friend and teacher Lavoisier to the guillotine, or at least not exerted himself with sufficient force to save him, could never be disproved, and persistently clouded his reputation.[21]

Fourcroy in fact embodied all the risks of patronage at a time of political upheaval. Nor was the Terror simply a matter of episodes in the lives of individuals. In 1794, the finances of the Muséum hung in the balance, and were only settled by Daubenton's promise to find employment in the Muséum for Oliver Marat, an amateur entomologist, brother of the Jacobin hero assassinated by Charlotte Corday. It was a promise which was conveniently forgotten after Thermidor; but the very existence of such a bargain shows the extent to which the revolutionary ethic of natural science, the martyrology of the Terror, and the financial instability of the Revolutionary government could all combine.[22] Botany, sensibility, virtue and Terror formed a continuum.

It was against this background that Cuvier campaigned for admission to the Muséum, and it is against this background that much of his career within the institution must be understood. His search for admittance to the staff of the Muséum was a long-drawn-out affair, as even Cuvier himself admits. It supplies a further contradiction to the impression given even by Cuvier's contemporary biographers, that Cuvier's rise to fame was of meteoric rapidity. In reality, it was a matter of a long and slow campaign to become known and to justify claims with achievements. The first move was made in 1791, shortly after the retirement of the d'Héricy family to Ficquainville, and the final assumption of his vocation as a naturalist that we have already traced. In that year, Cuvier placed himself in contact with Lacepède, and put forward the idea that on Lacepède's election to the Legislative Assembly, he should become his deputy in the Jardin.[23] The idea did not meet with much favour; it is now impossible to reconstruct why, though financial difficulties in the Muséum and Cuvier's lack of reputation may well both have contributed. However, as we have seen, Cuvier remained on friendly terms with Lacepède, and condoled on his enforced departure from the Muséum in 1793.[24] Meanwhile, Cuvier was broadening the base of his campaign. It is certain that he was in contact with Haüy by 1793, possibly having elected him as a replacement figure for Lacepède, whose absence from the capital was of uncertain duration.[25] The surviving correspondence with Haüy is friendly in tone, and reveals nothing of the hostility

Families, friends and institutions

which was to mar their relations from 1795. It is extremely possible that Lamarck, in 1790 a highly respected botanist, and in 1793 Professor of the zoology of insects and *vers* at the Muséum, was also one of Cuvier's most important contacts in this period. Unlike Lacepède, Lamarck was in Paris continuously, and again unlike Lacepède, and Haüy, was in good odour with the revolutionary government. A contemporary German account of the Muséum, using information likely to have been supplied by Cuvier himself, mentions a correspondence with Lamarck, as one of the most important ways in which Cuvier was brought to the notice of the authorities of the Muséum.[26] All trace of such a correspondence has now disappeared, and in fact letters of any sort between Cuvier and Lamarck are now exceedingly rare.

The conflict between Cuvier and Lamarck which became obvious after 1800 should not lead us to overlook how important Lamarck may have been in the period between 1793 and 1800 as a patron of the new entrants to the Muséum. His friendship with Haüy left him especially well placed in this respect, for the latter's residence in the Collège Cardinal Lemoine had enabled him to meet and be in daily contact with some of the most promising of the younger generation of aspiring naturalists. Chief among those who passed from friendship with Haüy to friendship with Lamarck was, of course, Geoffroy St Hilaire. This was also the channel which resulted in the introduction of Latreille to the Muséum in 1797, and to his continuing patronage by Lamarck.[27] In his campaign for entry to the Muséum, Cuvier's very broadly based education in Germany stood him in good stead, and enabled him to attract the attention of men working in fields as widely separated as those of Haüy and Lamarck.

The final stage in Cuvier's assault on the Muséum came when in January 1795 he asked Mertrud to report to the Assembly of the Professors on scientific papers he had written.[28] As we have already seen, the Muséum was uncertain as to whether to prefer his candidacy or that of Richard for the post of *suppléant* or substitute for the aging Mertrud. That Cuvier should have triumphed was partly due to his own outstanding success in achieving visibility in the Parisian scientific societies, and in forging social links in the world of science and politics in the preceding months. His collaboration with Geoffroy may well have seemed to some to have given him standing already within the Muséum, but it still remains that the decision to appoint Cuvier was not unanimous, and this left deep marks on his position in the Muséum. It became easy, as we have seen, for him to be viewed as a threat to Geoffroy's position, and thus to arouse the enmity of Geoffroy's patrons Haüy and Daubenton. This hostility was returned with interest by Cuvier.[29] On his return to the Muséum after his tour of conquered Europe and Thouin, Faujas de St Fond showed himself to be no less hostile. Cuvier after all had been elected in his absence and moreover was beginning to move rapidly and successfully into the field of palaeontology where Faujas himself had developed a major interest in the course of his European journey.[30] The later controversies between Cuvier and Faujas over the classification of fossil animals were undoubtedly fuelled by these factors, as well as by Cuvier's irritating superiority in anatomy and zoology over Faujas. According to Cuvier, Faujas not only became his personal enemy, but did all he could to disrupt his friendship with Lamarck.[31]

Cuvier did little to make life easier for himself with his inaugural lecture at the Muséum of 1795, where his condescending attitude towards the achievements of the older generation of naturalists could hardly have softened Daubenton's attitude towards him.[32] In any case it is obvious that Cuvier's achievement of a post in the Muséum as *suppléant* to Mertrud, and then as titular professor of comparative anatomy, did not mark the end of his troubles, but rather their beginning. The extent of the personal hostility which he aroused in the Muséum which was increased by the hegemonic claims of his new form of zoology, meant that the Muséum was hardly the secure base of authority for him that many writers have imagined. Comparison of his career in the Muséum with that of his future collaborator, Pierre André Latreille, shows the extent to which seeking entry into the Muséum could easily have led to the achievement of nothing more than a continual insecurity in income, prestige and position.[33] Latreille entered the staff of the Muséum in 1797, after having mounted much the same campaign for appointment as Cuvier. After completing his education at the Collège Cardinal Lemoine, he became the friend of Haüy who, in turn, introduced him to Lamarck. Meanwhile, he repeatedly sent papers to the Assembly of the Professors, through Lamarck, for comment. On Lamarck's suggestion, he was eventually made an assistant *aide-naturaliste* on 19 July 1798, and full *aide-naturaliste* on 4 November 1799. The similarities with Cuvier's campaign are obvious: the acquirement of an important patron within the Muséum, the preparation of the ground by the submission of work in natural history, culminating in the eventual appointment. But there are also important differences, differences which tell us much about why Cuvier was successful in achieving an important position in the Muséum, and Latreille for many years was not. First of all, Latreille concentrated his attentions on a smaller number of patrons than Cuvier had done. Whereas Cuvier had mobilised support from both outside and inside the Muséum, Latreille confided his cause to Haüy and Lamarck alone. In other words, while Cuvier had made sure that he controlled not only the entrances but the approach roads, Latreille was forced into a direct assault on the portals of the Muséum unsupported by a broad base of outside patronage. Latreille also entered the Muséum at a time when there were no full chairs left to distribute. Forced to occupy the lowly and badly paid position of *aide-naturaliste* for many years, he remained dependent on his original patrons at a time when in the corresponding stage of his career, Cuvier was in a position to become a patron in his own right, and gradually dissociate himself from dependence on the men who had originally obtained his post for him. In Latreille's case his fortunes waned as Lamarck's position in the Muséum declined. In 1807, for example, Lamarck tried to induce the Assembly of the Professors to apply for special funds to set up a separate chair of entomology for Latreille, and failed to do so. It was a significant blow for his protégé, who was forced to earn additional funds by writing for popular publications in natural history, and by collaborating with Cuvier on the entomology sections of *Règne animal*. It was only in 1818 that he obtained a lodging in the Muséum, and only in 1820 that be became Lamarck's *suppléant*. It had taken him a quarter of a century to achieve, in institutional terms, what had been Cuvier's starting point.

On Lamarck's death in 1827, his chair was split between entomology and malacology, and Latreille obtained that of entomology, which he enjoyed until his death in November 1832. Except for these last few years, Latreille's institutional position never matched up to his professional reputation, and he was frequently miserably poor.

Latreille's career not only demonstrates the importance of the cultivation of patronage and friendship; it also points out the inability of the Muséum, as an institution, to help individuals without such contacts. Financial constraints throughout the period of Cuvier's association with the Muséum were such that few could hope for financial security without an income from private sources or from an outside post. In the early years of the Muséum salaries were frequently not paid, and institutional subsidies fell into arrears. For his first few years in the Muséum, Cuvier was clearly reduced to living on credit, and it is difficult to imagine that he was the only one of his colleagues in this position.[34] The financial constraints on the Muséum made it impossible to ameliorate the position of those such as Latreille who had entered the Muséum at a low level of payment, or to create positions for them worthy of their merit as naturalists. Financial crises in the Muséum closely followed the pattern of events in the world outside. No institution directly dependent on the Ministry of the Interior for its funds was able to escape the effects of the great French banking crisis of 1805-6, and certainly no institution in the Empire was able to escape the retrenchment of 1813 after the disastrous invasion of Russia in the preceding year. Real financial security only came after the budget of 1823 had guaranteed substantial funds.[35] In these circumstances, forward planning in the Muséum was never easy to carry through, and the hope of its charter of 1793, that henceforward invidious distinctions between members of its staff in income and status would be avoided, could hardly be realised. Latreille's four francs a day contrasted sharply with the yearly 5,000 francs of the full professors; and his three-monthly contracts with their life tenure.[36]

These simple considerations should lead us to pose the question, therefore, of how the Muséum, as an institution,

Families, friends and institutions

could be helpful to Cuvier's achievement, and the more we consider the Muséum, the more inescapable the conclusion becomes that to consider it *as an institution* may not be the most helpful way of trying to understand its effects on Cuvier's life and work. For a start the idea of an institution in the modern sense usually implies some sort of continuity and unity of outlook: whereas the Paris Muséum in this period does nothing so much as reproduce the incompatibilities in the world of French natural science as a whole; it provided a place where many of the different views of what nature was, and who was to control and explain it, uneasily jostled together within the same physical space.

In human terms, the Muséum presents not so much the picture of a group of men concerned with the advancement of natural science, but rather of a collection of different individuals linked together by many different types of loyalty. The bonds of patronage have already been mentioned in this chapter as have those created during the Terror which often reinforced each other.[37] The next most obvious group was that of the family. In 1823, Deleuze estimated, in his study of the Muséum, that fifty families lived within its walls.[38] Many of the staff of the Muséum as we have seen, were related to each other, and were often descended from holders of positions within the old Jardin du roi. Contemporaries were eager to argue that family relationships amongst the Muséum staff were likely to encourage harmony in the working of the institution.[39] The reality, of course, was different. It is clear first of all that some family groups in the Muséum were also the centre of political groups. André Thouin's sister, for example, married the regicide Deputy Leclerc, the intimate friend of the Director Larévellière-Lépaux.[40] The alliance formed a nucleus for those in the Muséum of moderately radical, republican and anti-Catholic viewpoints, since Lépaux was the inventor and exponent of the new religion of Theophilanthropy which aimed to worship without benefit of the Church. Around him gathered a circle consisting not only of the Thouins but also of the Professor of botany, Desfontaines, the librarian of the Muséum, Toscan, and even to some extent Cuvier himself.[41] In turn, Thouin, who shared his house within the grounds of the Muséum with his sister and Leclerc, was friendly with the naturalist Bosc, a future Professor of the Muséum, and himself a close friend of Mme Roland, wife of the Girondin Minister of the Interior. On the fall of the Gironde, which heralded the rise of Robespierre and the opening of the Terror, it was Bosc who sheltered Larévellière-Lépaux from the fury of the political victors.[42] This Girondin–theophilanthropic group within the Muséum were unlikely to have felt particularly close to such colleagues as the Jacobin Fourcroy, or to the monarchist Lacepède. Such considerations also point up the fact that the community of the Muséum cannot be limited simply to those people who happened to hold office there, in an institutional sense. Not only did many members of the Muséum live with their extended families within its walls; they also employed informally many other individuals as secretaries and assistants. Cuvier, for example, as we have already seen, very quickly built up a group of Montbéliardais around him, most of whom were employed by him personally, rather than by the Muséum, and who lodged in his house. Georges Duvernoy and Charles Laurillard, as well as his cousin Charles Cuvier, are the figures who come most easily to mind in this connection, but such others as the Irish naturalist Joseph Barclay Pentland also occupied for many years a position of responsibility in Cuvier's 'laboratory', and in his family, without ever appearing on the payroll of the Muséum.[43] Pentland's functions included assistance with Cuvier's scientific correspondence, overseeing the manufacture of plastercasts of fossils, and the care and arrangement of the collections of the Cabinet of comparative anatomy as a whole; they even included the duty of providing a social escort to Mme Cuvier when her husband was detained by official business. What we are faced with here is a small research group some of whose members had instituted affiliations with the Muséum, some of whom had not; direction and control came from Cuvier rather than being dictated by the imperatives of the Muséum as such. There was, in fact, no sharp line between families and the Muséum, between the work performed within the family or household and that supported by the Muséum as an institution. This is particularly true when we consider the important role played by women like Sophie Duvaucel in the production of illustrations and the sorting of material for such

Families, friends and institutions

large-scale, collaborative productions as the *Histoire Naturelle des poissons* edited by her stepfather Cuvier.[44] From this point of view, the Muséum can best be seen as a series of households: there was no sharp line between the domestic and the institutional resource. It is clear that, especially in the Restoration, Cuvier's work became increasingly affected by its style of social organisation. His basic materials may have been provided by the collections of the Cabinet of comparative anatomy which lay under his control as titular professor; in form, however, his large-scale, encyclopaedic works were singularly well-adapted to being produced by a large number of collaborators – larger by far than the Muséum as an institution could have afforded to provide him with – working within the same household. When Charles Lyell produced his famous description of Cuvier's working methods, he was not, as he seemed to think, describing a work scheme designed to maximise the efficient use of time by one person, but rather a scheme designed to be accessible to a whole team of people working on different aspects of the same project.[45] This, after all, was why Cuvier was so anxious that the anatomy galleries under his care should directly communicate with his own house in the Muséum's grounds.

After 1815, it was on the shoulders of the household that scientific work increasingly fell. Laurillard has left a vivid description of the impact of Cuvier's political functions outside the Muséum on his subordinates within it: in 1817, he wrote to Duvernoy:

I have hardly the strength left to climb the stairs to go to bed ... You will have some idea of what I mean when I explain that our elephant has died, that M. Cuvier, who has been unwell, and who has much other business in any case, has not been able to attend to its dissection, so that I had to do it almost completely single-handed. For my relaxation, an ostrich also took it into its head to die the day after I had finished the drawings from the elephant.[46]

It was also from within the family that vocations were formed and informal teaching of natural history was begun. Cuvier has left us a picture of his own teaching of his small son Georges from pictures and models of animals, in just the same way that his own imagination had first been touched by the pictures in his uncle's copy of Buffon thirty years before.[47] These were scenes which must have repeated themselves in the many families who lived within the walls of the Muséum. It was accident that the majority of Cuvier's children did not reach maturity. Had they done so, there is no reason why they should not have formed a family group as tightly knit as that of the Brongniarts.

The power of families within this situation is perhaps best illustrated by an examination of the most closely-knit group within the Muséum, that of the Brongniart family. Related to Fourcroy, Alexandre Brongniart, Cuvier's collaborator on the geology of the Paris basin, whose sister Cuvier had unsuccessfully courted, produced three children from his own marriage, all of whom arrived at maturity and all of whom married. His son Adolphe gained for himself a chair at the Muséum, as did his sons-in-law, Victor Audoin and later, the chemist, J. B. Dumas. The whole family group collaborated on the founding and editing of the *Annales des Sciences naturelles*, which as we have seen, for many years maintained an eclectic approach which refused outright to support Cuvier in his struggle with Geoffroy and Lamarck. It was an alternative source of opinion to the *Annales du Muséum*, and one whose foundation closely coincided with increasing personal tension between Alexandre Brongniart and Cuvier.[48]

Other relationships within the Muséum were ostensibly highly institutionalised: they were the *aides-naturalistes*, assigned as assistants to particular chairs, and the *suppléants* or substitute lecturers, appointed when titular professors were too old, infirm or busy to lecture themselves. However, as we have seen in the case of both Cuvier and Latreille, such appointments did not, in fact, depend on any formal examination of competence; they depended far more on family relationships and the organisation of efficient patronage.[49] Enthusiastic amateurs were regularly welcomed by the staff of the Muséum, and it was often from this class of men that the *aides* and *suppléants* were drawn.[50] Blainville, for example, who became one of Lamarck's successors on the division of his chair after his death, had a primarily medical training, and knew Cuvier simply because of his assiduous frequentation of the comparative anatomy gallery.[51]

We should be clear, therefore, about the kind of allegiances

Families, friends and institutions 175

we are talking about in the case of the Muséum. We are not dealing with a group of men brought together by a formal institutionalised process of certification, examination and appointment. The institution, rather, existed to give the final seal of ratification to relationships of other kinds, which were already in being. They ratified family relationships, personal debts – especially the debts accumulated during the Terror – and often had at their back campaigns for the accumulation of patronage stretching far beyond the confines of the Muséum.[52] If this interpretation is accepted, it carries another consequence: that it is not possible to assess the importance of the Muséum simply in terms of the collections it accumulated and made available to its staff. The answer to the question of why the Muséum became a scientific focus lies only at the most simple level with objects: the real answer lies with people, with their ideas about science, and about the functions of the Muséum. Neither ideas about the institutionalisation of science, or about the newer 'institution' of science have much meaning when confronted with the Paris Muséum of Natural History, which possessed coherence only at the most formal legal level.[53] The Muséum was not so much an institution as a catchment area for ideas and attitudes about natural science.

How then did the Muséum affect Cuvier's achievement? It is clear that the increase of the Muséum's collections, in ways which have already been discussed, massively accelerated the progress of Cuvier's work. Instead of having to rely on descriptions or incomplete representatives of many genera, he was able to begin his encyclopaedic projects of the listing and categorisation of the animal kingdom. Animals from the Statholder's collection, for example, form the subject of many of his early papers, and of the lengthy study of living and fossil elephants.[54] Nonetheless, Cuvier was still heavily reliant on gifts and descriptions from outside the Muséum. Nothing is a more frequent feature of his correspondence than this reiterated demand for specimens or casts of specimens. If the Muséum's collections could in the nature of things not hope to contain representatives of all known species, such collections nevertheless had another very important role to play: that of the exemplification of his system of classification.[55] From the beginning of his career as titular professor, the order of

Cuvier's galleries of comparative anatomy rigorously followed that adopted in the *Leçons d'anatomie comparée:* in other words, the galleries differed from the older collections in that they followed an order dictated by physiological systems and their hierarchies, rather than either zoological order or aesthetic consideration. Cuvier's galleries were full of objects to be looked not *at,* but *into.*[56] It is certainly in terms of the construction of the comparative anatomy galleries that Cuvier himself presented the major achievement of his career in the Muséum. The autobiography lays stress on this point:

> I began the anatomy collection from the moment of my appointment in the Jardin du roi. The Jardin had just acquired the vast buildings which had formerly belonged to the administration of the hackney carriages of Paris, and which backed right on to the building which had been given to me (as living quarters). I had a hole made in the party wall of the attics and had carried up three or four skeletons which had been mounted by Mertrud. I went to look in the cluttered *cabinet* to see what remained of the skeletons mounted by Daubenton which Buffon had had piled up like bundles of firewood: and it was in pursuing these enterprises, with the help of some Professors, and against the hindrance of others, that I succeeded in making my collection so important that soon nobody dared to oppose its further enlargement.[57]

It was also a view which Cuvier stressed at the time by publishing in the *Annales* of the Muséum a description of the enlargement of the collections in comparative anatomy which poured scorn on the achievements of his predecessors.[58]

He quoted statistics of numbers of preparations to show that his efforts through purchase and the exchange of gifts from other collections had increased the number of specimens fivefold in his first eight years in the Muséum. In place of the chaotic arrangements of Buffon and Daubenton, which mixed preparations of organs with entire skeletons, and split the collection between cellar and attic so that it was impossible to view it as a coherent whole, he had substituted an arrangement on a physiological basis. In 1806, the galleries were for the first time since 1793 opened to the public.[59] They not only fitted in with the craze for dioramic displays of nature which was so characteristic of Parisian consumption of culture at this time, and well into the Restoration; they also afforded maximum publicity to Cuvier's own system of classification, and seemed

Families, friends and institutions

to provide striking visual evidence of his capacity to justify his claims to be able to provide an ordering of nature. It was in the galleries of the Muséum that Cuvier's 'legend' as some sort of magician of nature, the possessor of a universal understanding, was born, and it was in its lecture theatres that it was confirmed.[60] By the end of his life, the collection stretched over fifteen rooms, and contained over twelve thousand specimens. For Cuvier, in fact, the Muséum functioned perhaps most importantly as the only place where his brand of élite, expert science could gain validation from public display, without thereby losing its character as true science. The Muséum offered the ultimate refinement of that visibility which Cuvier had sought as the way of making his career in Paris ever since 1795.

It was in this sense that the Muséum provided for Cuvier the 'institution' of his science: not in the sense that the Muséum was the locus of a coherent enquiry into natural science, but rather in the sense that it was here that the physical objects of his science, their intellectual ordering, their examination by experts, and their exposure to the wider world of the public could come together in an environment consecrated to nature alone, and set apart from the cultural marketplace: a veritable Elysium.

But the comparative anatomy galleries were not seen as an indisputable benefit by some of Cuvier's colleagues. The contemporary historian Deleuze, employed as an *aide-naturaliste* in the Muséum since 1795, is clear that the building of Cuvier's galleries, in the situation of financial uncertainty under which the Muséum laboured, necessitated the cutting off of funds from Geoffroy's menagerie.[61] It may be that Frédéric Cuvier's appointment in 1805 as keeper of the menagerie was an effort by Cuvier to forestall the hostility of Geoffroy. Cuvier himself also hints that he encountered opposition from his colleagues in the enlargement of his collections. This impression is confirmed by Geoffroy, who implies, further, that the alterations to the buildings of the Muséum which Cuvier described as the first stage in the enlargement of the collections, were undertaken on Cuvier's own initiative, rather than in accordance with a decision of the Assembly of the Professors.[62] This, taken with Cuvier's scorn for the work of his two elderly predecessors Daubenton and Mertrud, would by itself have been quite enough to arouse opposition from many of his colleagues. It was also true that the way Cuvier arranged his specimens challenged their scientific ideas quite as much as had the works of natural history of which the comparative anatomy collections were the physical embodiment. In the *Leçons d'anatomie comparée*, Cuvier had already attacked those who thought it illegitimate to use anatomical and physiological data in a work which purported to be one of natural history. In doing so, he was challenging all the old distinctions between the disciplines, distinctions which were vital to the natural history of the 'classical age'. The arrangement of his galleries along physiological rather than zoological lines contained precisely the same challenge. They also contained a further threat, and one which was specific to their arrangement as galleries, and not as a 'cabinet'. Cuvier in fact repeatedly opposed the idea that arrangements of animals should be confined by a cabinet's demands of ease of recognition and conservation. He also appeared unwilling to accept that the aesthetic demands of the old cabinets should any longer be conformed to, or that the limits of the collection should be set by the physical dimensions of the rooms provided by their housing, rather than by the dimensions of nature itself.[63] The question of the arrangement of specimens, of course, also involved him in the old debate between those who wished to place emphasis on external characteristics as the main basis for classification and those who like himself, wished to probe the intimate organisation of the organism for such a basis, in particular, conchologists such as Lamarck, whose arrangements of shells had fulfilled an aesthetic purpose as well as proclaiming their allegiance to the principle of an external system of classification over one based on physiological organisation.

Just because the collections of the Muséum made manifest so decisively classificatory choices, so they also reproduced and reinforced debates within the institution. The collections of the Muséum in fact displayed as many different classificatory systems as there were chairs to which Cabinets were attached.[64] It is thus not really possible to take the comparative anatomy collections, important as they were to Cuvier, as a

Families, friends and institutions

simple index of Cuvier's dominance within the institution. The social and constitutional arrangement of the Muséum ensured that such a position was in fact very difficult to obtain, and the uncertainty prevailing in ideas of classification ensured that bids to do so through the use of arrangements of collections would generate as much hostility as they would establish authority.

However claims for superiority in the Muséum continued to centre on the issue of the collections because of their function of awarding supreme visibility to systems of classification. This is why Geoffroy also lays stress on his foundation and control of the menagerie and the zoology collections.[65] Like Cuvier's own claims in other contexts, however, those of Geoffroy seem sometimes to have arisen as much from a need to justify as from the wish to report accurately on the past. Contemporary visitors were in no doubt that, comparing the two collections, Cuvier's was by far the larger and better arranged. The Dutchman Martinus van Marum, for example, who visited the Muséum in September 1802, found a 'very extensive collection ... distributed over several rooms'.[66] In the zoological gallery run by Geoffroy, however, he commented on the numbers of unidentified specimens, and found little that his own institution, Teylor's Museum in Haarlem, did not already possess.[67] The prestige of Cuvier's collection was bolstered by his adroit use of propaganda. Serious contemporary guidebooks to the Muséum, such as that published by the German naturalist Gotthelf Fischer in 1802, made much of Cuvier's claims and achievements. Fischer treated Cuvier as a master of science, and as single-handedly responsible for the revival of natural history in France.[68] Using information which could only have been provided by Cuvier himself, he sketched his career, and then lyrically described Cuvier's qualities as a 'man, a colleague and a friend'; encomia which many of those in the Muséum would have disputed.[69] Fischer's book, however biased in its section on Cuvier, illustrates the extent to which Cuvier's position – however difficult it may have seemed from the inside of the Muséum – could be bolstered by the praise of those outside it. In the same way, the vast network of correspondence which Cuvier established in Europe, largely through the hunt for fossil specimens, and which he maintained in being throughout the Empire through the use of patronage in the administration of education, fed back on to his reputation in Paris.[70]

The size of his collections in palaeontology and comparative anatomy indicated a corresponding grasp of the network of exchange and patronage. As he said himself, after the collections had reached a certain size, no one dared to interfere with their further increase; this was not simply because of their intrinsic scientific value, but because of the strength of the networks of support at Cuvier's command which their very size implied.[71] This was especially true in the case of the palaeontological specimens. Because palaeontology itself was a relatively new field, it was less likely that such specimens would form part of the captured collections donated to the Muséum. In fact the evidence is overwhelmingly that Cuvier had to construct his own census of such material and that he acquired the collection that he did in this field largely through personal contacts. It is perhaps a mistake to place too much emphasis, at least in Cuvier's case on the influx of material into the Muséum under the Empire. To do so leaves unexplained the rapid increase of such collections into the period of the Restoration.[72]

Another way in which Cuvier had obtained an outstanding position in the Muséum was, Fischer implied, through his lecture courses.[73] Teaching in the Muséum traditionally consisted of public lectures, often attended by large numbers, and where appropriate, accompanied by demonstrations, herborisations, and for the interested few, access to the Professor's own collections and library. The Muséum, like the Collège de France, was not an examining body, and awarded no diplomas, though certificates of attendance at lectures could be obtained by students as evidence of assiduity. Although lectures were only given in the summer months, the lecture audiences contained all gradations of interest, from those who, like Blainville and Audouin graduated through them to personal contact with the Professor, and hence to involvement in his private research work, through medical students broadening their scientific outlook, to interested amateurs, and simple sightseers. Because the entrance fees to the courses were cheap, and entry unrestricted, it also served as a major channel

Families, friends and institutions

for the education of women in science and its auxiliary techniques. Feminine dominance in the audience for Desfontaine's lectures on botany, and Van Spaendonck's classes in natural history drawing, for example, was often remarked by contemporaries.[74] In other words, this heterogeneous audience shaded imperceptibly over the full range of response to nature, from the serious aspiring professional, to those who came to the Muséum for relaxation, for open-air uplift, and to acquire a little extra knowledge of the objects which they encountered on their wanderings through the gardens and such of the galleries as were open to the public. Audience numbers under these circumstances tended to be large. Cuvier's own lectures, even on such unpromising subjects as the anatomy of molluscs, were frequently crowded out.[75] Although Cuvier often implied to his distant correspondents that numbers such as three hundred auditors made him unique in the annals of the Muséum, in fact such figures were easily doubled by his colleague Desfontaines.[76] Paris in fact was gripped by a vogue for the natural sciences which was the reaction from the contentious, politically orientated debates in the literature of the same period. From science, the Parisians expected non-contentious display of the beauties of nature, an aesthetic and intellectual treat which would refresh rather than inflame.

Such audiences imposed special strains on those who lectured to them. Their very size made exposition into a histrionic display, and placed emphasis on the visual elements of explanation. Cuvier correspondingly developed a clear enunciation, a stage presence consciously modelled on that of the great tragic actor Talma, and a remarkable facility for drawing instantly recognisable animals and organs on the blackboard as he spoke.[77] Difficulties of presentation to such a heterogeneous audience also loomed large. It seems likely, according to one recent interpretation, that such difficulties may well have influenced the whole of Geoffroy's attempts to reduce the quadrupeds to a single common 'plan', to increase ease of exposition.[78] Cuvier himself considered the problem at length in his inaugural lecture of 1795. He remarked on the confusing effect of attempting to teach natural history by referring to different animals one after the other, and decided that systems in the physiological sense, traced through the various zoological orders, were easier to grasp by an amateur audience, and more rapidly converted into a genuine overview of nature, rather than the array of confusingly unrelated facts produced by examination of different species one after the other.[79] If we can accept the view that Geoffroy's style of exposition and actual approach to the ordering of nature was strongly influenced by the expository demands of the Muséum audience, there is no reason not to adopt this approach for Cuvier also. Although the physiological approach was present in his work long before he arrived in Paris, the experience of lecturing in the Muséum may well have accelerated the arrangement by physiological systems which was not only already implicit in his work but was already familiar to those of his audience who combined attendance at his lectures with that of the classes of Bichat in the Faculty of Medicine. There were in fact numerous other pressures on Cuvier's exposition of the order of nature other than the dramatic rise in the numbers of known species and the increase in the size of the Muséum's collections. It may well have been that the Muséum audiences, as much as the Muséum's collections, played a part in leading Cuvier to emphasise the kind of arrangement of nature which became his special contribution to science.

It is also true that the style of science practised in the Muséum had negative effects on Cuvier's achievement. As we have seen, the community of Professors was hardly at one in its view of nature, employed no common system of classification, and was engaged in violent internal disputes on classification, identification of specimens and the very bases of natural science for the greater part of this period. If Cuvier's work in the Muséum was representative of no common programme, it also had other drawbacks. Cuvier regarded his entry into the Muséum almost as synonymous with the abandonment of field natural history. Though he was to influence the zoological enquiries of many of the great expeditions of the nineteenth century, he was hardly ever again to work with living animals. The adult animal became the taxonomical standard, and a developmental view of physiology, let alone of the history of life, became unobtainable. Lamarck's particular form of transformism repeated this

Families, friends and institutions

failing, even though for the opposite reason, that the practice of dissection played almost no part in the formation of his scientific views. Henri Daudin pointed out long ago how the fact that Cuvier had never seen alive, or young, most of the animals he examined, led to misinterpretations of anatomical features, and a complete obscuring of questions relating to the social life of animals, and their capacities for adaptation.[80] It was precisely these questions that Cuvier's brother Frédéric, working daily in the menagerie, was to make peculiarly his own. It also enabled him to go on collaborating with Geoffroy long after fundamental disagreements had occurred between the latter and his elder brother. Frédéric in fact was highly scornful of a natural history which could deal only with the dead animal. This was the obverse side of Cuvier's reputation as the 'master of the charnel house'.[81]

In conclusion we must examine a further question. What was it, in other words, which made the Muséum so important that it was able to accord visibility to those, such as Cuvier, who were inclined to use it for that purpose? The extent to which an ideal of the Muséum existed in the public mind, and how that ideal changed over the period of the Revolution, Empire, and Restoration has rarely, if ever, been approached in the literature on Cuvier. Yet the existence of such a public presence for the Muséum was one of the key factors in making it able to confer visibility on those who worked there. The Muséum, from its foundation, had been presented to the public as the embodiment of a national institution. Its position as a former royal possession lent additional piquancy to its position after 1793 as a public resource. Propagandists pointed out its uses as an instrument of national education, and as a way of gaining prestige in the eyes of foreign nations.[82] From the outset, therefore, the Muséum was established with an 'image' which linked it closely with the revolutionary patriotism of the 1790s, an image which was reinforced by its reception of the collections taken from the conquered territories of Europe. In the succeeding few years, as the pressures of the Revolutionary Wars on France lessened, the Muséum began to be portrayed increasingly as a sort of accessible Utopia, open to the public, and portraying the unspoiled beauties and intricate organisation of nature. Guidebooks studiously emphasised these Rousseauist aspects of the grounds of the Muséum and its collections, and laid particular stress on the animals in the menagerie, and their supposed characteristics.[83] It was a utopic view of the Jardin, produced, as Walter Benjamin has suggested, as most utopias are produced, to provide reassurance at a time of rapid cultural change, and to hide the social tensions which had gone into the making of the Jardin itself, and into the science which was practised there.[84] The public who resorted to the Muséum to enjoy the pleasures of nature, did not after all want to be confronted with a science which would reveal these tensions to them; what it wanted was to be confronted with the unbroken fabric of nature rather than with the increasing complexities of political and social life in the Empire and Restoration period. It is in fact noticeable that generally speaking lectures in the Muséum were not used for the prosecution of controversy; the favoured medium for this remained the printed word and the lectures at the Lycée de Paris.

If the image formed in the public mind of the Jardin was utopic, so also was the existing ideal of what natural history consisted of. The Muséum offered to its public not an argument about the order of nature, but the order of nature displayed and arranged, and also, a tableau of the unspoiled virtues which popular writers located in the animals of the menagerie, and with the true practitioners of the study of nature. In the age of egoism, the reassurance that virtue was natural, to be found even in the beasts, was especially valuable.

Under the Restoration, the emphasis shifted again, and while not losing its former functions, the Muséum also started to symbolise a popular consumption of natural history. The clearest indication of this came during the famous episode of the giraffe. This animal, a gift from Ali Pasha of Egypt to the French government, was received in the Muséum on 30 June 1827, having walked to Paris from Marseille with its favourite keeper and a goat to provide it with milk. Popular interest in its arrival, the first such animal in Paris for many years, was such that not only were the streets lined to see it pass, but it gave its name to dances, bonnets, and many other articles of consumption, and influenced popular art for a considerable time. Odes to the giraffe were written and sold, and fashionable

Families, friends and institutions

young men, such as Stendahl, arranged to have places on a launch when it was decided that, to avoid the crowds, the animal should arrive by the river entrance to the Muséum[85] An element in the great spectacle of nature was sold in effigy many times over. The episode of the giraffe was of course the culmination of the process which had been begun by Cuvier and Lacepède's successful publication of a popular picture book about the animals of the menagerie in 1802; an enterprise which played upon a large enough market to be repeated by Cuvier alone a few years later.[86]

In these ways, the public image and the public's use of the Muséum did indeed contain within it many of the images of science which we have already traced in this work; science as a national story, as consumption, as spectacle, as epitome of virtue and authenticity, and as utopia. Precisely because these images were so confused and ambiguous, they were also very powerful, and combined with the actual scientific work going on within its walls, to give the Muséum great visibility. It began to be used as a model for other similar institutions. In England, the newly formed Zoological Society, for example, considered its form and finances when drawing up its original prospectus.[87] Precisely because it had such public presence in Paris, it became a public forum worth fighting for. In the increasing political unrest of the Restoration, liberal reformers such as Louis Lefebvre, for example, alternately mocked and satirised the Muséum, and fought to be allowed to give free courses within its walls.[88]

The idea of the Muséum also began to change for the professional scientists. Although Cuvier himself profited enormously from the 'mass' audiences of the Muséum, he could never, as we have seen, bring himself openly to endorse any ideal of popular science. His friend de Candolle, however, who had become director of the botanic garden in Geneva, increasingly endorsed the view that the public should have full access to natural history collections, even if this turned out to be at the expense of the high-level science being pursued within the same institution.[89] Deleuze, in his study of the Muséum, put forward the same point of view. This was not surprising coming from a man whose main concern outside the Muséum was with the popular 'pseudo-science' of phrenology:

but it was tempered with a more complex realisation than De Candolle's of the varieties of different types of person such public institutions increasingly had to serve: 'the man of science', 'the meditative man', the 'studious youth', the 'curious', and the 'man of letters and the artist'.[90] It was to all these that Cuvier was indebted for the visibility which ensured his career in Paris, and which also ensured the insertion of science into the cultural fabric of France; and this made possible the many public faces of Cuvier.

The Muséum, of course, had for many years possessed its own organ of publicity, the *Annales du Muséum d'Histoire Naturelle*, to be succeeded in 1832 by the *Nouvelles Annales du Muséum d'Histoire Naturelle*.[91] Founded by Fourcroy, the *Annales* published papers written by the Muséum staff or the Muséum's correspondents, and occasionally published items of interest from those who, like Humboldt, were not officially attached to the Muséum. The *Annales* had other uses than the simple reporting of research results, or the relying of controversy. It also existed to make a history and mythology of the Muséum. A long series of historical articles written by Antoine-Laurent de Jussieu, for example, attempted to establish the Muséum's continuity with the Jardin des Plantes which, as we have seen, was far from the case in any legal or constitutional sense. Deleuze often contributed to its pages obituaries of notable field naturalists, especially those of the Muséum's accredited travellers, and thus played his part in creating a niche in the martyrology of field natural history which should belong specifically to the Muséum.[92] Whereas the 'ideology' purveyed in the pages of the *Annales* was concerned with the establishment of institutional and personal continuities, that proposed by Cuvier for the *Nouvelles Annales*, was concerned directly with the issue of good and bad science. In many ways, Cuvier's prospectus for the new journal was the final episode in his conflict with Geoffroy. The two men quarrelled over the editorial policy devised by Cuvier, which was to stress positive facts and discoveries at the expense of theoretical speculation. It was an obvious swipe at Geoffroy, and it was also the first time that the *Annales* had attempted to dictate the views underlying the articles which were to be published within its pages.[93] This was also the first

Families, friends and institutions

time that controversy had been allowed to appear openly within the official activities of the Muséum. It thus foreshadows the increasing polarisations of debate that, as we have already seen, marked the approach of the great conflict of 1830 between Cuvier and Geoffroy.

By 1832, in fact, the popular and social Cuvier pictured by Pfaff in 1800, had clearly become seriously unpopular in the Muséum.[94] The collapse of his relationships with Geoffroy, with Lamarck and with Blainville had all left their mark, as had the earlier hostility from Haüy and Daubenton. The Brongniart group also displayed a notable coolness towards Cuvier, as we have already seen, although this never resulted in outright hostility, and was gradually softened between 1830 and 1832. Socially and politically, therefore, the Muséum hardly provided the secure basis of support for Cuvier which many commentators have implicitly ascribed to it, and it certainly could not insure Cuvier against Geoffroy's challenge in the Academy of Sciences. While Brongniart had created an extended family support-group, Cuvier's collaborators were less closely related to him, and could offer him little aid in conflicts which took place at the highest levels of the scientific community. Nor was the Muséum itself capable of providing him with effective support, for the simple reason that it lacked either the human or institutional coherence to do so. Nor could he join in competition on the marriage market of the Muséum to strengthen his position. Both of the most bitter controversies of Cuvier's scientific life were conducted with his colleagues in the Muséum, Lamarck and Geoffroy, and another scarcely less violent, but of less wide-ranging implications, with Faujas over the identification of fossil specimens. His arrogation of the comparative anatomy collections, and the way his lectures and books frequently trespassed on the territory of his colleagues and most notably on that of Lamarck, did not help matters. Cuvier's campaign for entry into the Muséum had begun his career by causing a violent internal dispute, and his career within it continued to create hostility amongst his colleagues. Nor is it possible to show Cuvier as the really dominant figure within the Muséum, in spite of the fact that he became President of its Assembly in 1808–9. Its constitution in any case made this very difficult for a single individual to achieve, and indeed had been designed expressly so that no person could ever again achieve Buffon's dictatorial position. Cuvier's period as President of the Assembly of the Professors has therefore to be balanced against his long periods away from Paris under the Empire, and the increasing pressure of his administrative duties outside the Muséum under the Restoration, which were often enough to cause him to delegate even scientific enquiry to his subordinates. Nor did the Muséum really contribute all that much to the professionalisation of science within this period. It produced no coherent view of the order of nature, its appointments were dominated by patronage and family connections rather than by a recognised *cursus* of merit and certification, and the effective workers within its walls always contained many, such as Pentland and Sophie Duvaucel, who were not part of the Muséum's official payroll.

Where the Muséum really did affect Cuvier's work was in the facility it gave him to exemplify his ordering of nature, and through its collections, enormously to speed up their detailed construction. Further, its position as a national institution of public access, and its 'image' to the broad public as an accessible utopia, gave Cuvier, through his lectures and collections, a complete visibility to all sections of the Parisian public in a way which could also be guaranteed to be genuinely scientific. Authenticated by the existence of this privileged spot, public in a way the Institut was not, Cuvier could at last achieve an uncompromised visibility as the interpreter of the natural order.

IX
Patronage and the post-revolutionary élite: enquiry and conclusion

The preceding pages should have made it clear that Cuvier's career could not have taken the form it did without his successful manipulation of patronage. This book has emphasised Cuvier's tactics as both patron and client, rather than stressing his institutional involvements. This was done deliberately, and reflects a judgement on the part of the author on the need to reorientate studies of French science in this period away from a dominant concern with institutions, and issues such as the 'professionalisation' of science, and towards a closer examination of the nature of the exchanges between individuals which constituted a substantial part of the exercise of power in this period.[1] This is not of course to argue that patronage exists in a vacuum. Institutional resources are obviously one of the most important prizes a patron has to offer to his clients. Rather, it is to argue that until we understand both the nature of the institutions of science, and the interchanges of power which went on around them in the shape of patronage, we will not understand the nature of science in this period. Emphasis on institutions in the literature has also encouraged the assumption that scientific institutions and scientific patronage were somehow coterminous. But in a world where the major patrons in science also controlled patronage in a considerable number of other fields (Cuvier in the Conseil d'Etat and the University of France, Lacepède in the Sénat and the Légion d'honneur, Chaptal in the Ministry of the Interior, to take only a few examples), this assumption is clearly a dangerous one, and can cause misleading conclusions to be drawn about the importance and operation of patronage. This is particularly so because we are in the interesting position of possessing many studies of institutions in this period, many biographies of individuals, many discussions of 'issues', such as professionalisation of science; but we do not possess a single comprehensive, precisely argued, historically detailed account of the exercise of patronage. This book, which has set out to be as much issue orientated as biographically orientated, represents a first step towards this goal.

We can expect little help in this task from the findings of general history. This too has concentrated overwhelmingly on analysis of institutions and on individual careers. There are, of course, some notable exceptions, especially in recent work. Nonetheless, we are still without a generally acceptable characterisation of how power was created and wielded in terms of patrons and clientèles. It is curious that this situation should persist, when the opposite is true for studies of the Restoration.[2] In these circumstances, the close analysis of Cuvier's actions as a patron over a period covering both the Empire and the Restoration, has value as a detailed case study closely linked to a general characterisation of the changing political life of the two periods. Such case studies enable us to build up generalised characterisations and typologies of action in this period, typologies which if they are adequately formulated, could be applied to give general significance to the incidents described in many of the biographies of this period, and would enable us to answer, for a given career, questions relating to its typicality or otherwise. The fact that Cuvier was a peculiarly self-conscious client and a peculiarly self-conscious patron means that his individual case is well worth studying. Few can have been so consciously aware of the pitfalls and advantages of each move in the game of the attraction and dispensation of patronage, few men have been classed so highly by their contemporaries as effective patrons, whether for good or for ill. In his own autobiography Cuvier is often at pains to explain the calculations behind particular moves at the turning points of his career. Although, like all autobiographies, Cuvier's conceals as much as it reveals, its narrative is far closer to an unvarnished account of the world of career-making than is for example that of Lacepède, whose romantic sentimentalism on the subject of nature often obscures the personal contacts leading to specific stages in his career.

Patronage and the post-revolutionary élite

To counterbalance the inevitable emphasis of this book on the problems encountered during a single career, this concluding section will also aim to draw together much of the comparative material on career patterns which has been scattered through the body of the book, and notably in Chapters III, IV, V, VI and IX, particularly in relation to the careers of Latreille, the Brongniart family, and those close to Cuvier such as the collaborators on the *Règne Animal* or his protégés Flourens and Blainville. At the same time, enough material exists on the careers of men such as Biot and Gay-Lussac, who stood outside Cuvier's immediate orbit, but who were engaged in the game of career-making at the same time.

We must now commence to raise some more general points. Firstly, to definitions. The central word at issue, 'patronage', is one that the literature has found hard to define. It is easy to recognise a patron or a client or an act of patronage when one sees it, far less easy to offer a precise definition. In part, this reflects the diffused and personalised nature of patronage in pre-industrial societies. In part it also reflects the clear logical difficulties of defining actions that take place within society. Such definitions have very little meaning unless they are accompanied by descriptions of the context within which patronage takes place. For this reason, I have decided to content myself in this section with a minimalistic definition of patronage as 'the creation and manipulation of a relationship of dependence between a superior in power and an inferior in power', and to accompany it with detailed descriptions of precise acts of patronage, and their context. This may seem to constitute a cavalier rejection of much sociological and anthropological work. But on examination, such studies tend to produce analyses of patronage that are inapplicable to the context with which we are dealing. Such models tend to relate far more to the relatively primitive societies studied by most anthropologists, or to deal with complex societies where the role of the state is far more dominant than it was even in the later part of the period with which we are concerned. Napoleonic and Restoration France tends to fall between two stools as far as these definitions are concerned, as being on the one hand a highly complex and sophisticated society in terms of its political interactions, and yet at the same time a society where the state played nothing like the same sort of effective and intrusive role that it does in the twentieth century. A further point must also be made in discussing the applicability of these models. It is that models of patronage which relate to the analysis of the general politics of a given society may not be applicable to actions constituting intellectual patronage. Political patronage, for example, generally does not aim or expect to change the status of the client. It may also fairly easily be restricted to a single or a few precise actions. On the other hand, the very object of intellectual patronage, with its profoundly educational ideology, is to secure the development of the protégé often over a long period of time. Intellectual patronage has within it, to far greater extent than has 'normal' patronage, extremely old ideals of the development of character in the protégé, of role modelling on an admired individual teacher, and even of the use of that teacher as a substitute for close family relationships, which are all absent or diminished in importance in 'normal' political patronage. Thus our first problem is to be very clear about the ways in which patronage within the world of science differed from the 'political' patronage which the same patrons might be exercising in the wider political stage.

Our second major task to relate the nature of patronage to the nature of public life as a whole. Here, comparative studies may be of considerable value. Historians for example have always taken for granted the great publicity with which patronage operated in this society, both in the intellectual sphere, and in that of general political life. They see nothing strange in the fact that the great patrons were publicly known as such, and that their clients were, generally speaking, not hesitant about proclaiming their links with their patrons. It was a way of ensuring that one's intellectual genealogy was known and respected, a way of entering the 'good' intellectual families. But such open, publicity-seeking, participation in the world of patronage would seem, for example, totally alien to the world of the modern Mafia boss, whom all would recognise as a patron figure. Typically, such men will minimise their role or deny it completely, representing themselves as merely humble citizens, without more authority than the next man, though perhaps with a little facility for resolving problems

Patronage and the post-revolutionary élite

which is made use of by his neighbours. Patronage in Cuvier's world, in other words, was a profoundly public exercise. In other societies, it insists on being tacit, hidden. Why the difference? The answer lies partly not just in the differences between intellectual patronage and Mafia patronage, but also in the difference between the state systems of two different historical periods. Silent or dissimulated patronage tends to occur when, as in modern Italy, there is a gross disjunction between the institutions of power and the way power is actually wielded. In cases where the reverse is true, which would apply to most European pre-industrial societies, the mechanism of central government comes second in importance to the patronage cliques which it harbours, and there is not so much of a perceived gap between impersonal bureaucratic ideologies and the profoundly personal nature of patronage. All power in traditional societies, was seen, from that of the monarch downwards, in personalised terms. In other words, it was not institutional position as such, but the very public use of the patronage power given by various kinds of prestige and position, which conferred visible authority. When bureaucratic ideals are relatively weak, then the exercise of power cannot take place without an audience. The Mafia boss on the other hand, dissimulates his power precisely because it depends on the play-off between two sets of values, between his power, and impersonal, universalistic, bureaucratic ideals which govern the overt apparatus of power. By this sort of comparison of factors about patronage which historians too often take for granted in this period it is thus often possible to arrive at general conclusions which link the nature of patronage with the nature of authority as it is exercised generally in the society to which one is referring.

The existence of an audience for the exercise of patronage is also of vital importance in understanding the nature of scientific patronage in particular. Patronage throughout this society is carried out in virtue of an audience. Scientific patronage in particular makes it essential for every aspirant to the scientific community to be able to satisfy the demands of the audience of the scientific élite, those who decide on the norms of good science. The patron therefore has to take care to select and foster only those clients who can be relied upon to perform well for this audience, and thus increase his own prestige in front of it. Scientific patronage thus contains risks which much of political patronage need not, in virtue of the fact that such patronage does not simply exist as a transaction between patron and client, but also as a transaction between patron, client and audience. A further risk to the patron stems from the fact that this audience adjudicates performance in the light of impersonal norms. This makes it an audience quite unlike the audience for general politics, which is concerned above all with the effectiveness of given actions in gaining desired ends. The scientific audience, on the other hand always possesses the potential of judging a protégé according to the accepted norms of 'good' science, rather than in virtue of the power of their patron. In other words, the existence of the audience means that protégés can fail, fail publicly and fail in a way that cannot necessarily be ascribed to personal hostilities. The risks carried by the patron in adopting a particular client are therefore higher. The existence of an audience actuated by impersonal norms also means that clients who find themselves in disagreement with their patron can turn to that audience for validation, and in such circumstances are not wholly dependent on their patrons. Blainville's quarrel with Cuvier, for example, was rapidly followed by the publication of work attacking Cuvier's system of classification. This was an appeal to the wider audience of science over the head of his former patron. This appeal to an even wider definition of the interested public was also to be used with great effect by Geoffroy St Hilaire in his conflict with Cuvier in 1830, as we have seen.

However, it must not be thought that in this analysis, patrons, clients and audience are everything, and institutions nothing. Clearly, without institutions, patrons would have had no posts at their disposal to distribute to their protégés. This was not the only resource at a patron's disposal, but it was one of the most important, because it gave both visibility and income to the protégé, and often ensured for the patron at the same time a multiplication of his own visibility through such means as for example as *suppléance* at lectures. But the effectiveness of a patron can more truly be measured not simply in terms of the institutional patronage at his disposal,

Patronage and the post-revolutionary élite

but in terms of the variety of combinations of different *kinds* of resource he could command. A patron who commanded the disposition of posts across a whole range of different areas of public life was far more powerful than one who commanded posts on only one. The network of relationships to which such wide-ranging powers gave rise exerted a multiplier effect on the whole range of influence.[3] In the case of both Cuvier and Laplace, their period of greatest scientific influence was also that of their highest standing outside the scientific community. A patron's 'capital' consisted not simply of his power to dispose of institutional places, but also of the network of relationships and informal influence upon which he could call. Such influence could be as much the product of family relationships or political collaboration as it was either of scientific expertise or of institutional power. This means that we need to know as much about the networks which enmeshed each patron as we do the patronage resources of individuals.

This is not the place to embark on a full-scale examination of that sociological technique known as 'network analysis'.[4] But put briefly, it would seem that there are many dangers to the historian in the use of this type of analysis. The fieldwork behind network analysis encounters frequent difficulties arising from informants' use of key words such as 'friend' and 'neighbour' in many different senses. Such terms can only be understood in terms of individual usage and language. But whereas questioning and cross-checking with informants on the meaning of the words they use is perfectly possible if the informant is alive, the process becomes more tricky when the informant is dead, and has left only written testimony to guide the historian. In order to estimate degrees of closeness or distance between individuals in the past, the historian is impelled into a far more prolonged exploration of the nature of 'friendship' or 'neighbourliness' in the period with which he is dealing. Network analysis also has difficulty in coming to terms with the qualitative evaluation of the relationships it maps. But it is precisely the 'content' of a network and its reputation in the eyes of other individuals and networks, in which the historian is often most interested. What ideas or ideologies did a given network endorse or contain? How far was a given network regarded as having high status by other individuals or networks? How, in the fluid world of the post-revolutionary French élite, is one in fact to say where one network ends and another begins? Again, this is a relatively easy matter to determine if one is working with a small number of living individuals, and a complex matter if one is dealing with a large community of the dead.

It might in fact be more helpful for the historian to think in terms of each patron as a sort of transmission belt. By passing into contact with the transmission belt, the protégé was able to come into contact also with the whole range of opportunities and human resources represented by the network. Thus, our next theme must be the identification of the social institutions through which the protégé was most likely to come into contact with the network. We also need to be able to identify the chronological turning points in a patronage relationship, the 'moments'.

It is obvious that in Cuvier's case, for example, the major social institution at his disposal was the *salon*, just as, for Laplace, the most effective were the informal meetings at his country house at Arcueil, chronicled by Maurice Crosland. This was the transmission belt which fed aspiring members of his network into contact both with its already accepted members and with other patrons whose notice they might also be capable of attracting. Far more attention needs to be paid to informal social institutions like the *salons*, for their very prevalence in this period is an indication of their importance. We need to know far more about their membership, whether that of one *salon* overlapped with another, their political role, and their function as recruiting grounds for potential members of the élite. It is also the existence of such social institutions that enable us to answer the basic question: why were patrons necessary at all? In a world where so much science was produced by amateurs, outside the Parisian networks, and of independent financial means, this question needs to be asked. It may become clearer if we link patrons specifically to the making of careers in science, from which by definition the wealthy provincial amateur is unlikely to gain much profit. Clearly also, for those who are bent on making a career in science in Paris, the patron controls all sorts of access to institutions, formal and informal, to cash, and to the audience

Patronage and the post-revolutionary élite 197

of peers which the aspirant has to convince of his capabilities.

But a study of any major Parisian scientific patron of this period will also reveal him in relations which can only be described as those of patronage and yet which do not conform to the Parisian 'career' model briefly outlined above. Cuvier's relations with provincial *savants*, which I have examined elsewhere,[5] are clearly relations of patronage, include the exchange of services and information. But this 'patronage at a distance' differs in several ways from the Parisian model. It is carried on by letter, rather than face to face. It is not educative in the sense that Cuvier is not primarily interested in training the provincial *savants*, already men of considerable expertise. What goes on is rather an exchange of information, in which there is little feeling of a great gap between the scientific standing of the different parties involved. In return for the sacrifice of claims to the ownership of the information which the provincial *savant* passes on to Cuvier, he gains access to Cuvier's own stock of information, and to the wide range of political services that Cuvier can perform. The prime example discussed in this book is Cuvier's efforts on behalf of Fabbroni, which necessitated the mobilisation of political support across a wide range of acquaintance, which extended, indirectly, as far as Napoleon's sister, Eliza Bacchioci. Patronage at a distance is thus often a far more equal relationship than direct patron–client relations. It was a perception of forced inequality that induced Blainville to revolt against Cuvier.

The other major division in types of patronage is that between formal and informal patronage, the former being defined as patronage relations which take place between those who are not otherwise linked, and the latter typically between members of the same family. The Brongniart family group would be the best example explored in this book, but Cuvier himself at the beginning of his career took care to promote the careers not only of his brother Frédéric, but also of his more distant relatives Duvernoy and Laurillard, as well as Charles Cuvier at a later stage. Relations which were both of patronage and of familial tie were clearly likely to be stronger than those which depended merely on the effectiveness of the patron and the gratitude of the client. But they were also more dangerous for the patron in the sense that a family member who proved inadequate to maintain the patron's reputation could not be discarded as easily as could a protégé who was not related to him. Reliance on family members as protégés could also lead to accusations from the rest of the community of nepotism or favouritism, accusations which a patron already in an insecure position for other reasons, might well wish to avoid. We have seen already in discussing Cuvier's career under the Restoration how such accusations could be used to embroil his position, and how Cuvier's own increasing vulnerability was translated into attacks on other members of his family holding posts in areas quite unrelated to his own. The Brongniarts remained relatively invulnerable to this sort of attack because, unlike Cuvier, their public commitments were neither wide-ranging nor in the most sensitive areas of political debate. These were factors which greatly reduced Cuvier's capacity to contain the dimensions of threats to his own position.

We now need to focus more specifically on Cuvier's own career in terms of this question of patronage. Until genuinely large-scale comparative work has been done, questions such as the typicality of Cuvier's career are going to continue to be difficult to examine in a meaningful way. At the moment it is simply possible to say that Cuvier's career was not regarded by his contemporaries as being typical but rather as having registered the extremes of successful power. Cuvier is certainly untypical in his early and conscious refusal to rely on the support of any one patron to facilitate the transition from the status of gifted provincial amateur to that of a recognised Parisian professional. This was a decision that was certainly facilitated, however, by the fluidity of the society which Cuvier encountered in Paris in 1795. The post-thermidorean world was no longer dominated by the constraints of the Terror, and had yet to experience the sharp focusing on the founts of patronage controlled by the future imperial family. It was notoriously a time when the control of power shifted daily between different groups and individuals, a process intensified by the frequent political purges of the Directory. It may well be that the process of attracting and dispensing patronage returned after Napoleon's seizure of power in 1799 which were closer to those of the old regime where so many of his servants had learnt their business. Men such as Biot,

Latreille or Gay-Lussac who were making their career after 1799, may well have been more likely to focus their efforts on a single patron rather than do the conscious 'shopping around' that men such as Cuvier and De Gérando, active before 1799, were liable to do. Another factor in the stabilisation of patronage must also have been the re-establishment of a central élite body for the intellectual classes, the Institut de France. A young man arriving in Paris at the beginning of 1795, twelve months before the formal opening of the Institut, would be in a position to make maximum use of the competition for good protégés which must have taken place among the surviving members of the scientific community as one of the means of improving their chances of election to the new body. In all respects, therefore, the year 1795 was an auspicious one in which to begin to make a Parisian career.

But if the initial stages of Cuvier's career may well have been atypical, then his actions as a patron after his own establishment were probably less so. The establishment of the Institut and the return of political stability defined the arenas for the exercise of patronage more clearly than they had been before. The actions of Cuvier and many like him, such as the Brongniarts, in establishing part of their clientèle among their family may well also have contributed to the further stabilisation of the system. If Cuvier's early career offers us little indication, unlike Geoffroy's, of the turning points in a client's career, the significant 'moments' of adoption and acceptance by an older patron, the point at which Cuvier himself began to be perceived as a patron in his own right, is fairly clear.[5] By about 1800, he was certainly being used by his native town as the man they turned to to gain needed support in their difficulties with the Parisian authorities.[7] This perception at a distance, which came some time before his election as Permanent Secretary to the Institut, or even his appointment to the full chair at the Muséum, is surely the crucial turning point, and points up the dominance of informal influence through personal contacts over institutional position, in contemporary assessments of the degree of power at the disposal of individuals.

Cuvier's success as a patron and as a 'reference figure' for the period after 1800 until 1830 hardly need to be further established. But the events of 1830 tell us much about the patronage systems of the Empire and the Restoration, and their essential weakness. Cuvier's concern, which has so often been documented in this book, to exclude the broad public from the inner workings of the scientific life, was not only motivated by a wish to produce a natural history which should be expert, technical and positivistic; it was also motivated by an acute awareness of the fact that the patronage system as he knew it functioned well only as long as it remained an affair between patron, client and expert audience. Once the general public were asked to adjudge the issues of the scientific world, then power based on control of patronage within the scientific community began to be challenged. Geoffroy's *succès d'opinion* in 1830 was not due to a victory on the substantive scientific issues involved, nor was it due to his pre-existing power in the community of science. Geoffroy's victory was due to his successful appeal to 'opinion', a force so powerful, especially on the eve of revolution, that it nullified the accumulated prestige of Cuvier. Geoffroy's challenge was dangerous because it went outside the limits of the normal challenges issued by one patron to another, and included an appeal to public opinion. The nature of Geoffroy's challenge also pointed up another inherent weakness in the tripartite relationship between patron, client and audience. The public ideology of science was a strongly other-worldly one, which condemned the very world of manoeuvres for advantage which constituted that of the patron and client. It also placed a strong emphasis on the retention, for the ideal scientist, of that very personal autonomy which submission to the will of the patron could well erode in the client. This is why patronage systems in science always contained the roots of their own decay, because at any moment their moral validity could be challenged. Taken with the extent to which the possessors of wide-ranging political positions could be affected by instabilities in the political position as a whole, and the challenge to Cuvier's position caused by the events of 1830, should cause little surprise.

In conclusion, we must pose one further question. To what extent did the patronage system in science affect the content of scientific work itself? We have already seen that there were in fact many different patterns of patronage in this period. Equally, few would attempt to argue that the science produced in this period was homogenous in style or in the character of its assumptions. Probably, to try to relate specific research programmes to the character of scientific patronage would be a hopeless undertaking. But some more general conclusions do seem possible. The patronage system, just because it was so profoundly personalised and so based on the *education* and development of the protégé, was unable to produce coherent and lasting schools of work which lasted beyond the life time of the patron. Laplace's programmes and patronage power collapsed even before his death, as Robert Fox has shown. The same occured with Cuvier's own patronage power, as we have seen, with the defection of Blainville. The science of the Empire and the Restoration is above all characterised by its absence of consensus on research objectives, norms of enquiry, and standards of evidence. The patronage system provided no clear statement of what was meant by doing good science. Hence, surely much of the urgency in Cuvier's arguments for a positivistic science. We may also speculate about other effects of the patronage system on the conduct of science. One effect may have been the high premium placed on the production of massive encyclopaedic works in the natural sciences, such as Cuvier's *Règne Animal*, and *Histoire Naturelle des Poissons*, or Lacepède's *Histoire naturelle des poissons* or Laplace's *Méchanique Céleste*. Such large-scale projects were ideal as resources for the attraction, training and testing of the protégés. The tasks involved in their production were of a kind that could be parcelled out amongst several different workers without too much affecting the coherence of the whole. The patron had much work done for him, and the protégés gained expertise and prestige. This may also have had the result that highly speculative, non-experimental, non-encyclopaedic works, such as those of Lamarck, were those which could not be used as patronage resources. As we have seen, Lamarck himself discouraged even those who like De Candolle, did wish to become his protégés. It is significant that even when Candolle was accepted by Lamarck it was to rework the old edition of the *Flore française*, a work of listing. Lamarck's later and more philosophical works were all written by himself.

So great was his deficiency in clients that Lamarck was forced to underscore his public position not in virtue of the numbers of his followers, but in virtue of his disdain for that part of the world of science which was articulated by the publicity-seeking manoeuvres of patron and client; hence the growth of the myth, fostered by Lamarck himself, of Lamarck as a solitary martyr to the machinations of the great patrons, and Cuvier in particular, the epitome of the public man of science. Lamarck was in fact exploiting to the full that ever-present gap between the real world of science and its asocial ideology.

The final way in which the patronage system may have influenced the presentation of science was that it may have given experimentally replicable science high value for the patron. Results by a protégé which replicated effectively in front of the audience of the patron's scientific peers were clearly one of the ways in which the patron could raise or maintain his own status. Cuvier's most successful experiment in that direction was clearly with the early work of Flourens on the localisation of the functions of the brain. Thus, although the operation of patronage may be difficult to link directly to the actual content of the science produced, it certainly could well have influenced the form of its presentation, and the dominant emphases in French science towards a positivistic, experimentally based science, and its denigration of the speculative philosophical school represented by Lamarck and to a lesser extent by Geoffroy. This trend in turn fought back by appeal to public opinion or to asocial ideals of science, but only started to make real headway after the publication of Darwin's work in 1859 found the French in need of an indigenous proponent of some form of transformism. This set up the denigration of Cuvier, the patron and public man who had used his power to repress Lamarck, which has influenced all subsequent historiography on this topic. It is hoped that this book will have gone some way towards showing how misguided such an interpretation of the public world of science has been.

Notes

Note to Introduction
1. All quotations retain the original spelling.

Notes to Chapter I
1. See Goguel, 1864; pp. 21–2, reprints the birth certificate.
2. Coleman, 1964, devoted only pp. 6–8 of his 212-page study to this period; Febvre, 1953, p. 329, dismisses the years in Montbéliard as 'secondary' and 'negligible' in importance.
3. For general accounts see Viénot, 1895, and C. Duvernoy, 1891.
4. E.g., Georg-Friedrich Parrot, born in Montbéliard in 1767, became first President of the University of Tartu in Russian Estonia, and Secretary to the St Petersburg Academy of Sciences.
5. For genealogies, see Haag, 1859–68, s.v. Württemburg, IX.
6. Estimated as 3,143 in 1769 and as 3,996 in 1794, by Debard, 1974–5, and Sahler, 1911.
7. The first and second years of Cuvier's life were also marked by a particularly acute crisis; food shortage may well have contributed to his bad health as a child and adolescent.
8. Cucuel, 1914, quoting BNP MS fr. 8548, fol. 91.
9. Tuefferd, 1862, p. 28.
10. *Ibid.*
11. See genealogical table of Cuvier's family, and note 15 below.
12. Oberkirch n.d., p. 36; C.-L. Duvernoy, ed. M. Menot, 1955–9, pp. 289–90.
13. Viénot, 1895, p, 149.
14. Oberkirch, n.d., *passim*, relates these visits and others like them; Renard, 1967, gives full details of visits by the Grand-Duke Paul of Russia; Fallot, 1903, points out the opportunities for travel in Germany which could accrue from attendance at Court.
15. Goguel, 1864, p. 8 *et seq.*, incorporates work by G.-L. Duvernoy on Cuvier's family tree; see also Roy, 1887, Emonot, 1897; Mauveaux, 1913, pp. 265–6; Salomon, 1927; Viénot, 1932; Mathiot, 1932, gives details of the life of the surgeon Jehan Cuvier, Cuvier's great-grandfather.
16. Mauveaux, 1913, pp. 265–6, gives the armorial of the Cuvier family in the Red Book of the *bourgeoisie.*
17. Waldner was an uncle of Mme d'Oberkirch, whose memoirs of life at the court of Etupes have already been cited. Jean-George Cuvier

joined the regiment in 1758, and held the rank of lieutenant in 1769. For the regiment, see Grouvel, 1945.

18. Cuvier's autobiography (MS Flourens 2598) of the library of the Institut de France, puts the family's annual income at 800 francs at this period.

19. Debard, 1974–5, p. 280.

20. Goguel, 1864, p. 204, gives Frédéric's godparents as his mother's brother Samuel-Frédéric Chatel, a teacher at the town's infant school, and a military colleague of his father, Jean-Frédéric Richard, a lieutenant in his regiment.

21. For accounts of Cuvier's childhood, see Lee, 1833, pp. 8–14; C. L. Duvernoy, 1833, pp. 8–11, also quoted in Trouessart, 1909; Viénot, 1932, pp. 6–14 quotes material from Duvernoy's source C.-N. Cuvier, omitted in all previous accounts, except that of Bourdon, 1844, p. 98.

22. G.-L. Duvernoy, *ibid*; Trouessart, *ibid.*, p. 110; Viénot, *ibid.*, pp. 10-11.

23. Boas, 1966, pp. 1–31; Coveney, 1967, p. 48; Cuvier, 1819–27, I, pp. 37–8, II, p. 313.

24. E.g. Lee, 1833, p. 11.

25. Wetzel, cited in Godard, 1893, pp. 191–2.

26. Viénot, 1932, pp. 10–11.

27. Viénot, 1885, *passim*; C. Duvernoy, 1891, p. 386 *et seq.*; Viénot 1932, p. 9.

28. Marchant, 1858, pp. 59–60. Letter of 14 October 1788.

29. Cramer and Hermehnle, 1906–53, confirms this story. There is no record of Cuvier's matriculation at Tübingen; II, pp. 329, 323, records the matriculation of his cousins Charles-Nicholas Cuvier in 1785 and Louis-Christophe Cuvier in 1784.

30. I can find no confirmatory evidence of the story recounted in Lee, 1833, p. 13, of Cuvier reaching the Grand-Duke's notice by his delivery of a ceremonial speech of welcome on the occasion of this visit, nor is this event mentioned in the autobiography.

31. Batz, 1784, p. 92.

32. *Ibid.*, p. 39.

33. Raeff, 1975.

34. Batz, 1784, p. 48.

35. Fallot, 1903, p. 18, gives an account of a meal at the Academy in 1773, witnessed by the Montbéliardais D.-C.-E. Berdot: 'Tous les élèves s'étant mis en marche très cadencée, défilent deux à deux pour se rendre chacun à sa chaise où ils s'arrêtent pour attendre le commandement d'un bas-officier qui après leur avoir fait faire un demi-tour à droite, commande la prière qui se fait à haute voix par un des élèves placé dans un cathèdre qui se trouve à l'autre extremité de la salle. Cette prière faite, les jeunes gens se mettent à table et à peine le Duc a-t-il dit, "Mangez, Messieurs", que chacun porte la cuillière à la bouche . . . le tout se fait avec la dernière précision militaire'. See also Batz, 1784, p. 205.

36. For the reminiscences of a contemporary of Cuvier at the Academy, a Polish nobleman, see Longin (ed. anon.), 1914.
37. Batz, 1784, p. 9.
38. Raeff, 1975; Mack Walker, 1978.
39. Longin (ed. anon.), 1914, p. 230, relates the peculiar practical jokes which the Grand-Duke was liable to play on the students, but comments that nevertheless, he 'avait porté sur cette institution toute son affection, et c'était celle d'un tendre père plutôt que d'un protecteur. Il donnait constamment des marques de bienveillance aux élèves, et les prodiguait surtout aux plus jeunes, qui ne le voyaient jamais sans avoir reçu de lui quelques paroles caressantes; il savait par coeur les noms de tous, et les nommait sans hésiter. Les bâtiments de l'Académie étaient attenants à son palais; il n'avait qu'un couloir à traverser pour s'y rendre.'
40. Those in authority possessed great power as the focus of adolescent emotion. *Ibid.*, p. 233, recounts how after attending a Grand-ducal ball 'Je trouvai la Grande-Duchesse si belle que de trois semaines elle ne sortit pas de l'esprit. Je la vis danser un menuet . . . je devins mélancholique et je pleurais la nuit'.
41. Batz, 1784, was clearly written to rebut such charges; see its preface, and pp. 210–91: 'C'est de la méchanceté et de l'ingratitude de ces mauvais sujets qui ont lassé la longanimité [sic] du Duc, que viennent en grande partie les noires calomnies qu'on a répandues contre l'Institution'.
42. D'Harcourt, 1928, pp. 28–46. Cuvier displayed his fellow-student Danneker's bust of Schiller in a prominent position in his home in Paris at the Jardin des Plantes.
43. Pfaff, 1858, p. 16; for another example of Cuvier's physical immobility, see *ibid.*, p. 17.
44. *Ibid.*, p. 22.
45. Anon., 1791.
46. [Jean-Simon Kerner], 1786, *Vorrede*, no pagination: 'Auch finde ich sehr billig hier offentlich dem Hrn chevalier von Marschall und Hrn Cuvier, welche in der Botanik unter den zoglingen der höhen Carls-Schüle gegenwärtig die meiste kenntnisse haben, meinen lebhaften Dank abzustatten . . . .' This is very probably the first mention of Cuvier in print.
47. Pfaff, 1858, pp. 17–19. Similar stories that Cuvier opened a natural history society at school in Montbéliard should be taken as a reading back of the incidents of Stuttgart. There is no evidence for such a society in Montbéliard, and one is not mentioned by Wetzel. Such stories are typical of the biographical tradition's propensity to over-use a limited range of key incidents and by doing so create a monolithic, static view of its subject. For this story see e.g. Lee, 1833, p. 13.
48. Pfaff, 1858, p. 15. See Brunschwig, 1973, p. 316, for the cult of friendship in the rest of Germany.
49. D'Harcourt, 1928, p. 46.

50. Published Oeringen, 1788. For the ethic of cosmopolitanism, see McKillop, 1965.
51. Marchant, 1858, p. 52, Cuvier to Pfaff, 10 September 1788.
52. 4 vols, Neuchâtel, 1779.
53. Cuvier to Saussure, n.d. (1788–9), BIFC 3214/1. His account of this journey is at BIFC 3312/ 1-3.
54. Pfaff, 1858, pp. 294-6, examines Cuvier's relationship at this time with Kielmeyer. I follow the chronology of their acquaintance as established by Pfaff.
55. Brunschwig, 1973, pp. 208–80.
56. See note 4 for Parrot's subsequent career.

Notes to Chapter II

1. Cuvier described the decision as follows: 'Il fallait prendre un parti pour ma famille et pour moi, et j'en pris un qui parut désespéré à tous mes camarades et qui cependant a été l'origine de ma fortune subséquente', Flourens, 1856, I, p. 171. Again the use of the reversal technique indicates the depth of the contemporary dislocation.
2. Marchant, 1858.
3. Petit & Théodoridès, 1961, recount the archival history of the *Diaria*.
4. As will be seen, my interpretation of this correspondence is in direct opposition to that contained in Bourdier, 1971: 'Between the ages of nineteen and twenty-three, Cuvier acquired the basic ideas that he developed between 1804 and his death in 1832'.
5. BIFC 3312 (1–3), 2 October 1788.
6. Landesbibliothek Stuttgart, Cod. hist. 4° 333; Duvernoy, 1833, pp. 123–7; Ahnne, 1906. Johann Georg August Hartmann, 1767–1851. See also note 46 to this chapter.
7. BIFC 3214/1, 2 April 1791; LBS, Cod. hist. 4° 413. Authenrieth, 1772–1835.
8. BIFC 3214/1; East German Academy of Sciences; Schiller National-Museum, Marbach-an-Neckar, MS Z 424, 19 February 1791. Karl Friedrich Kielmeyer, 1765–1844.
9. Cuvier's mother died in 1793. For the annexation see Roy, 1887; Sahler, 1911.
10. Earlier biographers who rely almost exclusively on the correspondence with Pfaff for this period should therefore be used with these points in mind. E.g. Viénot, 1932, pp. 22–75.
11. Marchant, 1858, p. 52, letter of 10 September 1788.
12. *Ibid.*
13. Galland, 1891, p. 380; Beaujour, 1877, pp. 491–6.
14. De la Rue, 1820, p. 268, for maps of this part of the town.
15. Perrot, 1975, p. 96. References are to vol. I.
16. Marchant, 1858, p. 54. Achille d'Héricy, Cuvier's pupil, was born in 1776. His grandfather, the old Marquis d'Héricy, the proprietor of the house in Caen, had been royal Governor of Lower Normandy.

Notes to Chapter II

The Marquise d'Héricy, Achille's mother, was born Marie-Elizabeth le Parmentier de Criquetot in 1756, married in 1775, and died in 1829. See also note 30 and Dollfus, 1925, for further details about the family.
17. Perrot, 1975, p. 102.
18. Marchant, 1858, pp. 88–90, 125.
19. Moreau, 1962.
20. Farin, 1781. Cuvier's opinion of the classification was not high: Marchant, 1858, p. 125, letter of August 1789.
21. Marchant, 1858, p. 172, letter of April 1790. Flourens, 1856, I p. 179: 'M. Conte, épicier, qui logeait sur le marché aux poissons, s'était fait un cabinet ichtyologique préparé par lui-même, et où je fis mes premières études dans cette partie'.
22. Marchant, 1858, p. 136, letter of February–March 1790.
23. *Ibid.*, p. 56, letter of September 1788.
24. *Ibid.*, P. 155, letter of 1–2 April 1790. Other books mentioned in this correspondence as read by Cuvier include: p. 52, Gmelin's edition of Linnaeus, in Latin; p. 67, Pliny, Aristotle, *Historia animalium* and *De partibus*; Gessner, *De aquaticis*; p. 95, Linnaeus, *Faune suédois*; p. 131, Lavoisier, *Traité élémentaire de chimie*; p. 144, *Journal de physique*, 1789; p. 150, Rousseau, *Confessions*; p. 177, F. d'Herbigny, *Dictionnaire du conchyiologiste*; p. 196, *Mémoires de l'Académie des sciences de Paris*, 1753; Haller, *Supplément de l'Encyclopédie*; p. 197, Fourcroy, *Entomologia parisiensis*, 1785; p. 208, Lacepède, *Histoire naturelle des reptiles*; p. 218, *Mémoires de l'Académie des science de Paris*, 1759; *Annales de Chimie*, VII; Priestley, *Expériences et Observations*; Kirwan on phlogiston; Fourcroy, *Expériences sur les matières animales*; p. 247, de Jussieu, *Genera Plantarum*; p. 253, Adanson, 'Mémoire sur les coquilles'; p. 262, Deluc, *Lettres à M. de la Methérie*.
25. See Courtaux, 1911.
26. Marchant, 1858, p. 47, letter of 10 September 1788.
27. *Ibid.*, p. 160, letter of 1–2 April 1790.
28. *Ibid.*, p. 286, letter of July–August 1792.
29. *Ibid.*, p. 271, October 1791.
30. Courtaux, 1911; Magny, 1863–4, I, pp. 84, 151, 154, 164, 169, 171, 172, 173; II, p. 138; Caumont, 1849.
31. Marchant, 1858, p. 60, letter of October 1788.
32. Fregnac, 1966, p. 50; d'Estaintot, 1888–9.
33. De Bernardy, 1961, genealogical appendices.
34. Oberkirch, n.d., *passim*.
35. Magny, 1863–4, I, pp. 151, 169; Gosselin, 1963, recounts the biography of his wife Marie-Judith de la Rivière.
36. Marchant, 1858, p. 146, n.d. (spring 1790); Perrot, 1975, pp. 296–7, sums up the outlook of the upper classes of Caen in rather more charitable terms: 'la défiance envers les charlatans, la sincérité, la douceur, le goût du savoir utile, et le respect des arts, l'inclination pour la liberté morale plus que politique'. Later, Cuvier was more succinct in his description of the nobility as 'rien moins qu'éclairée,'

Marchant 1858, p. 204, letter of 31 December 1790.
37. De la Rue, 1843, II, p. 430.
38. Marchant, 1858, p. 120, letter of 10 August 1789.
39. Vanel, 1907, especially pp. 8–36.
40. Cuvier described her in 1790, as 'une des plus ferventes patriotes du royaume; aussi a-t-elle été forcée de renoncer à la société de plusieurs personnes de son rang et même de ses parents', Marchant, 1858, pp. 204–5, letter of 31 December 1790.
41. Mourlot, 1912, pp. 87–9, 234, 239.
42. Vanel, 1907; anon., 1794, p. 4.
43. Brunschwig, 1973, p. 253 et seq.
44. Marchant, 1858, p. 226, letter of 19 February 1791.
45. Ibid., p. 228, letter of 21 July, 1791.
46. See Cuvier's reproaches to Hartmann for his delays in correspondence and neglect of the common project, letter of 18 November 1790, printed in Duvernoy, 1833, p. 120. The original of this letter is in the Schiller National-museum, Marbach-an-Neckar, MS Z 656.
47. Marchant, 1858, p. 218, letter of 19 February 1791.
48. See the description of his work on the anatomy of the frog in his letter to Kielmeyer of 19 February 1791, Schiller National-museum, Marbach-an-Neckar, MS Z 424; of bivalve molluscs, Marchant, 1858, p. 237, letter of 3 September 1791; and on the comparative anatomy of the vocal apparatus in birds, ibid., p. 275, letter of 13 May 1792. It is clear that Cuvier's interest in comparative anatomy was aroused long before the discovery of fossils near Fécamp in 1792 to which it is usually attributed, even by Cuvier himself, and certainly by the biographical tradition: Flourens, 1856, I, p. 179; Lee, 1833, p. 20. Dollfus, 1925, places the geography and fauna of the Pays de Caux as itself the central formative influence on Cuvier's work at this period, and ignores possible influence from Stuttgart and Kielmeyer.
49. Marchant, 1858, p. 237, letter of 3 September 1791: 'La méthode de Linné est vague et incertaine, et surtout combien il est rare que les caractères génériques conviennent à toutes les espèces du genre'. Still the most thorough study of the debates on classification is H. Daudin, 1927.
50. Marchant, 1858, p. 179–80, letter of 25 June 1790. See ibid., pp. 198–9, letter of 31 December 1790: the first rule of classification is 'de choisir une partie qui soit facile à décrire d'une manière précise, et assez composée pour donner une quantité suffisante de caractères différents. De plus, cette partie doit être formée semblablement chez les genres semblables, afin d'éviter les séparations ou des réunions qui ne seraient pas naturelles.'
51. Ibid., p. 270, letter of October 1791; similar opinions in Cuvier to Kielmeyer n.d. (1790s), BIFC 3214/1.
52. Marchant, 1858, p. 139, letter of February–March 1790.
53. Ibid., p. 143, letter ibid.
54. Ibid., p. 281, letter of 13 May 1792.
55. E.g. Bourdier, 1971.

Notes to Chapter II

56. Marchant, 1858, p. 286, letter of July–August, 1792.
57. E.g. *ibid.*, p. 279, letter of 13 May 1792, contains news of the most recent *séances* of the Académie des sciences in Paris, and the experiments of Berthollet, Pelletier and Vauquelin on respiration.
58. In the *Journal d'histoire naturelle*, II, 1792, 'Mémoire sur les Cloportes'. A debate on classification preceded publication: Cuvier to Olivier, n.d., BIFC 3214/1; Olivier to Cuvier, 21 July 1792, BIFC 3215 fol. 7; reprinted in Théodoridès, 1961, p. 183.
59. Cuvier to Lacepède, 9 March 1792, MHNN; BIFC 3214/1, 9 February 1792. The letter of condolence is in APS, Misc. Ms Collection, n.d. (1793). These letters refer to others which can no longer be located.
60. The only surviving text of the autobiography is that prepared for publication in Flourens, 1856, I, by Mme Cuvier; Brianchon, 1876–7, however indicates the existence of another text, perhaps the original, in the keeping of Cuvier's nephew Charles-Frédéric Cuvier, at that date. On his death in 1893, it does not seem to have accompanied the rest of his uncle's papers to the Institut de France.
61. De Beaurepaire, 1866.
62. See Lee, 1833, pp. 21–3; 273. Accounts dependent on Lee include Menault, 1859; Pariset, 1840.
63. Flourens, 1856, p. 179.
64. Lee, 1833, pp. 21–2.
65. See note 62.
66. De Beaurepaire, 1866, dates this letter as 10 February 1795, and states that Tessier alerted Garat and Ginguené to Cuvier.
67. Cobb, 1952, p. 256 *et seq*; Fallue, 1841, pp. 457–63.
68. See the notes described in Dehérain, 1908–22, p. 19.
69. Later relations between Cuvier and Tessier are obscure. No letters from Cuvier to Tessier survive, and only a few, on scientific affairs, from Tessier to Cuvier.
70. *Ibid.*, p. 68.
71. In the autobiography account: 'On me destina donc à lui servir de suppléant, et ce fut par l'espérance qu'il y consentirait qu'on me détermina à venir à Paris.'
72. Lerond, 1975.
73. E.g., 'Le Prince est toujours ici mais il paraît qu'il n'avance à rien. Pour moi, malgré des lenteurs auxquelles je ne m'attendais pas, je suis tout près du but' (Cuvier to Achille d'Héricy, n.d., APS, Mis. Ms Collection). Another such obscure letter is printed in Ardouin, 1970, pp. 62–4, and reassures the d'Héricy that it is 'impossible qu'une loi contraire au droit naturel dure longtemps'.
74. Such moderates would have been more helpful at this point than would either Garat or Ginguené. After a brief spell as Minister of the Interior in 1793, Garat had been forced to retire to a chair of philosophy at the Ecole normale in 1794. He became a member of the Institut in 1795. After an unsuccessful diplomatic mission to Turin, Ginguené retired to the editorship of the *Décade philosophique*

(1795–7). After the proclamation of the Empire in 1804, his *idéologue* and republican sympathies were too pronounced for him to remain in public life.

75. Flourens, 1856, I; Larévellière-Lépeaux, 1895, does not however mention Cuvier. See also Martineau, 1948, s.v. Brack.

76. Hahn, 1971, p. 271 *et seq.*

77. Isidore Geoffroy St Hilaire naturally ascribes the decisive appeal to his father (pp. 60–1); Lee, 1833, pp. 22–3, to Millin de Grandmaison; Pariset, 1841, p. 361, to Tessier's suggestion that Cuvier should share his house in Paris; Flourens, 1845, p. 70, ascribes it to Daubenton and Lacepède; the *Nouvelle biographie universelle* article on Tessier asserts that Cuvier was called to Paris by the Société philomathique.

Notes to Chapter III

1. Duvernoy, 1833, p. 11: 'Quelques conversations avec des savants dignes de l'apprécier, quelques mémoires lus à la Société d'histoire naturelle de Paris, avaient suffi dans ces temps historiques où l'orage de la Révolution commençait à se calmer... pour placer M. Cuvier dans une position digne de lui, la plus propre à montre toute l'étendue, toute la puissance de son génie'. See also I. Geoffroy St Hilaire, 1847, pp. 65–6; Coleman 1964, pp. 10–11.

2. Quoted in L. Royer, 1930, p. 62.

3. See, e.g., R. Darnton, 1971.

4. Descriptions of Cuvier as a lecturer are to be found in Duvernoy, 1833, p. 73; Moreau de la Sarthe, 1824, p. 356.

5. For Cuvier's borrowing from Talma, Bourdon, 1844, pp. 116–7. Candolle, 1862, p. 149, describes his love of amateur theatricals.

6. Calculations from Monglond, 1939–63, give the following figures for scientific publications: 1793, 24; 1794, 21; 1795, 40; 1796, 43; 1797, 58; 1798, 78; 1799, 102; 1800, 110; 1801, 112; 1802, 137; 1803, 118.

7. Letter of Cuvier to A. G. Camper, 27 floréal on VIII (17 May 1800), Amsterdam University Library; Cuvier & Lacepède, 1801.

8. Cuvier himself received many mentions in such journals. A rapid examination of the *Magasin Encyclopédique* reveals references and publications at I (1795), pp. 205–7, 326; II (1795), pp. 165, 433, 550, 137; III (1795), p. 147, 451; V (1795), pp. 145–55; VI (1795), pp. 130, 294; VII (1796), p. 285; VIII (1796), p. 227; IX (1796), pp. 134–8; XII (1796), pp. 438–9, 526; XV (1797), pp. 150–51; XVII (1797), pp. 146, 507–22; XVIII (1797), p. 32. Even in his first few years in Paris, Cuvier had clearly profited from the existence of such journals. Kitchen, 1965, does not examine this aspect of journal publishing. At this period, numbers of subscribers for the major French journals were approximately as follows: *Moniteur*, 2450; *Journal des Débats*, 8150; *Décade*, 1000, *Journal de Paris*, 600. Such figures should be multiplied by around ten to give an indication of the real numbers of readers.

Specialist publications founded in this period include the *Annales du Muséum* (1802): the *Bulletin de pharmacie* (1811): the *Annales de chimie* (1789); the *Journal de physique* (1794).
    9. Outram, 1980 b.
    10. This historiography is fully examined in *ibid.*
    11. Hahn, 1969.
    12. Adrien de S...n, 1807, p. 10. The author is not identified in Mortier, 1955.
    13. Dalberg, 1802, p. 43, quoted in Bénichou, 1973, p. 116.
    14. Contemporary accounts, such as Biot, 1803, hence placed great stress on ideas of science as a national resource, the saviour of the nation during the Revolutionary wars. A contemporary review of Biot is in the *Décade*, 10 pluviôse an XI, pp. 206–11. This work, originally compiled as the introduction to the *Journal des Ecoles Normales*, had a wide circulation. For similar arguments see Cuvier 1810, pp. 292–5.
    15. Outram, 1980 b.
    16. See for example the denigration of Fourcroy by Cuvier because of his too successful public lectures: one of Fourcroy's major weaknesses was his openness to the pressures of public disapproval. 'Recherchant toujours vivement une approbation immédiate, il ne songeait point que . . . les succès s'imposent qu'autant qu'ils ne sont point trop balancés par des échecs.'
    17. Commission temporaire des Arts: Millin *(Autobiography)*; *suppléance* of Mertrud's chair at the Muséum: Geoffroy, Lacepède and Millin *(Autobiography)*; Chair of natural history at the Ecole centrale du Panthéon: a jury including the Abbé Bathélemy *(Autobiography)*; Full professorship at the Muséum: de Jussieu and Lakanal (letter of Cuvier to de Jussieu, 12 brumaire XI (3 November 1802), printed in Charavay Sale catalogue, 6 April 1846, p. 5, letter of Lakanal to the Commission of public instruction, n.d. BNP, n.a. fr. 1305, f.59. Collège de France: Miot de Mélito and Lucien Bonaparte *(Autobiography)*; Permanent Secretary of the First Class of the Institut de France: Fourcroy (Dehérain, 1916).
    18. I. Geoffroy St Hilaire, 1847, p. 65 n.
    19. Flourens, 1856, I, p. 182.
    20. Tuetey, 1912, I, pp. xxxv–vi, records the membership of the Commission as including Lamarck, Thouin, Richard, Vauquelin, Berthollet, Monge, Deyeux, Prony and L'Héritier de Brutelle.
    21. Societies joined by Cuvier in this period included the Société philomatique (3 germinal, III: 23 March 1795); Société d'histoire naturelle de Paris: proposed by Geoffroy, 11 frimaire, an III, elected 1 pluviôse, III; Société philotechnique de Paris (1 messidor IV: 19 June 1796) Société libre des pharmaciens de Paris (11 vendémiaire V: 2 October 1796) Société de santé de Paris (22 nivôse V: 11 January 1797) Comité d'administration de l'école de médicine de Paris (10 vendémiaire IX: 2 October 1800); Société de médicine de Paris (5 brumaire XII: 27 October 1803).
    The *Bulletin* of the Société philomatique recorded twelve papers by

Cuvier between 1795 and 1799. In May alone of 1795 he read two papers to the Société d'histoire naturelle. For details see Duvernoy, 1833, p. 19; Appel, 1975, p. 144. These papers were of crucial importance to the establishment of his reputation. However, many of them were written in collaboration with Geoffroy: e.g. the 'Mémoire sur une nouvelle division des mammifères et sur les principes qui doivent servir de base dans cette sorte de travail', *Magasin Encyclopédique*, II, 1795, 164–90; 'Lettre du Citoyen Geoffroy et du Citoyen Cuvier sur le rhinocéros bicorne', *ibid.*, I, p. 90; 'Mémoire sur les rapports naturels du Tarsier, *didelphus macrotarsus*', *ibid.*, III, 1795, 147–54; 'Histoire naturelle des orang-outangs: des caractères qui peuvent servir à diviser les singes', *ibid.*, III, 1795. Membership of such societies also enabled Cuvier to exercise patronage beyond the boundaries of Paris: foreign *savants* admitted to membership of the Philomatique on Cuvier's initiative, for example, included Camper, Fabbroni and Candolle. Of all these societies, the Philomatique was undoubtedly the most important in terms of the claims to priority which the rapid publication of its *Bulletin* enabled its members to stake; on the other hand, the Société d'histoire naturelle was largely composed of older men, members of the Institut and the Muséum, and may well have been the more serious forum for a new entrant trying to establish a scientific reputation. It should not be forgotten that such societies allowed Cuvier to establish himself not simply as an adroit social manipulator, but also as a talented naturalist.

22. Flourens, 1856, I, p. 182.

23. In joining the Société philotechnique, Antoine Vincent Arnault, for example, made the following calculation: 'Se mettre en rapport avec eux était pour moi d'un double avantage: à l'agrément que je pouvais retirer de leur commerce se joignait l'espérence de m'assurer leur suffrage, si jamais j'étais porté sur la liste des candidats de l'Institut, où les nominations se faisaient alors par toutes les classes assemblées, qu'elle que fût la classe à laquelle appartint le fauteuil vacant'. (Arnault, 1833, II, p. 309.) After the reforms of 1803, the separate classes no longer combined in elections.

24. Calculations based on material in Institut de France, 1939.

25. Flourens, 1856, I, p. 181, relates Haüy's efforts to turn Geoffroy against Cuvier; I. Geoffroy St Hilaire, 1847, p. 65 n, for Daubenton's hostility to Cuvier for the same reason. BIF MS Flourens 2598/3 f 32 accuses Faujas de St Fond of trying to stir up trouble between Cuvier and Lamarck, at the same period.

26. An account of the election is to be found in Flourens, 1856, I, p. 183.

27. Such memoirs are catalogued in Tulard, 1971. Cuvier is mentioned in Villemain, 1864, I, p. 466, as a member of the salons of Mme Lavoisier, of Barbé-Marbois and later, of that of the Duchesse de Duras; in Vauthier, 1913, p. 21, as a member of that of the poet Delille; Brifaut, n.d., I, pp. 192–3, 290–91, mentions Cuvier as a member of that of Mme de Rauzan, the daughter of the Duchesse de

Duras, and of that of Mme Lavoisier; a letter of Cuvier to Sir Charles Blagden of 1805 records his introduction to Mme Gauthier; (RSL, MS BLA c. 148). Portal's fortnightly gatherings are recorded in Van Marum, ed. Forbes, 1969, II, p. 373; for Mme Pastoret, see Bassan, 1969, p. 25. We must also assume that Cuvier was on intimate terms with Prony and his wife (see note 86). Dupin, 1823, is lacking in information on this score.

28. Brifaut commented on the salons, 'quelle source d'instruction et de connaissances pour un novice avide d'apprendre', (pp. 290–91) Stendahl commented: 'Vous serez quelque chose dans le monde, vous pourrez espérer de plaire à une femme aimable quand vous serez porté par deux ou trois salons. Au bout de dix années de constance, ces salons . . . vous porteront à tout'. Stendahl, 1973, p. 380. The intensive schedule of meetings imposed by both the private scientific societies and by the Institut, also increased ease of contact. Members of the Société philomatique, for example had to attend meetings at least once a week or risk a fine; a monthly banquet characterised the Société philotechnique, which met in addition once a week. The Institut met twice a week, had twelve monthly general meetings, four quarterly public meetings, as well as sectional meetings and special committee meetings.

29. Frankel, 1978, details from BU for De Gérando, on whom no full-length study exists.

30. Szramkiewicz, 1974, pp. 38–9. Delambre married in 1804 the cousin of Alfonse-Jean Buffault, Regent of the Bank of France: Arnault had married a sister-in-law of the same man.

31. The Society held weekly meetings, and had two public sessions every year. Cuvier's participation in it is described in Crosland, 1967, p. 186; Depping, 1840–41.

32. Martineau, 1948, p. 88.

33. Goguel, 1864, p. 133 and Salomon, 1927, reproduce respectively the certificates of the civil and the religious marriage of Cuvier, which both took place on 12 pluviôse XII (2 February 1804) with the same witnesses.

34. Arnault, 1833, I, pp. 115, 211; Szramkiewicz, 1974, pp. 114–23.

35. Duvernoy, 1833, p. 149, 'Note supprimée'.

36. Luce de Lancival, 1907. Lancival, a priest who had renounced his vows under the Revolution, also held strong republican views, Bénichou, 1973, p. 124. Survey of the scraps of information which we do possess about Mme Cuvier suggests that her links with the learned world may already have been strong by the time of her first husband's execution in 1794. Tuetey, 1912–17, shows that inventories of his property and library, confiscated after his death, passed before the committees of the Commission tempraire and would certainly have been available to Cuvier. Cuvier's colleague at the Institut, Phillipe Duvaucel the mathematician, later mayor of Evreux, was certainly related to the tax farmer Duvaucel. (Durand, 1971, p. 246. This book is otherwise disappointingly sparse in its

information on the Duvaucel family.) Again before 1789, Phillipe Duvaucel, Cuvier's brother-in-law, the tax-farmer Braq (see genealogical table), and Cuvier's patron, Lacepède, had all been members of the French anti-slavery society (Anon, 1789; Perroud, 1916). At the time of her marriage to Cuvier, Mme Duvaucel is stated by the marriage certificate to have been living at 1125 rue de Tournon. A check through the *Almanach Impérial* for that year, section Institut de France, revealed that this was also the address of two other colleagues of Cuvier, the architect Gondoin, and the chemist Deyeux. Cuvier was certainly on friendly enough terms with Deyeux, who was also the son-in-law of another regent of the Bank of France, Moreau (Szramkiewicz, 1974, p. 268), to ask for his help in the writing of the sections on chemistry in Cuvier, 1810 (Cuvier to Deyeux, 10 June 1807, Wellcome Library, Autograph Collection). Cuvier's acquaintance with Deyeux could also have been pursued through the Commission temporaire (see note 25), and the Société libre des pharmaciens de Paris.

37. For the use of the *Minutier centrale* of the Archives nationales, see Newton and Uttée, 1974; Daumard and Furet, 1959.

38. Viénot, 1905, gives some indication of the extent to which Cuvier, barely abreast of his duties in science, education and the Institut, relied heavily on Duvernoy to get the *Leçons* to the press.

39. For Laurillard, see Mathiot & Duvernoy, 1940; for Charles Cuvier see *idem*, 1881; for Curie, grandfather of the physicist, see Leuilliot, 1955; Brandt, 1938.

40. See letters of Cuvier to Guizot, 13 October 1814, Henry E. Huntington Library, San Marino, California; to the School at Montbéliard, 1 February 1799, Viénot, 1932, 114–15. Duvernoy, 1833, p. 79, relates an incident which shows how much Cuvier's position as the patron of Montbéliard in Paris had strengthened by 1809. Returning from a tour of inspection of German universities, he was met at Strasbourg by a deputation which had seized the chance of his passage to come all the way from Montbéliard to enlist his support and engage him to watch over their interests in Paris.

41. Coulmann, 1862-9, especially volume 1; André, 1896, *passim*, especially pp. 1–110. Mme Prony was also a close friend of Josephine.

42. BIFC 3297/4–5.

43. For the social ascent of Treuttel and Würtz, see Barber, 1969; for Bartholdi, see Szramkiewicz, 1974, p. 67.

44. *Ibid.*, p. 67. In 1830, Coulmann joined Cuvier in the Conseil d'etat, and in 1831, became a *député* for the Bas-Rhin.

45. Tulard, 1970, estimates income in the quartier du Roule of Paris, whose inhabitants included Chaptal, Daru and Lacepède, at an average of 40,000 fr. per year. Cuvier arrived in Paris with 12,000 fr. in assignats (*Autobiography*). From the Commission temporaire des arts, he earned 2000 fr. The salary was the same at the Ecole centrale du Panthéon but may well not have been regularly paid (Suratteau, 1961). As Mertrud's *suppléant*, he would earn 2500 fr., half of Mertrud's

salary, as well as gaining free lodging in the Muséum. As full professor at the Muséum, he retained these lodgings and earned a salary of 5000 fr. At the Collège de France his annual salary was 5000 fr. As Perpetual Secretary of the First Class, his salary was 6000 fr., and was drawn with the payment of 1200 fr. due to him as a member of the Institut. As a member of the Légion d'Honneur after 1803, Cuvier drew a further 250 fr. With fluctuations in audience size, he would have taken about 1200–1500 fr. at the Athénée de Paris (Lycée républicain). Academic salaries would have been reduced by payments to *suppléants*. A further 2000 fr. came after 1812 from his *dotation* on lands in Hanover, but this would have ceased in 1814. Finally, his post from 1802–3 as an Inspector of Public Instruction brought him for that year 12,000 fr. Literary earnings are hard to judge from the remaining documentation, but participation in the Levrault *Dictionnaire des sciences naturelles* probably brought about 4,000 francs. All salaries of state institutions were often in arrears. E.g. letter of Cuvier to Hermann of 1800, printed in Lee, 1833, p. 27, states his pay is a year in arrears at the Muséum. Sources for this note: BIFC 3296/18, decree of 19 vendémiaire an XI; BIFC 3346 *bis*, imperial decree of 11 January 1812; Flourens, 1856, I, p. 183; letter of Cuvier to Thouin, 5 brumaire XI (26 October 1802), ANP: AJ XV 561; Dehérain, 1916, p. 369; Delaunay, 1940, p. 85; Powell, 1978; Crosland, 1967, p. 222. Comparison with the income of another member of the Institut, the artist Moitte, whose total income came to 5000 fr. pa, shows, however, that Cuvier may well have been rich in comparison with some of his colleagues. See Bertaut, 1944, p.109; Cottin, 1932, *passim*. Income levels even within the Institut were thus far from homogenous.

46. It is curious that the stories examined in Chapters I and II of Cuvier's foundation of such juvenile societies, find an echo in many other scientific biographies such as, for example, that of Lacepède (Hahn, 1975a). The unprecedented expansion of such private societies in the later eighteenth century and the revolutionary period, point to the importance of science and learning generally as the carrier of new forms of informal social institutions. From another point of view, the Société philomatique was crucial to the later development of Cuvier's own social forum, his salon. As the meetings of the Société widened to include family members, so their character changed into informal social gatherings. See Candolle, 1862, pp. 96–7. Agulhon, 1977, surveys the later development of some similar social forms.

47. Arnault, 1833, II, p. 310.

48. Biot, 1803, p. 32, describes the scientific community as including both the rich, and 'les autres, sortis par leurs talens de la classe obscure où le hazard les avait placés, n'étaient, quoique moins riches, ni moins éstimés, ni moins accueillis; il semblait que le mérite melât les rangs dans la société'.

49. Pfaff, 1858, pp. 29, 35.

50. Cuvier, 1795 c, p. 148.

51. E.g., Appel, 1975, p. 180; Bourdier, 1973.

52. The generally held opinion that Geoffroy and Cuvier shared lodgings almost from the time of Cuvier's arrival in Paris should also be modified. I. Geoffroy St Hilaire, 1847, p. 63, states that Cuvier moved into Geoffroy's apartment in the Muséum directly after his appointment as Mertrud's *suppléant* in July of 1795. However, Cuvier's contract with Panckouke of 1 vendémiaire IV (23 September 1795) gives Cuvier's address as rue de Varenne, 659 (BIFC 3303/44). It should also be noticed that Cuvier himself asserts (Flourens, 1856, I, p. 183) that 'aussitôt que j'eus un logement, j'y fis venir mon pere âgé alors de plus de 80 ans, et mon frère' – a heavy influx to impose on Geoffroy's rooms, even if Frédéric delayed his arrival in the capital until 1797. Other sources state that Cuvier occupied not Geoffroy's but Mertrud's apartment in the Muséum after he had agreed to Cuvier as his *suppléant*. This is borne out by the letter from Cuvier to Thouin previously cited (note 45). It has seemed worthwhile to emphasise what seems such a trivial point, because it is such assertions, with their implications of great emotional closeness between Cuvier and Geoffroy, as well as a strong scientific collaboration, which underpin accounts of the collapse of their friendship.

53. Flourens, 1856, I, p. 185. Cuvier's friend Prony made the same decision and refused to go to Egypt.

54. I owe this point to Hannaway, 1969, pp. 578–81.

55. E. T. Hamy, 1901.

56. BIFC 3159, 'Analyse d'un ouvrage de M. Humboldt intitulé: Tableaux de la nature ou considérations sur les deserts, sur la physionomie des végétaux et sur les cataractes de l'Orenoque, traduit de l'allemand par J. B. B. Eyries'. Cuvier's hostility to Humboldt may well also have come from his identification of him as the field naturalist *par excellence*.

57. For Geoffroy's later journeys to Spain, see Hamy, 1908.

58. Flourens, 1856, I, p. 184.

59. Dehérain, 1916, reprints the letter of Geoffroy to Cuvier of 19 pluviôse XI (8 February 1803) in which these manoeuvres are described.

60. BIFC 3339/1–18. E.g. letter of 23 May 1811 relates Geoffroy's intrigues against Blainville: '... il y a dans tout cela une duplicité et une intrigaillerie dégoutante.'

61. E.g. Flourens, 1856, I, p. 186. 'Indépendement de mes mémoires sur les fossiles et sur les mollusques dont je remplissais les Annales du Muséum, j'avais mes deux cours à faire, mon secrétariat et l'administration de mon Cabinet d'anatomie à conduire; je faisais même le soir une leçon à l'Athénée de Paris, enfin je rédigeais avec M. Duvernoy les trois derniers volumes de mon anatomie comparée qui ont paru en 1805 ... [lacuna in text] A ces occupations qui auraient pu suffire à plus d'un homme laborieux, il s'en joignit une autre qui me détourna longtemps ... un rapport sur les progrès des sciences devait être présenté aux Consuls en fructidor an XI.' (This

Notes to Chapter III

eventually became Cuvier, 1810.)

62. Letter of Cuvier to Camper, n.d. (1799); *idem* to *idem*, 14 fructidor XI (1 September 1803), both in Amsterdam University Library.

63. Cuvier to Camper, n.d. (1799), Amsterdam University Library.

64. Letter to Cuvier to Camper, 28 Janury 1803, 'Je suis écrasé de travail pour l'organisation de l'Université. J'en ai même contracté des douleurs de poitrine qui commence à m'inquiéter ... Si je ne dois pas vivre longtemps, je voudrais au moins laisser un enchatillon de la manière dont je l'avais concu' (his work on fossils): Amsterdam University Library. Similar comments by Duvernoy on the state of Cuvier's health make it seem likely that he had contracted tuberculosis (Duvernoy, 1833, p. 129).

65. E.g. letter of Cuvier to his Stuttgart friend Boigeol, 25 nivôse an IV (15 January 1796) elaborates Cuvier's delight on his election to the Institut 'de me réunir tous les soirs avec tout que la France a produit de plus illustre, profiter de leurs leçons et de leurs examples, admirer surtout l'étonnante simplicité de la plupart de ces hommes dont le nom rétentit dans toute l'Europe': Charavay sale catalogue, 9 February 1863, p. 18. This letter was discovered too late for inclusion in Outram, 1980 a.

66. Cuvier, 1819-27, I, pp. 91-2. This passage comes from the *éloge* of Lemonnier, read to the First Class on 7 October 1800.

67. Letter of Cuvier to Camper, 23 vendémiaire an XII (16 October 1803), Amsterdam University Library.

68. Delaunay, 1940, p. 86. Emilie married in 1800 Jacques Pichon, French envoy to the American states; Martineau, 1948 p. 88.

69. Evidence for this conjecture is based on a letter from Cuvier to Mme Prony, wife of the Director of the Ecole des Ponts-et-Chausées, and hostess of a well-known *salon*; 'Ma belle et généreuse amie, Je ne sais trop ni ce que je fais ni ce que j'écris depuis ce matin; après dix projets de lettres, voici celui auquel je m'arrête. Daignez y jeter les yeux; vous êtes de sang-froid; vous verrez mieux que moi s'y il n'y a rien d'inconvéniant; en le fesant [*sic*] mettre ensuite à la poste, personne ne se doutera que vous l'avez lu. C'est le dernier service que je réclamerai de vous dans cette triste aventure. Peut-être mon desir de les voir encore est-il une ruse d'un amour mal éteint qui me trompe moi-même; mais j'avoue que je ne puis y renoncer volontairement. Daignez être persuadée de ma vive et éternelle reconnaissance. G. C.' The letter is dated 24 prairial an IX (13 June 1801), and is MS N.A. fr. 15778, f. 103, of the BNP.

70. The decree, dated 17 nivôse XI (7 January 1803), is printed in Aucoc, 1889, pp. 67-72.

71. Dehérain, 1916, p. 370.

72. *Ibid*.

73. Viénot, 1905; Dehérain, 1916, is also at pains to suggest that Cuvier maintained a stoic abstraction from such matters.

74. Dehérain, 1916, p. 370.

75. Cuvier, 1819–27, I, p. 305. This comes from the *eloge* of Michel Adanson, which was read on 5 January 1807.

76. Crosland, 1967, p. 186; Mandelbaum, 1982. La Métherie who had rejected Cuvier's first papers for publication, became Cuvier's *suppléant* at the Collège de France, having failed in the competition for the full chair. 'C'était me venger assez noblement', was Cuvier's comment in his autobiography (BIF MS Flourens 25983, fol. 42) Lefranc, 1893, p. 302, charts the early manoeuvres in this appointment. Cuvier at first attempted to gain from La Métherie the reversion of his chair in the Ecole centrale du Panthéon, as an alternative to the *suppléance* of his post at the Collège de France. Cuvier's other *suppléants* included the following:

H. M. Ducrotay de Blainville: replaced Cuvier in the Athénée de Paris, 1811, at the Collège de France in 1812 and 1813 and at the Muséum, 1814–16. Professor at the Muséum in succession to Lamarck, 1830; quarrelled with Cuvier, 1816, succeeded to his chair in the Muséum, 1832.

A. M. C. Duméril: Replaced Cuvier at the Ecole centrale du Panthéon, 1800–04. Collaborated with Cuvier on the *Leçons d'anatomie comparée*.

J. La Metherie: Replaced Cuvier at the Collège de France, 1800–12.

M. J. P. Flourens: replaced Cuvier at the Collège de France, 1828–30. Succeeded him at the Collège de France, 1832, as Permanent Secretary of the Academy of Sciences, 1833.

77. Letter of Cuvier to Fabbroni, n.d. (1803, Fabbroni papers, APS.).

Notes to Chapter IV

1. For general survey of this process see Vaughan & Archer, 1971. Negrin, 1977, came to the author's attention too late to be used in this chapter.

2. See Appendix.

3. For example, both Napoleon's Minister of Finance, Martin Gaudin, and the *Architrésorier* of the Empire and Third Consul Lebrun, had already achieved recognition before 1792, while Mollien, the Minister for the *Trésor publique*, had first achieved prominence as a protégé of Lebrun. See Mollien, 1898; Gaudin, 1826.

4. Arnault, 1833, IV, p. 5; III, p. 292. Unfortunately, Arnault ends his memoirs with the *coup* of *brumaire*, and thus deprives us of direct evidence on his attitude towards the Imperial University.

5. Brunschwig, 1973, pp. 210–12.

6. Rota, 1907.

7. Schama, 1970.

8. Flourens, 1856, I, p. 172 ff.

9. Van Duzer, 1935; Williams, 1953.

10. The creation of the *écoles centrales* had been given over to the Conseil d'Instruction publique, of which De Tracy was the head, by decree of 8 ventôse an VII. See Destutt de Tracy, 1801.

Notes to Chapter IV

11. Destutt de Tracy, 1819, section 4, p. 455.

12. It is important to note that neither Napoleon nor the *idéologues* had any idea of education as a means of increasing social mobility in society as a whole; Destutt de Tracy, 1801, pp. 332–5 specifically rejects such a notion, and Napoleon was even more violently opposed to it; Vaughan and Archer, 1971, pp. 186–91; Marquiset, 1913, pp. 71–2: 'Vous ne pouvez pas dire au peuple qu'il y a une autre lumière que celle de la réligion, celle de la raison naturelle . . . Au lieu que vous avez de petits coqs de village qui viennent on ne sait d'où . . . et perdent la génération.'

13. Puget, 1932; Vauthier, 1911; Lanzac de Laborde, 1916.

14. BIFC 3726, Carnet.

15. Cuvier to Fabbroni, 6 pluviôse an XI (24 January 1803), APS, Fabbroni papers.

16. Letters to A. P. de Candolle of 24 frimaire an XI (15 December 1802) and 15 germinal an XI (5 April 1803), printed in Candolle (ed.), 1862, pp. 541–3; letter to Duvernoy from Fréjus, 15 frimaire an XI (6 December 1802): 'On se fait pas une idée des chemins de ce pays-ci. Autant vaudrait voyager dans les montagnes bleues, ou dans les Apalaches que M. Chateaubriand vante tant.'

17. Moore (ed.), 1969, p. 61. Cuvier himself often expressed his dislike of Napoleon's schemes of conquest: e.g., letter to Camper of 1799, printed in Coleman, 1963.

18. De Gérando, 1868, pp. 48–9, letter of De Gérando to Mme de Staël, July 1802.

19. Stocking, 1964; Bouteiller, 1959; Moore (ed.) 1969; Cuvier's instructions to Baudouin are in the WHM, Autograph 68159. Meetings of the Society are reported in the *Magasin Encyclopédique* XXXI (1800), pp. 409–10; XXXII pp. 531–2; XL pp. 540–41; XLI p. 256. The Society is treated in Moravia, 1974, *passim*.

20. Moore (ed.) 1969, p. 61.

21. *Magasin Encyclopédique*, XXXI, 1800, pp. 409–10.

22. Of course, this atmosphere of working always in the short term fed back on to the actions of the governing class. Many, such as Fontanes himself, regarded the Empire merely as a stepping-stone on the way to the achievement of another form of government, such as a constitutional monarchy. The strain of working in one regime whilst waiting for its transformation into another led many into situations of internal conflict which in Fontanes' case showed themselves in repeated attempts at resignation from his post as Grand Master. See Vauthier, 1911.

23. Marchant (ed.), 1858, p. 33.

24. De Staël, ed. Tieghem, 1959, p. 420–21. Fontanes' attacks on the book appear in the *Mercure* of 16 thermidor an VIII. Earlier, Fontanes had collaborated with Lucien Bonaparte to produce the pamphlet *Parallèle entre César, Cromwell et Bonaparte*, published on 1 November 1800, but almost immediately suppressed by Napoleon as revealing too well his ambition for supreme power.

25. The original review was in the *Mercure* of 8 nivôse an XI (29 December 1802).
26. By Ginguéné, on 30 prairial, and 10 and 20 messidor.
27. Roederer, an XII, pp. 13–14.
28. BIFC 3161, pp. 6–8; printed in the *Moniteur* of 3 November 1807, p. 1186 (Cuvier, 1807) For similar attitudes, expressed earlier by Cuvier, see *Eloges historiques*, I, pp. 165–85; Sarton, 1922.
29. BIFC MS Flourens 2598/3, ff. 53–5. The full version of the report only appeared in 1810 (Cuvier 1810).
30. Campe performed the function of keeping Cuvier up to date with German work in this field; see BIFC 3276, Carnet, p. 65, 'note remise par M. Campe des principaux auteurs pédagogiques d'Allemagne'. For Guizot, see Johnson, 1963, chapters 1–4.
31. Both the autobiography and Aulard, 1911 are silent on this point, which Fontanes' destruction of his private papers shortly before his death also renders obscure. The remains of this collection, now in Bibliothèque publique et universitaire, Geneva, contains no correspondence with Cuvier.
32. Both brothers had been expelled from the Ecole normale in 1796 for refusing the oath of hatred towards monarchy. See Jeannin, 1968; Ste-Beuve, 1948, II, pp. 279–80.
33. Pailhès, 1900, p. 202, 286; Reynal, 1883, p. 77, prints without indication of source Fontanes' demand that Joubert be appointed Inspector-General.
34. For Fontanes' friendship with him, see BIFC 3235, f. 3, letter of Fontanes to Cuvier and Coiffier, 1 May 1813. His amnesty is in ANP F7 3335, 2e état, prairial an XI–germinal an XI; Baldenspurger, 1924, II, pp. 41–2, examines his literary works.
35. By 1811, however, Napoleon was strongly to suspect that the central direction of the University was working towards the restoration of royalism, and was using the revival of loyalty to the Church to this end; see Schmidt, 1905.
36. E.g. a request from Portalis to Cuvier to compile a report on female education in the Empire concluded, 'C'est surtout à l'égard des femmes qu'il faut faire entrer en considération les moeurs de chaque contrée, et je vois avec quelle intélligence et avec quel soin vous les avez observés dans les pays où vous avez rempli avec tant de succès votre mission', BIFC 3318, f. 2, Portalis to Cuvier, 18 December 1811.
37. BIF MS Flourens 25983, p. 60 is conspicuously lacking in mentions of contributions by either Fourcroy of Fontanes to the discussions immediately preceding the opening of the University, many of which took place in special sessions of the Conseil d'Etat open to outsiders under the personal supervision of Napoleon. It is difficult to substantiate what Cuvier's real contribution to the form of the University was, and he certainly found, as we will see, many aspects of its constitution uncongenial. The opinion of Poirier, 1932, that Cuvier took no part in these discussions cannot be substantiated. The anecdote of Lee, 1833, p. 230, of Cuvier's victory over Regnault de

Notes to Chapter IV 221

St Jean d'Angély, in a discussion before the Conseil and his subsequent rise in Napoleon's esteem, equally cannot be disproved.

38. Members of the Faculty of Sciences in Paris were Lacroix, Biot, Poisson, Gay-Lussac, Thenard, Haüy, Desfontaines, Francoeur, Geoffroy St Hilaire, Alexandre Brongniart, Mirbel and Duvernoy. Lacroix's appointment in particular is well documented. As Miot de Mélito's brother-in-law, Cuvier regarded his appointment as a debt of patronage. His recommendation of Lacroix is at BIF Fonds Lacroix, III, p. 51, letter of 26 April 1809.

39. Robert, 1961, p. 49; Bourgeaud, 1909.

40. In the United Provinces and the Hanse towns, May to September 1811; in Italy July 1809 to January 1810, and again for the first half of 1813. Reports of these first two journeys are respectively Cuvier and Noël, 1811; Cuvier, Coiffier and de Balbe 1810; quotations in this chapter are from the MSS in BIFC from which these reports were written up.

41. ANP F17*, 1751-8, record the meetings of the Conseil between 1 October 1808 and May 1815. Amplification of these registers may be obtained, for some sessions, from F17 12818-12821. The last volume of F 17* 1758 covers only the period from March to May 1815.

42. BIFC 3270, fol. 9. Gerbod, 1966, confirms this impression of the weakness of the inspectorate in the Imperial University.

43. Legée, 1970; Cuvier visited Amsterdam, Bremen, Franeker, Haarlem, Hambourg, Göttingen and Stuttgart.

44. BIFC 3262, f. 21.

45. Cuvier and Noël, 1811; BIFC 3260, ff. 16-22; Schama, 1977, p. 540. Between 1795 and 1798 Noël had been French envoy in the United provinces, until his over-sympathetic attitude to Dutch complaints necessitated his replacement by Charles Delacroix. The account of Noël in the *Nouvelle biographie universelle* does not mention his tours in Holland with Cuvier.

46. Works directly dependent on Cuvier and Noël, 1811, include d'Alphonse, 1813, especially p. 144; Cousin, 1838, pp. 257 ff. This report was also used as the basis of the reorganisation of primary education in the new state formed by the union of Belgium and Holland after 1815; see letter of van den Ende to Cuvier of 24 July 1818, BIFC 3240, f. 27. Van den Ende had been instrumental in forming the Dutch school system. See Schama, 1970. The influence of the report in France after 1832 is indicated in Gontard, 1959, p. 257.

47. BIFC 3297, f. 7, letter of Fontanes to Cuvier, 15 April 1813.

48. Schama, 1977, p. 532-41.

49. BIFC 3260, f. 2 mentions reports by Martinus van Marum and by Adriaan Camper. Cuvier's and Noël's report was in turn sent to the Maatschappij tot 'Nut van't Algemen.

50. Letter of Cuvier to Camper, 7 February 1812, Camper papers, University Library, Amsterdam.

51. 'Nous aurions peine à rendre l'effet qu'a produit sur nous la première école primaire où nous sommes entrés en Hollande. C'était

précisement une de celles que la charité publique entretient pour les enfants des familles les plus indigéantes, pour ceux qui en tant d'autres pays seraient reduits à traîner leur misère sur les grands chemins pour y faire le métier de mendians [sic] en attendant qu'ils ayent la force de faire celui de voleur.' BIFC 3260, f. 4.

52. Duvernoy, 1833, p. 79.

53. *Ibid.*, p. 147.

54. Flourens, 1856, I, p. 172: 'En Allemagne, où l'on enseigne tout par méthode, on apprend plus de choses en biens moins de temps qu'en France où les connaissances universelles ne se puisent guère que dans la pratique.' Cuvier goes on to attribute his own success in French public life entirely to his German training.

55. Poirier, 1932, p. 99.

56. Letter of Laurillard to Frédéric Cuvier, Göttingen, 6 August 1811, BIFC 3318, f. 11. 'C'est en fossiles que notre mission est plus riche; M. Cuvier met à contribution tout les cabinets, tant publics que particuliers et même les livres qu'il ne possède point, qu'il ne peut point se procurer et qui traîtent de cette matière; il sera probablement obligé de faire un supplément général pour mettre au jour plusieurs morceaux, plus complets et plus décisifs qui ceux qu'il a déjà publiés.'

57. BIFC 3262, f. 2, 4. Camper and Brugmans showed their gratitude in 1815, when they stopped the return to Holland of the collections captured by the French. BIF MS Flourens 2598/3, f. 76.

58. Cuvier to Autenrieth, n.d. (1799), LBS, Cod. hist. 4° 413; Cuvier to Camper, 20 nivôse an IX (10 January 1801), Camper papers, University Library, Amsterdam.

59. In the later eighteenth century, the whole idea of nationality was highly controversial. An ideological separation between nation and ruler had marked not only the French revolution itself, but also the movements for reform in many other European states of that period, such as the United Provinces (Schama, 1977, ch. 1) After the French conquests in Europe, anti-French feeling fed a revaluation of national culture in many cases, such as Prussia, Lombardy and Piedmont. In keeping clear of the issue of national allegiance, Cuvier was thus avoiding an extremely delicate topic.

60. ANP, F17 1570, dossier, 'Personnel du lycée de Gênes, 1809–13, rapport sur le personnel du lycée de Gênes'; Outram, 1974, p. 258. See Boudard, 1962 for fuller treatment of the Imperial University in Genoa. While in Genoa, Cuvier stayed with his brother-in-law Charles Bracq, then head of Customs in Liguria. See Anon, 1847, and genealogical table.

61. BIFC 3263, section Turin, f. 3; Viara, 1942 points out the similarities between the Imperial University and the Piedmontese system.

62. AST, Fondo Balbo, contains many letters between the two men. Like Cuvier, De Gérando elected to spend much of the Empire outside France. Between 1805 to 1806 he supervised the annexation of the republic of Genoa, and from 1808 to 1814 formed part of the governing

Notes to Chapter IV

body of the former Papal states.

63. See Turi, 1969, for analyses of the years between 1799 and 1807 in Tuscany.

64. BIFC 3263, ff. 5–10.

65. Cuvier assured the University of Genoa, for example, that 'les idées étroites et les préjugés nationaux, obstacles invincibles des lumières, seront bannis de leur enseignement'; BIFC 3345, f. 29, printed 'Discours de M. Cuvier aux Facultés de l'Académie de Gênes . . . le 26 novembre 1809'.

66. BIFC 3263, ff. 1–5.

67. This episode is reviewed in more detail in Outram, 1982, which prints the correspondence between Cuvier and Fabbroni in full.

68. Fabbroni to Cuvier, 27 March 1807, BIFC 3228, f. 7.

69. Bassan, 1969, provides an ideal tool for tracing many similar webs of friendship centring on the Pastoret family. Their friendship with Balbo, for example, is shown here and in the family papers held at BNP N.Acqu.fr. 24151, 12945. Cuvier, De Gérando, and the Pastorets were also mutual friends.

70. Fabbroni protested to Cuvier about the infiltration of priests into higher education in a letter of 8 February 1808, BIFC 3230, f. 11. Fabbroni's friend Santi wrote to him on 12 September 1811 about his desire to 'stabilire un sistema nuovo e non molto favorito dei Preti' (APS Fabbroni papers). Cuvier recommended Santi for the rectorship of Pisa in 1813 (ANP F 17 1601, dossier Faculté des Sciences 1810–12, report of 3 February 1813). As Inspector of the Academy of Pisa from 1808, Santi made his view that the French regime continued the work of Peter Leopold explicit in his 'Rapport d'une tournée faite . . . pendant l'été de l'année 1811', ANP F 17 1601, dossier 'Faculté des lettres'. Santi's contributions to the *Recherches sur les ossemens fossiles des quadrupèdes* of 1812 are acknowledged in II, 'Additions et corrections', p. 17. (This edition of the OF is not continuously paginated.)

71. ANP F17 1600, dossier Collège de Volterra, 1811–13, Cuvier to Fontanes, 17 October 1813.

72. Schmidt, 1805.

73. BIFC 3263, ff. 7–8, section 'Turin'.

74. Neppi Mondona, 1969, for the events of 1799; petition of G. Nannoni for his father's chair, 16 September 1812, ANP F17 1601, dossier 'Faculté de Medecine'; letters in support of Rasis from the Comte de Borna, December 1812 and January 1813, *ibid.*; report of Cuvier to Fontanes, 5 November 1812, *ibid.*; Fontanes to Benjamino Sproni, Rector of the Academy of Pisa, 5 November 1812, *ibid.*

75. Of course, Cuvier's powers of appointment could seal scientific relationships in even more obvious ways. On hearing of his nomination as Inspector of the Academy of Genoa, the botanist Domenico Viviani wrote to Cuvier 'Je ne saurois pas, [sic] mon respectable et cher ami, vous témoigner assez ma reconnoissance pour ce que vous venez de faire pour moi dans cette circonstance. Comptez d'avoir un

ami à Gênes qui ne peut jouir du bonheur que vous lui avez procuré s'il n'a pas d'occasion d'occuper quelques moments pour vous tous les jours. Je veux absolument que vous me regardiez comme votre chargé d'affaires en Ligurie pour tout ce qui vous intéresse. Je m'y livrai d'autant plus voluntiers que je rendrai dans le même temps service à mon bienfaiteur et à la science': Viviani to Cuvier, 15 October 1810, MNHN MS 1889, tôme 6, no. 1006.

76. Flourens, 1856, I, p. 192, ' . . . rien ne console de pareils coups'.

77. Moulard, 1914. De Gérando sealed his friendship with Tournon by conducting the negotiations for his marriage.

78. Material relating to Cuvier's Roman journey is to be found in WHM 1898; BIFC 3259, 3264.

79. For such subsequent careers see Outram, 1976, pp. 632–3; for Holland, see Schama, 1970.

80. BIFC 3244, f. 31, letter of Fossombroni to Cuvier on the fossil elephants of Tuscany; Corsini kept Cuvier informed on the state of the educational institutions in Tuscany founded under the Empire: BIFC 3242, f. 48, letter of 30 April 1822.

81. See the following chapter; see also Lee, 1833, p. 33: 'the moderation and benignity of M. Cuvier knew how to soften inconsistencies . . .'

82. See also Bourgeaud, 1909, for his successful attempts to preserve the autonomy of Geneva within the Imperial University.

83. Flourens, 1856, I, p. 191; however, this passage also states that Cuvier suspected the direct influence of Napoleon or of the Conseil d'Etat in his nomination.

84. Parodi, 1974, p. 298-300; Puget, 1932, p. 308.

85. See Gerbod, 1977, Ch. 1; Fabbroni's decision to return to Tuscany is recorded in his letter to Louis Aubin Millin de Grandmaison of 27 January 1816, BNP N.Acqui.fr. 3231, f. 96.

86. Cuvier, 1817, p. xxxi.

87. *Ibid.*

88. Foucault, 1966, 275–92.

89. Cuvier, 1817, p. v.

90. Bryant, 1978, stresses the impact on individuals of increasing lack of conformity between public and private worlds, particularly in the case of those who served the ever more demanding government of Napoleonic France with considerable private reservations. However, this interesting article overlooks the extent to which the emotional pressures of employment by the state under these conditions were recognised, and formed the subject of publicly discussed therapeutic programmes such as that of the Société des observateurs de l'homme. That Cuvier's particular response through a certain idea of science was to prove less effective in the tighter confines of a national state, does not mean it was concerned with a pure retreat into privacy under the Empire: above all, it was concerned with an adjustment to the strains of public life, not a retreat from it.

Notes to Chapter V

1. In this chapter I am clearly indebted to Bourdieu, 1972. It should be noted that general histories of this period tend to make little connection between the dispute and the general political history of this period, beyond a vague connection with the outbreak of revolution in 1830; many more general histories in fact mention the conflict which followed the first night of Victor Hugo's *Hernani* (25 February 1830) as their example of cultural tension in this period, but there are few studies which attempt a detailed examination of the way culture and politics interacted over this whole period. These remarks stand for both modern and contemporary accounts. See Capefigue, 1837; Salvandy, 1855; Hamel, 1897; Lamartine, 1853; Maurin, 1850; Nettement, 1868; Pasquier, 1894–5; Molé, 1925; Bertier de Sauvigny, 1955; Artz, 1931; Montbel, 1913; Vidalenc, 1966; Vielcastel, 1860–78; Vaulabelle, 1874; Pinkney, 1972; Jardin and Tudesq, 1973; Charléty, 1921. Benjamin, 1973, offers interesting ideas on the fragmentation of culture under the Restoration and later.

2. See Hartman, 1972, for the capacity of this society to generate myth in another context, and its capacity to mobilise opinion.

3. Outram, 1978.

4. For contemporary inability to delimit the political sphere in social analysis, see Porter, 1970. Sennett, 1977, offers an interpretation of the redefinition of the public realm as a whole between the eighteenth and nineteenth centuries. Wolin, 1960, discusses the nineteenth century underestimation of the political sphere.

5. Both Cuvier himself (G. Cuvier, 1817, I, p. xx) and Pasquier, 1832, take the first view, Coleman, 1964, the second and Bourdier 1971, the last.

6. Bourdier, 1971.

7. E. Geoffroy St Hilaire, 1830.

8. For extended examination of this term see Boltanski, 1973.

9. Agulhon, 1978.

10. Fontvieille, 1976, pp. 1767, 1781, 2000–2001.

11. Gerbod, 1977.

12. Gerbod, 1977, p. 61.

13. Raspail, 1830, p. 153. More work needs to be done on the strategies governing marriage amongst the social and political élite. Trenard, 1958, and Vidalenc, 1969, also comment on the lack of firm boundaries between different types of power in this period, which is perfectly compatible with a high degree of conflict within the upper middle class in the Chamber and with great shifts in the structure of wealth; see Daumard, 1973.

14. E.g., the hopes of the liberal paper the *Minerve française* that 'on commence enfin à entendre en France le système représentatif, puisqu'on sent que l'unité de vues, des principes et des sentiments est nécessaire dans les hommes qui se chargent de la pénible tâche du gouvernement'. See Harpaz, 1968, p. 99; *Minerve française* IV, 1818, p. 422, 27 December 1818.

15. Beach, 1971, p. 157.
16. Speech of 28 January 1822; Mavidal & Laurent, xxxiv, p. 264.
17. O'Boyle, 1970.
18. E.g. (Imbert), 1816.
19. Gerbod, 1977, p. 98, points out the importance of frequent purges amongst the administration for the formation of a journalism of protest.
20. Spitzer, 1971.
21. *Ibid.*, p. 288.
22. For Japy, see the genealogical table and Leuillot, 1959–61, I, p. 326; for Bertrand, see letter of Cuvier to Bertrand (n.d.), Edinburgh University Library, Pollok–Morris papers, and Bertrand, 1824.
23. Spitzer, 1971, pp. 228, 247, 304; Leuillot, 1959–61, I, pp. 270, 321–5. The account in the *Dictionnaire biographique française* does not mention his involvement in Carbonarism. Brack's distinguished career was only resumed after 1830.
24. Bourdier, 1971.
25. Poirier, 1932, p. 89. The decisions of the Conseil, of course, may still be consulted in the *Moniteur officiel;* what is lost is the record of the discussions leading up to these decisions.
26. Laurillard, 1852, p. 589–9.
27. Even the account by Pasquier, 1832 and 1894–5, I, p. 205; II, pp. 396–7; IV, pp. 475–6, his colleague in the Conseil d'etat, devotes only a few paragraphs to Cuvier's public career. Lee, 1833, gives a more exhaustive account (pp. 35–47, 227–61) but plays down the conflicts and insecurities in Cuvier's position in order to produce a picture of Cuvier as a mediator figure, above politics because fundamentally devoted to science.
28. For such attacks see Anon (ed. A. Emory), 1815; Anon, 1815; Anon, in *Le Nain jaune*, 20 April 1815, p. 23.
29. See Appendix.
30. Gerbod, 1965, p. 137.
31. Gerbod, 1966, p. 81–6; Liard, 1894, p. 141.
32. His attempts to preserve its independence from the Church under the Empire have already been examined. See also his memoir of 1820 on this topic, BIFC 3270.
33. Olivier-Martin, 1941, p. 17, Puget, 1932, p. 309. Between 1824 and 1828, members of the Conseil did in fact hold office entirely at the King's pleasure. It should be noted however that when Cuvier himself made difficulties about his appointment to the Commission on the censure of the press in 1827, this did not result in his removal from the Conseil. Cuvier's letter refusing appointment is at BIFC 3297/29.
34. For one such dispute, between Cuvier and Villèle, see Mavidal & Laurent, session of 7 February 1817. For the latter's dislike of Cuvier, see Villéle, 1904, II, pp. 151, 156; V, p. 405.
35. Robert, 1961, pp. 333–43. Cuvier's papers in BSHPF are mostly concerned with the resolution of detailed problems and contain no letters or memoranda by him.

36. Mavidal & Laurent, XXXII, p. 227-8, session of 7 June 1821: '... moi qui, par une circonstance qui m'est personelle et que vous n'ignorez pas, étais peut-être le seul des fonctionnaires supérieures de l'instruction publique qui ne peut jamais prétendre à cette dignité.'
37. Molé, 1923-5, IV, p. 207.
38. Leuilliot, 1959-61, III, pp. 265-9. Letters by Georges and Frédéric Cuvier to J. G. Schweighaeuser (Bibliothèque municipale, Nancy, MS 1260) interpret this *affaire* primarily in terms of a decline in toleration for Protestants. Accusations of nepotism played a secondary role. That the religious issue was the dominant one is shown by the considerable difficulties experienced in gaining posts by Protestant pupils of Cuvier who were not related to him. See Genevray, 1940.
39. Genevray, 1940, p. 291. Constant's speech of 18 May 1827 is recorded in Mavidal and Laurent, LII. See also Leuilliot, 1959-60, III, p. 269.
40. Genevray, 1940, p. 291; Garnier, 1925, p. 316.
41. *Ibid.*
42. Molé, 1923-5, IV, p. 207.
43. *Minerve française*, 1818, IV, pp. 421-2, 27 December 1818.
44. In 1817, Cuvier had also refused insistent requests from the *département* of the Doubs that he stand as *Député*. See letter to Georges Duvernoy, n.d., printed in Viénot, 1932, pp. 133-4. Political correspondence in BIFC is extremely sparse, and offers no illumination of this episode.
45. Charles Cuvier, 1881, pp. 142-9. The new legislation had to do with the political functions of the prevotal courts.
46. Clémentine Cuvier's personality, and her activity in charitable enterprises as the founder of the Société de prévoyance et de secours mutuels in 1825, led to the production of many memoirs on her death, e.g., Wilks, 1832; Salvandy 1827.
47. Boltanski, 1973, p. 10: '... parmi l'ensemble des privilèges qui sont l'instrument et le produit du pouvoir, il n'en est sans doute pas de plus important que le capital des relations; par l'intérmediaire du réseau de rélations, familial et amical, s'opère un nombre important de transactions objectivement politiques ou objectivement économiques.'
48. Lee, 1833, p. 229.
49. Flourens, 1856, I, p. 172. 'En Allemagne, où l'on enseigne tout par méthode, on apprend plus de choses en bien moins de temps qu'en France où les connaissances universelles ne se puisent guère que dans la pratique. C'est ainsi que j'ai pu me faire en quelques années des idées sur toutes les parties du gouvernement assez justes et assez liés pour que longtemps après, quand je fus placé dans le Conseil de l'Université et dans le Conseil d'Etat, je me sois trouvé aussitôt au niveau de ma besogne.'
50. Flourens, 1856, I, *ibid*; the hostility of the Chamber of Deputies to the project is indicated in Mavidal & Laurent, LVIII, pp. 247-8,

session of 8 April 1829. ANP BB 30/251, dossier 61, indicates that this project was conceived in conjunction with the Comte de Serre, although neither Cuvier nor Serre (Lacombe, 1881) mentions this. See also Pouthas, 1926, p. 344.

51. Gerbod, 1965, p. 60. The place of science in the normal curriculum was to remain uncertain after 1830; see Trénard, 1958. A considerable anti-intellectual element was present in the thinking of Catholic conservatives such as Fraysinnous (see Schmidt, 1911), which cannot have helped Cuvier's schemes.

52. Mavidal & Laurent, XXXVII, pp. 494–5, session of 27 July 1822; Jeannin, 1968. Rioting reached such a pitch in 1822 that almost all institutions of higher education in Paris were closed, and it always remained potential at such symbolic events as the burial of the Napoleonic hero General Foy in November 1825. Villemain, 1864, I, pp. 387–437 contains a prolonged description of Foy and his relations with students. Threats to order certainly no longer came from the lower classes alone. It is however difficult to endorse an interpretation of 1830 as provoked to any large degree by generational conflict. Student disorder beforehand often merely showed up, or was the excuse for, conflict among the ruling class. Royer-Collard's resignation as Director of Public Instruction in 1819 for example was sparked off by student unrest, but was certainly not unpleasing to Catholic and conservative groups. (Liard, 1894, p. 141) Actual participation by students in the Carbonari or in the 1830 revolution itself was low. (Spitzer, 1971, p. 281; Pinkney, 1972 p. 269–70.) Nor, in spite of some contemporary feeling to the contrary, was this an age-resistant society; in fact the very instability of politics and the weakness of the bureaucratic *cursus* in the face of patronage, made it possible to achieve high position relatively young in a significant number of cases. (Mazoyer, 1938, p. 405; Abrams, 1970; Spitzer, 1971.) The severest attacks on Cuvier were in fact to come from his contemporaries such as Geoffroy; nor, as we have seen, can it be said that political attacks on Cuvier came from any one political tendency; in fact, by 1830, the French upper class was so fragmented that it is not surprising that Cuvier should have been attacked by so many different groups.

53. Gerbod, 1965, p. 96. Cuvier's long report on the abuse of seminary education is BIFC 3285/2 (1820); see also his letter to the Bishop of Bellay, ANP F7. 9768.

54. Johnson, 1963, *passim*.

55. Poirier, 1926, p. 233.

56. Poirier, 1932, pp. 101–5; BIFC 3270/5, 'Notes remises à M. Guizot lors de la rédaction de son ouvrage sur l'instruction publique'.

57. Guizot, 1816, p. 5, p. 10. As the social tensions caused by industrialisation became increasingly obvious, however, sections of the liberal bourgeoisie began to use primary and technical education to cultivate an alliance with the upper sections of the working class which was to be of a considerable importance in the shaping of the forces which supported revolution in Paris in 1830. Cuvier's friend

Charles Dupin was one of the leaders of this movement. See Cuvier's letter to François Bonnard of 15 January 1826 (BIFC 3323/11) for his endorsement of Dupin's projects. For this interpretation as a whole, see Newman, 1974.

58. For a list of members of the Society, see *Journal d'Education, publié par la société formée à Paris pour l'amélioration de l'enseignement élémentaire*, 1815, I, p. 98.

59. Gontard, 1959, pp. 287–375. BIFC 3270 describes the Lancastrian system as possessing 'avantages immenses sous le rapport de l'économie, de la rapidité des progrès, et des habitudes d'ordre et de subordination'. See Leuilliot, 1955, for the success of schools on this model founded by Cuvier's relative Ferdinand Curie, grandfather of the scientist.

60. Poirier, 1926, pp. 14–29; see his letter to the Vicomte de Montmorency of 27 April 1816 (WHM Autograph Collection) for one such licensing, of a school under the patronage of the Duchesse de Duras; his favourable report upon the Société, of 1819, urging the continuance of the subsidy is at ANP F17 5947.

61. His speech was rousing enough to be printed by order of the Chamber: 'Discours relatif à l'allocation de 50,000 fr. pour encouragements à l'instruction primaire de M. le Baron Cuvier, Commissaire du Roi, Chambre des deputés, séance du 12 juin 1821'; and to spark off a pamphlet controversy examined in detail in Gontard, 1959, pp. 373 ff.

62. Cuvier also played a considerable part in removing the implications of retroactive political legislation which surrounded the establishment of the prevotal courts. See Paillet, 1911.

63. Mavidal & Laurent, XXXIV, p. 265, session of 28 June 1822.

64. For a previous exploration of the public uses of the myth of science see Outram, 1980.

65. One speaker demanded, for example, 'Lorsque tant de jeunes gens adeptes se pressent aux portes de la science, pourquoi les répousser en accumulant sur une seule tête des emplois, chaires et pensions, qui répartis entre eux auraient soutenu leur zèle, fécondé leurs talents, enrichi la science . . .' (Mavidal & Laurent LVII, p. 733, session of 28 March 1829.) Professional journals repeated the same complaint, e.g. *Gazette de l'instruction publique: journal d'éducation national, de littérature, des sciences et des arts*, 2, p. 7, 11 June 1829.

66. See the sources quoted in note 28. Their very titles *(Protée, Girouette)*, point to the problem of lack of form or defined location as a grounds for denying the validity of their subjects' claims to participate in decent politics. Another aspect of these accusations is that of Cuvier's ability to adapt to service under different regimes – a question already treated in Chapter IV.

67. In 1831, for example, a speaker regretted the probable effect of the abolition of the legality of the *cumul* on the income of 'un homme riche de tous les dons de la nature, [qui] porte partout cette incontestable supériorite qui commande l'admiration et excite

l'envie; les dossiers déparent des mains savantes qui dotèrent la France de tous les trésors de l'Univers; l'Etat lui doit de la réconnaissance; mais la posterité et la science nous demanderaient compte un jour de tout le temps que les affaires ont dérobé à cette grandeur de l'esprit, à cette capacité prodigieuse d'un homme extraordinaire.' Mavidal & Laurent, LXVI, p. 332, session of 25 January 1831. Legislation proposed by Cuvier's colleague in the Conseil d'Etat, Cormenin, would in fact have made *any cumul* illegal: *ibid*, LXVII p. 752, session of 21 March 1831. Cormenin, 1842, p. 142 has a half-admiring and half-mocking portrait of Cuvier as Commissaire due roi.

68. 'Cuvier et Laplace cités à Paris comme des modèles également accomplis de talent et d'obséquiosité', remarked Henri Beyle, himself a much-disappointed seeker for office. Michel, 1964, p. 550. See Fox, 1974, for the collapse of Laplace's research programme and authority as a patron.

69. Outram, 1980.

70. Statement based on a sample of the careers of Cuvier's contemporaries in DBF and BU: Pastoret, Thenard, de Serre, De Gérando, Molé, Pasquier, Royer-Collard.

71. These demands were probably intensified in this period by the importance laid by governmental institutions – as distinct from the practice of politics – on the separation of powers as the guarantee of the Charter.

72. Recommendation of the brother of the Rector of the Academy of Toulouse for a sous-préfecture in a letter to Décazes of 22 December 1820 (WHM, Autograph Collection); patronage exercised on behalf of Montbéliard and the Doubs, letter to Guizot of 13 October 1814, Henry E. Huntington Library, San Marino, California; letter to Municipal Council of Montbéliard, 18 December 1831, printed in Goguel, 1864, p. 117; letter to Marquise d'Héricy concerning boundary disputes in Normandy which he undertakes to settle in her favour in the Conseil d'etat, of 4 July 1827, now in the Muséum de Rouen, and printed in Lerond, 1975.

73. For Dupin, see note 57; for Bertier, letter of Cuvier to Maréchal MacDonald of 26 September 1823, Charavay sale catalogue, 18 June 1843, p. 10.

74. Pilon, 1932.

75. MNHN, MS 756, premier cahier, p. 11.

76. Imbert, 1816, for example, sees the suitor for office as 'un acteur, placé sur un vaste théâtre, entouré de curieux qui cherche à lire dans ses régards les émotions dont il est agité ... le solliciteur, pénétré de l'esprit de son rôle, et versé dans l'art de dissimuler, n'a jamais un visage plus rayonnant que lorsqu'il maudit son étoile, jamais son pas n'est plus assúre que lorsqu'il vient de faire un fausse démarche', (pp. 122–2).

77. Geoffroy St Hilaire, 1830, p. 53.

78. See Agulhon, 1977 and 1978, for a characterisation of, for example, private societies as carriers of effective action; the sinking of political differences into the call for effective action for a 'neutral' objective such as public welfare in some shape or form accounts for the possibility of such organisations as the Société pour l'amélioration de l'enseignement élémentaire, to gather a large membership and expand rapidly in spite of the complexity of the political situations encountered at local and national levels.

79. *Annales des sciences de l'observation*, ed. Raspail and Saigey, 4 vols, 1829–30, Baudouin, Paris. Saigey (1797–1871) was a compatriot and former protégé of Cuvier who later became secretary to Victor Cousin; see Duvernoy, 1943, p. 28.

80. ASO, II, 1829, pp. 317–21, obituary of Abel.

81. *Ibid.*, III, 1830, pp. 159–60. See also the obituary of D. S. Leman in II, 1829, pp. 151–2, and the glorification of Picot de Lapéyrouse at the expense of Candolle, which uses the same vocabulary and intentions, IV, 1830, pp. 156–60.

82. Geoffroy St Hilaire, 1830, p. 30.

83. *Ibid.*, p. 34.

84. *Ibid.*, p. 165.

85. Appel, 1975, pp. 180–98. See also note 15.

86. Raspail, for example, placed on the one hand, as 'good naturalists', Geoffroy, Lamarck and Lapeyrouse, and on the other as 'bad', Cuvier, Ardouin, Mirbel, Adolphe Brongniart, Blainville and Candolle, ignoring both the hostility between Cuvier and Blainville, and his growing distance from the Brongniart group. See ASO, IV, 1830, pp. 313–19; 156–60; II, 1829, pp. 303–5; I, 1829, pp. 276–9; III, 1830, pp. 290, 408–13, 448–9; Geoffroy, 1830, pp. 31, 69, 78–9, 132, claims the allegiance of Cuvier's collaborators and protégés Dubrueil, Serre and Flourens.

87. Appel, 1975, p. 318.

88. *Ibid.*, p. 175; I. Geoffroy St Hilaire, 1847, p. 376.

89. It is worth noting that when Raspail tried to gain membership of the Academy of Sciences, Geoffroy's was the only vote cast in his favour.

90. The debate was also so interpreted by many sections of the newspaper press. Jean Guerin, for example, regarded Geoffroy's challenge as an epitome of 'the history of all scientific advancement'. (*Gazette médicale*, I, 1830, p. 417; Appel, 1975, p. 298.)

91. Frankel, 1972, pp. 347–50; Frankel, 1978.

92. Appel, 1975, p. 223. Lee, 1833, p. 310 records a quarrel between Cuvier and Arago of 26 July 1830, which broke out because Cuvier objected to remarks by Arago denigrating the incumbent Clermont-tonnère ministry, and felt that political discussion should not form part of the sessions of the Academy: in other words that its status as neutral ground should not be endangered.

93. Lyell (ed.), 1881, I, p. 133, letter of Charles Lyell to his father of 20 July 1823, recounting a dinner with Brongniart and his son-in-law:

'M. Pichon, who was cast out lately from the Council of State for giving it as his opinion that the King could not authorise the taking of the veil in convents without the Chamber repealing the existing laws against it. Cuvier, a Protestant, was President of the Council, and gave his vote the other way.' Pasquier, 1894–5, IV, pp. 473–5, also insists on Cuvier's propensity to give way to Catholic interests for fear of being thought to be biased in favour of those of the Protestants.

94. Appel, 1975, p. 209–63. It is difficult to say how far this change represented a genuine compromise, and how far an urge to close ranks within the Muséum against the radical threat posed by Geoffroy to both Cuvier and the Brongniarts.

95. Meyranx and Laurencet, 'Quelques considérations sur l'organisation des mollusques'. Cuvier's reaction to Geoffroy's report on this paper was printed in *Annales des sciences naturelles*, XIX, 1830, pp. 241–59, 'Considérations sur les mollusques'. It was not, of course, that Cuvier's work had previously failed to generate controversy. The dating of vertebrate fossils was always likely to produce debate (Gerstner, 1970), and recent discoveries leading to arguments for the existence of fossil man had also met with counter-arguments from Cuvier (Lyon, 1970; Cartailhac, 1884). Such conflicts rarely, if ever, went outside a boundary of 'normal' scientific discourse; challenge on the question of fossil man had also tended to come from young and unknown provincials such as Jules de Christol and Paul Tournal. In other words, these problems, though in 'internal' terms just as complex as Geoffroy's theory of analogies, were not presented in a way which challenged the structure of scientific debate from the inside as Geoffroy was to do. The debate between Cuvier and Geoffroy implied disagreement about the very nature of scientific argument, and hence made their resolution both impossible in itself, and a serious challenge to Cuvier's public position. Here I am indebted to the general argument of Appel, 1975.

96. Letter of Frédéric Cuvier *fils* to Richard Owen, 25 January 1884, Owen papers, IX, fol. 178, BM(NH): 'le cachet gravé sur pierre qu'il [Cuvier] portrait toujours sur lui, et représente *l'étude*, ainsi que je l'ai entendu lui-même expliquer'.

97. Mavidal & Laurent, XVIII, p. 71, session of 24 May, 1820; *ibid.*, LII, p. 136, 18 May 1827. In other contexts, Cuvier's presentation of scientific 'progress' is also deeply marked by the need to maintain its image as neutral ground. Even when he does not employ the language of the *éloges*, public and state support for science is justified by reference to its 'utility', conceived of as a quality from which all members of the collectivity are likely to benefit equally; in other words, the question of political impediments to the gaining of knowledge, and of the socially exploitative use of that knowledge in the process of the development of science-based industry, are ignored. See 'Rapport sur les progrès du science', pp. 29–30, for an image of science as a mediator in social conflict.

98. Robert, 1961, p. 334 n, quoting a report of Adolphe Monod to

the Consistory of Lyon of 14 February 1829.

99. Lyell (ed.) 1881, I, pp. 249–50.

100. See the emotional justifications of natural history explicitly mentioned in the *Règne Animal*, I, 1817, pp. xix–xx. 'It consoles the unhappy, it calms hatred. Once elevated to the contemplation of this harmony of nature ... how feeble and petty one discovers to be those provinces that depend on the free will of men ... I avow it proudly: these ideas have never been alien to my works and if I have sought with all my means to propagate their peaceful study, it is because, in my opinion, it is more capable than any other of feeding the hunger for activity which has so greatly contributed to the troubles of this century.' They could also feed the hunger for action in Cuvier himself, which could find no totally satisfying outlet in the political life of his day. These views have little to do with religious justifications for the contemplation of nature.

101. For an earlier presentation of this observation, see Outram, 1978, p. 161. The growth of 'Bohemia', and the overproduction of educated men in relation to the capacity of the state and the professions to offer them employment, were two factors contributing to this fragmentation of the élite. The 'battle' of *Hernani*, just as much as the Cuvier/Geoffroy debate, was a sign of increasing challenge to official culture caused by this social change. For more detailed exploration of the fragmentation of literary culture from this point of view see Bourdieu, 1972, pp. 71 ff. Contemporaries were, of course, well aware of the revolutionary potential of intellectual overproduction; Cuvier pointed out that the leaders of the Terror had almost all been men 'qui se sentaient des moyens supérieurs à leurs fortunes', BIFC 3270/5, f. 137.

102. E.g. Appel, 1975, p. 123 ff; Limoges, 1978. It is not that challenges to patronage authority were not important, but rather that a measure of their full impact can only be obtained by an examination of the ways in which the means of capturing control of cultural expression were changing in this period.

Notes to Chapter VI

1. For an individual example of one such medical student who also became a proficient botanist, see Théodoridès, 1967 a.

2. Cuvier, 1800–05, and Brongniart, 1837, for example both originated as textbooks. In the Restoration, Cuvier was offered a share of the profits of Selves' atlas for schools which amounted to 20,000 fr., and was offered almost the same by the publisher Dufour for the revised edition of the *Recherches sur les ossements fossiles des quadrupèdes*. His salary as Permanent Secretary was 6,000 fr. See C. Cuvier, 1881, p. 144.

3. For extended treatment of this theme, see Hahn, 1961.

4. Cobb, 1972.

5. Such accusations also serve (e.g. Bourdier, 1971), to reinforce an

image of Cuvier as an unscrupulous opponent of liberty and 'progress' in science.

6. E.g., Lee, 1833, p. 13; I. Geoffroy St Hilaire, 1847, pp. 62, 119; Duvernoy, 1833, p. 120; Appel, 1975, p. 74; Coleman, 1964, p. 174.

7. Lee, 1833, pp. 263–4, unwittingly reveals far more of a controversial Cuvier than is consistent with the ideal of unanimity: 'There is yet another sort of reproach which the inventors of systems overthrown by M. Cuvier have dared to bring against him. These, wounded by self-love, or contradicted in some cherished fancy, have not feared to attribute to pride, or even to a feeling of jealousy, very far from his noble heart, the reserve with which he admitted certain explanations of the phenomena of nature, and the resistance he offered to limited or defective theories ... This resistance, however, was one of the most beautiful parts of his character, for it proved his love of truth, and the ardour with which he knew how to defend it, even at the expense of his own tranquillity; and he fearlessly exposed himself to personal emnity, in order to turn students away from such views, the inevitable result of which was to stop the progress of science, by giving a false direction to the minds of those engaged in her cause.'

8. Cuvier, 1795 c; Cuvier 1795/9; Cuvier 1800–05, pp. iii, xvii.

9. Burckhardt, 1977, pp. 202, 209.

10. Cuvier, 1796/9; MNHN MS 628; Newth, 1952.

11. Geoffroy/Cuvier, 1795 a; Geoffroy/Cuvier, 1795 b; Cuvier/Geoffroy, 1795 a; Geoffroy/Cuvier, 1798.

12. Cuvier, 1812 a, p. 81.

13. 'Nous proposons de soumettre la classe des animaux à mammelles à une révision générale: de les ranger en ordres et en genres aussi naturels que peuvent l'être des agrégations qui, malgré tout le soin qu'on met à les former, n'ont toujours pour base que les abstractions des naturalistes' (Geoffroy/Cuvier, 1795 b).

14. Cuvier, 1812 b.

15. Geoffroy/Cuvier, 1798. Compare the 1799 version of Cuvier 1796/9; Cuvier opposes the idea that 'tous les quadrupèdes peuvent ne dériver que d'une seule espèce; que les différences qu'ils présentent ne sont que des dégénérations successives: en un mot, ce serait réduire à rien toute l'histoire naturelle, puisque son objet ne consisterait qu'en des formes variables et des types fugaces'.

16. Flourens, 1856, II, p. 182, points out the benefits that Cuvier's collaboration conferred on the almost unknown Geoffroy.

17. Cuvier, 1796/9; Cuvier et al., 1802.

18. See Chapter VII.

19. This may also help to account for the curious dichotomy in Lamarck's own work which arises from the combination of his proclaimed disbelief in the real existence of species, with much taxonomic work in botany and in the invertebrates.

20. Cuvier to Camper, n.d. (? 1798), University Library Amsterdam, Camper papers. For identification, the letter begins: 'C'est par un

Notes to Chapter VI

séjour...'

21. Cuvier 1800–05, I, 1800, p. xi, remarks that copies of the lectures to the Ecole centrale du Panthéon which formed the basis of the book '... ont été employés utilement dans quelques autres cours et même dans quelques ouvrages imprimés; abus très-léger, à la vérité, et qui ne m'empêchera point de continuer à faire connaître les observations qui me sont propres, à tous ceux qui pourront le désirer, mais suffisant cependant pour que je tâche de m'assurer par l'impression la date et la propriété de quelques-unes'. At the same date, Cuvier was defending his priority in publication on certain fossils against Antoine Gouan of Montpellier; Cuvier to Gouan, BL Add. MS 22935, f. 74, letter of 12 pluviôse an IX (12 February 1801).

22. Burckhardt, 1977, p. 186, quoting from Lamarck, 1809, II, p. 450.

23. Cuvier, 1795 b.

24. Except in my interpretation of the significance of Cuvier's collaboration with Geoffroy, I follow here the interpretation of Burckhardt, 1977, pp. 120–24, 190–95. Lamarck's lecture of 1796 was reported in the *Magasin Encyclopédique*, II, 1, 1796, p. 285.

25. Cuvier, 1798, p. vii; Cuvier, 1800-05, I, 1800, p. xix.

26. Cuvier, 1801, a, pp. 387–8.

27. Lamarck, 1809, I, p. 118.

28. BIF MS Flourens 2598/3, f. 33.

29. See note 24. Other workers on the same topic also gave scant recognition to Cuvier; e.g. Virey, 1798 and 1799.

30. Burckhardt, 1977, p. 199. Cuvier's review of Lacepède's *Histoire Naturelle des poissons* is in ME VI, 2, 1800, pp. 382–3; Lacepède's letter of thanks of 15 messidor VIII (4 July 1800) is BIFC 3222/27.

31. See Deleuze, 1813; for Duméril's adhesion to the Société de magnétisme, see Dureau, 1869, pp. 87–90.

32. Burckhardt, 1977, p. 280; Candolle, 1862, p. 58.

33. Delambre, who died in 1822, was succeeded by Fourier and in 1830 by François Arago.

34. Cuvier, 1810.

35. Outram, 1978; specific *éloges* embodying such research programmes would include those of Lamarck and Adanson: *Mémoires de l'Académie des Sciences*, XIII, 1836, pp. 1–31; Cuvier, 1819–27, I, pp. 267–308.

36. This also meant that Cuvier could comment on specialities outside the range of his teaching at the Muséum. Cuvier's reports to the Institut are most accessibly listed in RSL.

37. The admission of the public to the sessions of the Academy of Sciences forms the subject of his conflict with François Arago in 1830; the theme is already present in Cuvier, an IX.

38. Burckhardt, 1977, p. 191, 'Cuvier's magisterial and disapproving presence has long been recognised as a major factor in the poor reception of Lamarck's evolutionary theory by his contemporaries'.

Burckhardt, 1970 however, submits this view to more radical questioning.

39. Blainville, 1845.
40. Lamarck, ed. Giard, 1908, p. 564, 'Discours d'ouverture de l'an 1806': 'Dans un ouvrage qui vient de paraître sur la zoologie, l'auteur après avoir fait l'éloge de l'étude particulière des espèces, assure que la connoissance des espèces est ce que constitue le véritable naturalist'.
41. Letter of Marzari Pencati to H. A. Gosse, 20 floréal an XIII quoted in full in Plan, 1909, p. 1 xxxii–xxxiii, and in extract in Viénot, 1932, p. 100. The original is among the Pencati papers of the Biblioteca Civica, Vicenza. I owe this information to Pietro Corsi.
42. Cuvier, 1810, mentions Lamarck eleven times in 394 pages (pp. 154–5, 191, 272, 277–8, 292, 313–4, 316–7, 319) without discussing his views on species, although p. 314 revived the old quarrel by asserting that Lamarck had relied on Cuvier's arrangements of the invertebrates. However, such counting of references should also be supported by much greater attention to Lamarck's influence on contemporaries, which may well have been more extensive than is thought. See Corsi, 1978.
43. E.g. review of the *Hydrogéologie*, an X, pp. 530, 1292; of the *Recherches sur l'organisation des corps vivans*, 1802, II, p. 1462; of the *Philosophie zoologique*, 1809, pp. 1154–6.
44. E.g. *MU*, an XIII, p. 1497; 1807, pp. 234, 242. More attention needs to be paid to the effect on Lamarck's reputation of controversy with figures other than Cuvier.
45. Candolle, 1862, p. 160. 'Nous arrivâmes enfin à cette présentation. L'Empéreur, en voyant les quatre volumes, dit à M. de Lamarck, "Voilà un ouvrage bien considérable". "Sire", lui dit M. de Lamarck, "vos conquêtes ont étendu notre besogne", puis il me présenta comme son collaborateur. Tout cela se passa en deux minutes, et comme une affaire de forme.' It should also be noted that Candolle dates this anecdote to 1812, on the publication of the new edition of the *Flore*, and thus well after the incident usually placed in 1807 when Cuvier is alleged to have contrivé the insult to Lamarck by Napoleon which is said to have banished him from the court for ever.
46. *Ibid.*, p. 58: '. . . je ne tardai pas à m'apercevoir que mon travail chez M. de Lamarck m'était peu utile. Ce savant était alors absorbé par ses écrits contre le chimie moderne et par ses hypothèses relatives à l'action de la lune sur l'atmosphère. Quand je l'intérrogeais sur la botanique il me repondait par de la chimie ou de la méteorologie qu'il savait à peine. Je cessai donc peu à peu d'aller le voir.'
47. Cuvier, 1807, p. 413; Cuvier begins with 'Quelques réflexions générales sur la manière dont une compagnie, telle que la nôtre, peut et doit envisager ces sortes de recerches'.
48. Cuvier, 1807.
49. *Ibid.*, p. 413.
50. *Ibid.*
51. *Ibid.*, p. 421.

52. *Ibid.*
53. Cuvier, 1810, p. 5.
54. Letter of Cuvier to Villers, printed in Isler, 1883, dated 18 floréal X: 'Il est vrai que j'ai écrit à Gall, il y a longtemps et je ne sais trop pourquoi, mais il ne m'a pas répondu.' The almost illegible letter, BIFC 3224/56, 27 November 1802, which is ascribed by Dehérain to Gall, may thus not in fact be so. Geoffroy/Cuvier, 1798, however, pays serious attention to the use of facial angle in assessing the disposition of various species of monkey, and attempts to employ such essentially phrenological methodology as a means of classification.
55. Cuvier to Fabbroni, 17 frimaire an X, Fabbroni papers, America Philosophical Society. His opinion of Gall at this point was 'son affaire est à demi folle, à ce qui me semble'. Biographies of von Arnstein make no mention of this meeting, and there is no correspondence between her and Cuvier. See Spiel, 1962, *passim*.
56. Isler, 1883, pp. 60–61; Wittmer, 1907–9, p. 403. The original of the former is in the University Library, Hamburg, Nachlass Villers; the location of the latter is now unknown.
57. Villers, 1801, 1802.
58. *MU*, an XIII, I, pp. 707–8; 740–42, 763–4.
59. Wheeler and Barbour, 1933, p. 17. This lecture on Gall is undated, but is probably written before 1805.
60. Young, 1970, p. 24; Lantéri-Laura, 1970, p. 123. Although Cuvier was officially merely the *rapporteur* for the commission appointed to report on Gall, whose other members were Tenon, Sabatier, Portal and Pinel, Cuvier, 1808 b, ascribes sole authorship to him, as did Gall himself.
61. Cuvier 1800–05, II, 1800, 143–7.
62. This view was strongly expressed in contemporary comments on the struggle between Cuvier and Gall, even inadvertently by Cuvier's own protégés. Gall complained for example, of laudatory press reviews of the 1808 report which implied that the only merit of the work of Gall was to have forced the great Cuvier to produce 'un traité complet sur l'anatomie du cerveau': Gall and Spurzheim, 1809, pp. iii–iv.
63. Cuvier, 1812 c; Lantéri-Laura, 1970, p. 30.
64. Flourens, 1842, pp. 60–84; Cuvier, 1822.
65. Maine de Biran, 1924, V, 69–129.
66. *Ibid.*, p. 75: 'on peut donc voir combien serait illusoire toute parallèle entre les divisions physiologiques des fonctions vitales ou de leurs sièges organiques et la division psychologique des idées des facultés intimes du sujet pensant.' Those who make such equations 'ont dénaturé le sujet et le but de cette dernière science, l'ont entraîné dans une fausse direction, lui ont prêté une méthode et des instruments du moyens d'analyse, qui lui sont tout à fait étrangers'.
67. Gall and Spurzheim, 1809; MS MNHM 608, n.d.
68. *Ibid.*, p. 12; 'Je ne présente qu'une infinité de faits, soit purement empiriques, soit psychologiques, mais toujours des faits,

des observations, des phénomènes.'
69. *Ibid.*, p. 113.
70. Flourens, 1856, II, p. 189.
71. E.g., Cuvier described the crowd as that 'qui menacaient tous les genres de mérite', *éloge* of Cels, Cuvier, 1819-27, I, p. 242.
72. Cuvier to Kielmeyer, 30 January 1808, Academy of Sciences of the DDR.
73. Maine de Biran, 1924, pp. 92, 106.
74. E.g., Cuvier to John Gordon, 31 August 1817, printed in Ellis, 1823, pp. 86-7; Cuvier to Reimarus, 12 June 1809, University Library, Hamburg, MS Campe 2; Cuvier to Soemmering, 25 January 1812, Freien Deutschen Hochstiftes, Frankfurt-am-Main. Such correspondence reveals that there was no basic change in Cuvier's attitude to Gall after 1808. All the letters combine trivial criticisms of Gall's anatomical work, with complaints of his false claims to originality, and failure to distinguish between hypothesis and proof. The question of the novelty or otherwise of Gall's work of course only became important because of the part played in the making of scientific authority by the making of claims to priority and the sale of scientific goods, the newer the better.
75. Gall and Spurzheim, 1809, p. ii; Cuvier 1808 b & c; Cuvier, 1809. According to Gall, Cuvier had seized 'avec avidité tous les passages équivoques pour les divulger dans les feuilles publiques et dans les journaux littéraires . . .' It may be no accident that Biot's devastating portrayal of the scientific charlatan was also published in 1808, and has the same disdain of the public in science as did Cuvier.
76. W. R. Albury, 1977, treats Cuvier's relationship with Magendie.
77. Young, 1970, p. 46.
78. *Ibid.*, pp. 65-9; Gross, 1974, pp. 69-75; Gross, 1979, p. 241, establishes that this was Cuvier's view in 1808.
79. Gross, 1979, p. 255 ff.
80. Gall, 1821; Fossati, 1869, p. 351.
81. Fossati, 1869, p. 92.
82. E.g., Cuvier, 1810, pp. 254-5.
83. Cuvier, 1802; Gower, 1973, pp. 334-5.
84. Gower, 1973; Wetzels, 1971, p. 53.
85. Wetzels, 1971.
86. Cuvier, 1800-05, III, 1805, xvii-xviii.
87. Kielmeyer's letter does not appear in BIFC, and its present whereabouts is unknown. A printed version exists in Holler, 1938.
88. Cuvier to Kielmeyer, 30 January 1808, Academy of Sciences of the DDR.
89. List of Cuvier's reading drawn from *ibid.*, and from the catalogue of his library held in the Library of the Ecole normale supérieure, Paris, and kindly made available to me by its librarian, M. Ch. Petitmengin.
90. Cuvier to Kielmeyer, *ibid.*
91. Originally published in Budapest in 1800 as *Prolusiones ad*

chemiam saeculi deciminoni. See Snelders, 1970, for a survey of the relations between Ritter and Winterl. Gode von Aesch, 1940, contains no account of French attitudes to *Naturphilosophie*.

92. Cuvier to Kielmeyer, *ibid.*

93. Cuvier to Winterl, n.d., (1808), Staatsbibliothek, West Berlin, Darmstaedter Collection, MS. Lc. 1801 (3). Winterl's experiments had also failed earlier attempts at repetition by Guyton de Morveau.

94. Cuvier, 1810, p. 390.

95. Candolle, for example, gives an unusually frank account of the effect Cuvier's views could have on the presentation of work even by his friends: Candolle, 1862, p. 145 describes his 'polémique bénévole' with Cuvier over the new vegetable physiology inserted by Candolle into the new edition of the *Flore française*, which he had not dared to publish while canvassing for election to the Institut, 'dans la crainte qu'elles ne m'aliénassent mes plus zélés protecteurs, Cuvier at Desfontaines'.

96. For example, when Haüy could not repeat Ritter's experiments, Cuvier mentioned to Kielmeyer that 'M. Haüy s'est borné à ne point faire de rapport à la classe, comme c'est l'usage quand on ne veut pas causer de désagrément à des personnes d'ailleurs estimables comme Ritter l'est certainement'. (Cuvier to Kielmeyer, *ibid.*)

Notes to Chapter VII

1. The *Recherches* appeared in a four-volume edition in 1812, in an enlarged edition in five volumes in 1821–4, in a third in 1825, and in a fourth edition of ten volumes in 1834–6. Separate editions of the *Discourse* appeared in 1825 and 1826 under the title *Discours sur les révolutions de la surface du globe, et sur les changemens [sic] qu'elles ont produit dans le règne animal*. The sixth edition had been reached by 1830, and ran to 408 pages. The eighth was published in 1840, at 355 pages. The original 1812 edition, however, ran to 115 pages. Almost all the additional material was concentrated in the concluding historical section which attempted to use ancient legends and chronological systems, as well as recent archeological discoveries, to calculate the age of the ancient civilisations which had arisen after the last geological catastrophe. French editions of the *Discourse* incorporating new geological material appeared in 1854 and 1856 under the editorship of Hoefer, in 1870 under the editorship of A. E. Esquiros, and in 1881 under that of P. Bory. An edition by P. Wossidlo of the original text appeared in Berlin in 1881. English editions begin with *Essay on the theory of the earth translated from the French of M. Cuvier . . . by Robert Kerr FRS . . . with mineralogical notes and an account of Cuvier's geological discoveries by Professor Jameson* (Edinburgh, 1813). A second edition appeared in 1815, with additions which enlarged it to 322 pages. Many of the additions are designed to give a more specifically Wernerian tone to Cuvier's geology (e.g. *ibid.*, p. 228–30). A third edition of the

Jameson–Kerr version appeared in 1817, enlarged to 348 pages, and a fourth in 1822 enlarged to 454 pages; the fifth appeared in 1827, and was 550 pages long. Kerr's translation of Cuvier's text is nearly always faithfully literal. It should also be noted that although Jameson has often been castigated by later historians for his use of the term 'theory of the earth' in the title of the Kerr translation, this phrase in fact recurs many times in the body of the original French text as a description of the aim of the work; Rudwick, 1976, pp. 132–3; *Discours* pp. ii, 23–4, 34, 35, 36.

2. Examples of publications, apart from those by Buckland, concerned with these issues and using the *Discourse* as a springboard include Richardson, 1816; Bugg, 1826–7; 'Homo' 1815; Chalmers, 1836–42, XII, pp. 347–72; Fleming, 1826. Cuvier himself commented in his *Autobiography:* 'Ce discours a été en Angleterre l'objet d'une faveur particulière; il y a déjà été réimprimé quatre fois en anglais et deux fois en Amérique', BIF MS Flourens 2598-3, f 61. Cuvier nowhere offers any other comments on the various translations and editions of this work.

3. Haber, 1959, pp. 197–8; Bourdier, 1971, p. 526; Coleman, 1964, p. 110. Rudwick (note 1) has abandoned this interpretation.

4. Rappaport, 1978, pp. 1–18; see also Houtin, 1902. The problem is not mentioned in Reardon, 1975. It is also necessary to distinguish carefully what is meant by the term 'scriptural geology'. Not all those who took Biblical history into account, such as Buckland, rigidly stuck to a literal interpretation of the Bible account of the Flood. Cuvier and Buckland were able to work together because Buckland's geology tended to be internally independent from the Biblical history to which he attempted to attach it. Such was the confusion as to the permissible limits of interpretation of the Bible story, that in many quarters Buckland was viewed as not being a truly scriptural geologist at all.

5. Letter of Marzari Pencati to H. A. Gosse, 20 floréal, an XIII (1804), describing Cuvier's geology course at the Athénée de Paris, printed in Plan, 1909, pp. 1 xxxii–iv, says Cuvier 'n'est point très dévot'.

6. Duvernoy, 1833, p. 97. Lee's account of Cuvier's last lecture at the Collège de France, which she attempts to inbue with profound religious feeling, remains of doubtful value. Even she had to admit that the speech's 'Biblical quality' lay in its tone rather than in its content. See Lee, 1833, pp. 317–19. Lee, in her lengthy paraphrase of the *Discours, ibid.*, pp. 95–105, does not present it as an essay in scriptural geology, and her friend William Swainson went so far as to regard Cuvier as a materialist atheist. (Swainson, 1834, pp. 87–8.)

7. Such accounts are reviewed in Outram, 1976 b, pp. 101–37, 124–5, 133–6. Cuvier's *Autobiography*, MS Flourens 2589/3 of the Library of the Institut de France, does not discuss his religious views.

8. Wilks, 1838. The frontispiece to this work is wrongly entitled and is in fact an engraving of the portrait by Thomas Lawrence of

Notes to Chapter VII

Clémentine's stepsister, Sophie Duvaucel, which now hangs in the Louvre.

9. *Ibid.*, p. 43 ff.
10. *Ibid.*, pp. 128–30; 148–9.
11. See, for example, correspondence between Cuvier and Pastor Marron of the Eglise des billettes concerning the baptism of his infant son Georges, in Outram, 1980 a, s.v. Marron. Letters by Cuvier's wife printed in Théodoridès, 1966–7, pp. 55–64, also make it clear that repeated deaths within the family circle made it hard to cultivate an unquestioning religious faith.
12. Cuvier, 1819–27, I, p. 91.
13. *Ibid.*, pp. 91–2.
14. Robert, 1962, pp. 139–65.
15. Robert, 1961, pp. 333–43; Macler, 1932, pp. 253–7.
16. Cuvier, 1819–27, I, p. 386: 'cette liberté indéfinie de recherches que les Protestants autorisent même dans les matières qui touchent à la réligion'; Leclerc, 1969, 321–74.
17. Cuvier, 1819–27, I, p. 364. These views were very similar to those which guided Cuvier's educational thinking in general, of support for state institutions, and hostility to the control of the Catholic Church.
18. *Ibid.*, I, pp. 211, 234. The same opinions are expressed in Cuvier's article on Priestley in Michaud, 1823, pp. 83–8. 'Heureux s'il n'eût pas été détourné de travaux précis récompensés par des découvertes importantes, pour être lancé sans retenue dans des spéculations vagues de la métaphysique.'
19. 'Rapport de l'Institut national, Classe des sciences physiques et mathématiques, sur l'ouvrage de M. André, ayant pour titre: Théorie de la surface actuelle de la terre', *Journal des Mines*, 126, June 1807, pp. 413–30.
20. *Ibid.*, pp. 417–18: ' . . . pendant près d'un siècle, les ouvrages de géologie ne continrent que des efforts pour trouver des causes physiques de cette grande catastrophe, ou pour en déduire comme effet l'état actuelle de la surface du globe. Les auteurs oubliaient que le Déluge nous est donné dans la Genèse comme un miracle, ou comme un acte immédiate de la volonté du Créateur, et qu'il est par conséquent bien superflu de lui chercher des causes secondaires.'
21. *Ibid.*, p. 418: 'Ce pas une fois fait, les hypthèses ne conurent plus de limites. On vit renaître dans cette partie de l'histoire naturelle, la méthode systématique de Descartes que Newton semblait avoir bannie pour jamais de toutes les sciences physiques.' A similar point is made on p. 25 of the *Discours*, 1812 edition, from which all citations will be made. Unless otherwise indicated all such quoted passages are also to be found in the edition of 1826.
22. *Ibid.*, p. 413. ' . . . Il est devenui presque impossible de prononcer le nom de géologie sans exciter le rire.'
23. *Discours préliminaire*, pp. 118–38 (1826 ed.).
24. Rappoport, 1978, p. 14; Buckland 1820: Chateaubriand, 1802,

part 1, book IV, §V.

25. Cuvier seems also to have thought that although there were laws in natural history, such as that of the correlation of parts, their use would always have to be supplemented by observation. e.g. *Discours*, pp. 61–3. It is also noteworthy that Cuvier does not employ any of Laplace's cosmological arguments in the *Discourse*, and mentions Laplace's theory that geological 'revolutions' could have been caused by the tilting of the earth's axis only to dismiss it. Thomas Chalmers was the first to point out this discrepancy between the fulsome terms of the dedication and the substantive neglect of Laplace in the body of the work: Chalmers (note 2), pp. 350–5; after acknowledging Laplace's support in the Institut, Cuvier extols 'cet esprit sévère, fruit de l'heureuse association établie dans son sein entre les mathématiciens et les naturalistes': *Preliminary Discourse:* unpaginated dedication.

26. 'C'est un des résultats à fois les mieux prouvés et les moins attendus de la saine géologie, résultat d'autant plus précieux qu'il lie d'une chaine non-interrompue l'histoire naturelle et l'histoire civile', *Discours*, p. 85.

27. 'Et l'homme, a qui il n'a été accordé qu'un instant sur la terre, auroit la gloire de refaire l'histoire des milliers de siècles qui ont précédé son existence, et des milliers d'êtres qui n'ont pas été ses contemporains!', *ibid.*, pp. 115–16.

28. Cuvier, 1796, II, fructidor an VII, pp. 1–22. P. 2: 'La critique, qui s'occupe essentiellement de juger de la vérité des faits rapportés par les autres, est donc aussi nécessaire au naturaliste qu'à l'historie.'

29. Schwab, 1950; Diehl, 1978.

30. Outram (note 12), s.v. Champollion.

31. Schwab, 1950, pp. 676–86; Cuvier, Langlès, Delambre, Lamarck and Olivier, an XIV (1805). Works on comparative linguistics such as Friedrich von Adelung, *Mithridates oder Allgemeine sprachenkunde*, Berlin, 1806–17, were numerous in Cuvier's library.

32. 'J'essaie de parcourir une route où l'on n'a encore hasardé que quelques pas, et de faire connoître une genre de monuments presque toujours négligés quoique indispensable pour l'histoire du globe. Antiquaire d'une espèce nouvelle, il m'a fallu apprendre à déchiffrer et à restaurer ces monumens, à reconnoître et à rapprocher dans leur ordre primitif les fragmens épars et mutilés dont ils se composent; à reconstruire les êtres antique auxquelles ces fragments appartenient, à les réproduire avec leur proportion et leurs caractères, à les comparer enfin à ceux qui vivent aujourd'hui à la surface du globe; art presque inconnu, et qui supposoit une science à peine éffleurée auparavant, celle des lois qui président aux co-existences des formes des diverses parties dans les êtres organisés . . . et le règne entier des animaux s'est trouvé soumis à des lois nouvelles, à l'occasion de cet essai sur une petite partie de la théorie de la terre.' *Discours*, pp. 1–2.

33. In a modified sense, such claims had some justification. It is, of course, untrue to state that Cuvier was the first man to reconstruct

fossil animals, or to write about their distribution and the reasons for their extinction, as the plethora of quoted sources in the *Recherches* makes clear. Pierre-Simon Pallas had already discovered the famous mammoth bodies of the river Ob; Petrus, Camper in Holland had published studies of the two-horned rhinoceros on which Cuvier himself was to rely heavily, and nearer home, Cuvier himself gave the credit, in another context, to Daubenton as the first man to elucidate the principles of palaeontological reconstruction from scattered or damaged individual bones. See Cuvier's studies of Pallas in Cuvier, 1819–27, II, pp. 109–56; for Daubenton see *ibid.*, I, p. 62; Camper, an XI (1803), I, pp. 205–84. Blumenbach had already pointed out that most fossils must belong to extinct species, more or less different in type from those now in existence: *Beiträge zur Naturgeschichte*, Göttingen, 1790, pp. 6–8; it is, however, true to say that Cuvier was the first to attempt to make a full census of known fossil remains, and that he made both a greater number of successful reconstructions of extinct species and larger heuristic claims for such reconstructions, claims which emphasised both their importance for stratigraphy and for comparative anatomy. For Cuvier's census see Théodoridès, 1969, pp. 58–60.

34. *Discours*, p. iv: 'Quelques-unes de ses assertions sur les espèces dont viennent les os qu'il examine, ayant été attaquées par des savants estimables, il a été obligé, quoique bien à regret, de répondre avec détail aux argumens qu'on lui a opposés . . . Il espère s'être acquitté de ce devoir de manière à concilier ce que réclamait l'importance de ces documens avec les égards dus à l'âge et au mérite des personnes qui l'ont contraint de prendre, pour quelques instans, le rôle polémique si peu d'accord avec ses habitudes.' The rivalry between Cuvier and Faujas began when Cuvier challenged Faujas' identification of the large fossil animal found at Maestricht as having affinities with the crocodiles, and reassigned it to the lizards. Faujas de St Fond, *Histoire naturelle de la Montagne de St Pierre de Maestricht*, 1812, an VII (1799); Rudwick (note 1), p. 126; Cuvier, 1812, IV, seventh paper, contains Cuvier's controversy with Faujas over the classification of *megalonix*, and *ibid.*, eighth paper, over that of the *megatherium*. See also Cuvier, 1798; the controversy was retained into the second edition of the *Recherches*: 2nd ed., 1824, V, paper 2.

35. Lamarck is clearly meant to fall among those who 'disent que tout fut fluide dans l'origine, que le fluide engendra des animaux d'abord très simples . . . que, par suite de temps et en prenant des habitudes diverses, les races de ces animaux se compliquèrent, et se diversifierent au point où nous les voyons aujourd'hui': *Discours*, p. 28, attacking the *Hydrogéologie* and the *Philosophie zoologique* of Lamarck.

36. Georges Cuvier, 1801 b, I, pp. 60–82. Much of the subject matter of the *Discours* was also treated in Cuvier's 1808 lectures at the Collège de France, BIFC MS 3103.

37. Cuvier, 'Extrait d'un ouvrage', 1801 b, p. 72; *Discours*,

pp. 80–81. The same points occur in Cuvier, an VI (1798/9), pp. 315–18.

38. Cuvier & Brongniart, 1808, pp. 421–58; 1812, I, third *mémoire*. It should be pointed out that the *Recherches*, a collecton of reprinted articles bound together, does not have a continuous pagination, but retains the original page numbers for each article. This work was favourably reviewed in England as a successful example of a 'factual' non-theological geology: Anon., 1812, pp. 369–89. Further use of this study in England is discussed in Whewell, 1847, III, p. 570. Faujas de St Fond, 1803–9, I, pp. 58–75.

39. Lamarck, 1809, I, 77–8.
40. Carozzi, 1971, pp. 367–77; Laurillard, 1834–6; I, pp. 1–78, 56–7.
41. Lacepède, Cuvier and Lamarck, 1802, pp. 234–41.
42. J. B. Lamarck, I, 1802, pp. 299–312; pp. 302–4.
43. *Discours*, pp. 73–4.
44. *Mots et choses*, 1966; *The order of things*, 1970. Quotations are taken from the English translation, pp. 131, 137–8.
45. *Ibid.*, p. 149; Jameson makes the same point in Cuvier, ed. Jameson, 1827, p. 420.
46. 'La vie a donc souvent été troublée sur cette terre par des événements terribles, calamités qui, dans les commencements, ont peut-être rémué dans une grande épaisseur l'enveloppe entière de la planète, mais qui depuis sont toujours devenues moins profondes et moins générales. Des êtres vivans sans nombre ont été les victimes de ces catastrophes: les uns ont été détruits par des déluges, les autres ont été mis à sec avec le fonds des mers subitement rélévés; leurs races mêmes ont fini pour jamais, et ne laissent dans le monde que quelques débris à peine réconnoissables pour le naturaliste ... Mais ce qui étonne davantage encore, et ce qui n'est pas moins certain, c'est que la vie n'a pas toujours existé sur le globe, et qu'il est facile à l'observateur de reconnoître le point où elle a commencé à déposer ses produits.' *Discours*, pp. 11-12.
47. Rudwick (note 1), p. 119.
48. Carozzi, p. 371.
49. 'Je pense donc, avec MM Deluc et Dolomieu, que, s'il y a quelque chose de constaté en géologie, c'est que la surface de notre globe a été victime d'une grande et subite révolution dont la date ne peut remonter beaucoup au delà de cinq ou six mille ans; que cette révolution a enfoncé et fait disparoître les pays qu'habitoient auparavant les hommes et les espèces d'animaux aujourd'hui les plus connus; qu'elle a, au contraire, mis à sec le fond de la dernière mer, et en a formé les pays aujourd'hui habités; que c'est depuis cette révolution que le petit nombre d'individus épargnés par elle se sont répandus et propagés sur les terreins nouvellement mis à sec, et par conséquent que c'est depuis cette époque seulement que nos sociétés ont repris une marche progressive, qu'elles ont formé des établissements. élevé les monuments, recueilli des faits naturelles, et combiné des systèmes scientifiques.' *Discours*, p. 110.

50. '... lié d'une chaîne non-interrompue', *ibid.*, p. 85.
51. Haber, 1959, pp. 200–04.
52. *Discours*, p. 110.
53. *Ibid.*, p. 18; Carozzi, p. 371.
54. '... ce qui fait même l'objet définitif de tout mon travail, et établit sa véritable relation avec la théorie de la terre, c'est de savoir dans quelles couches on trouve chaque espèce, et s'il y a quelques lois générales relatifs soit aux subdivisions zoologiques, soit au plus ou moins de ressemblances des espèces avec celles d'aujourd'hui', *ibid.*, p. 68.
55. The significance of Cuvier's claim to be the Newton of palaeontology (*Discours*, p. 3) should now have become clearer; it was not a claim that palaeontology was an exact science, more a romantic self-portrayal by Cuvier as a discoverer of new worlds of as great a magnitude as Newton's, a claim to hegemony through emotional appeal which as we have seen was not altogether justified by the facts. Cuvier never hesitates to indicate that the claims of his new palaeontology, and the emergence of the romantic scientist, were indissoluble: such ideas, after all, 'm'ont poursuivi, je dirois presque tourmenté' (*ibid.*, p. 112) in fine Romantic style.
56. Cuvier's friend Maine de Biran pointed this out when he read the *Discours* soon after its first appearance: it interested him, 'par les grandes idées qu'il renferme, quoique le raisonnement ne soit pas toujours rigoureuse', Gouhier (ed.) 1954–7, III, p. 47, entries for 5 and 6 February 1813.

Notes to Chapter VIII

1. Cuvier was appointed Mertrud's assistant or *suppléant* at the Muséum from October 1795, and became full Professor of comparative anatomy *(professeur titulaire)* on 24 vendémiaire an IX (16 October 1802).
2. Coleman, 1964, for example, has no examination of the question of how the Muséum affected Cuvier's career.
3. An assumption fostered by the publications of Cuvier and his assistants: see Cuvier, 1803; Valenciennes, 1833; continued in Lee, 1833, pp. 24, 79–82, and R. Anthony, 1932.
4. This section is based on Hamy, 1893, and Taton, 1964, pp. 259–341.
5. Falls, 1934.
6. For Daubenton's attacks on Buffon in the Ecole normale of 1795, see Brown, 1966.
7. Deleuze, 1823, pp. 67–71, 75.
8. Taton, 1964, pp. 319–42. Professors appointed under the founding decree of the Muséum of the 10 June 1793, included René-Louiche Desfontaines as Professor of botany, Antoine Fourcroy as Professor of chemistry, Antoine Portal as Professor of human anatomy, Antoine-Laurent de Jussieu as Professor of field botany

(*botanique à la campagne*), Gérard van Spaendonck as Professor of iconography, André Thouin as Professor of horticulture, Antoine-Louis Brongniart as Professor of chemistry as applied to industry, Daubenton to the chair of mineralogy; Antoine Mertrud as Professor of the anatomy of animals (the designation of his chair was changed to that of comparative anatomy on his replacement by Cuvier), Barthélemy Faujas de St Fond as Professor of geology; Lamarck as Professor of the zoology of insects, 'worms' and microscopic animals, and Lacepède to the chair of the zoology of quadrupeds, birds, reptiles and fish. In 1793, on Lacepède's enforced departure from Paris, his chair was divided, and the zoology of mammals and birds given to Geoffroy St Hilaire. On Lacepède's return to Paris in 1794, he took over the resulting chair of the zoology of reptiles and fish. Of these men, only Geoffroy had not been connected with the Muséum before 1789.

9. Lamarck, Van Spaendonck, and the Lucas family, holder of the keys to the galleries, and general factotums, shared the large house in the Muséum grounds known as the Intendence (Deleuze, 1823, p. 136); Fourcroy and Haüy (appointed Professor of mineralogy in 1802) shared the Hôtel de Magny; Cuvier initially lived in Mertrud's lodgings in the Muséum, which he occupied entirely after the latter's death, sharing his rooms with Frédéric Cuvier and his assistant Laurillard. The only important member of the Muséum's staff to live outside its boundaries was Alexandre Brongniart, who lived on the rue St Dominique, near the Boulevard St Germain (Dalaunay, 1940, p. 140). Relationships among the Muséum's staff were common: Fourcroy was related to the Brongniart family; Alexandre Brongniart succeeded to the chair of his uncle Antoine in 1804. André Laugier, Fourcroy's *suppléant* from 1805, was related to both the Fourcroy and Brongniart families. De Jussieu was the nephew and great-nephew of Professors at the Muséum and was succeeded by his son Adrien. Thouin's brother Jacques ran the secretariat of the Muséum. Mertrud was the brother and grandson of professors of the Muséum. Cuvier's brother Frédéric was keeper of the menagerie of the Muséum from 1805, his stepson Alfred Duvaucel undertook to travel for the Muséum in the 1820s, and earlier he had unsuccessfully courted Alexandre Brongniart's sister Emilie. Nicolas Vauquelin, who succeeded Fourcroy in 1809, maintained a joint residence with Fourcroy's two sisters, the elder of whom made him her sole heir on her death. Daubenton was related to Buffon, to Vicq d'Azyr, who had briefly given lectures in the Muséum as *suppléant* to Petit in human anatomy, and his brother Edmé-Louis had also held office in the Muséum. Lacepéde married in 1795 the widow of A. Gautier, honorary librarian of the Jardin du roi. Victor Audouin, Latreille's *suppléant* and successor to Lamarck's divided chair in 1833, was Brongniart's son-in-law. Latreille, Lacepède's successor in 1825, was a former pupil of Haüy, as was Geoffroy St Hilaire. Cuvier's assistant Valenciennes was the son of Daubenton's former assistant.

Notes to Chapter VIII

Brongniart's son Adolphe became an *aide-naturaliste* in 1830. Another *Aide-naturaliste*, Oscar Leclercq, was Thouin's nephew. Sources: Kersaint, 1966; Delaunay, 1940; Silvestre de Sacy, n.d. (1941); Nadault de Buffon, 1863; Larévellière-Lépeaux, 1895, II; Taton, 1964; Hahn, 1975 b; de Jussieu, 1808; *Archives du Muséum*, 1935; Duvaucel, 1833.

10. Rice, 1951, p. 612, points out that before the completion of the Pont d'Austerlitz in 1806, the Muséum was only accessible from the Left Bank by ferry, or by a long loop round to a higher bridge.

11. See Chapter V.

12. Deleuze, 1823, pp. 75–100, describes this process of expansion; see also Thouin, 1808. The menagerie is described in Hamy, 1893; Geoffroy St Hilaire, 1838, pp. 143–85. Popular works about the Muséum concentrating on descriptions of the menagerie are listed in Denise, 1903, pp. 204–5; and Leblanc, 1842, III. Daudin, 1924, I, p. 31, shows how the *tarsier* and the elephant heads used by Cuvier in his early papers (Cuvier 1796; Cuvier and Geoffroy, 1795), were supplied by the new collections of the Muséum.

13. Bapst, 1892.

14. Boyer, 1971, 1973: Guillaumin, 1944.

15. Boyer, 1973; Cuvier, 1806.

16. Hamy, 1908.

17. De Jussieu, 1808, p. 18.

18. Nussac, 1934.

19. See Chapter III.

20. *Magasin Encyclopédique*, 2e. année I, pp. 284–7, 1795.

21. Hahn, 1959.

22. Bapst, 1892.

23. BIF MS Flourens 2598 (3), fol. 23.

24. See Chapter II.

25. Lacroix, 1932, reprints a letter of 1793 from Haüy to Cuvier.

26. Fischer, 1802, p. 446. Lamarck was also one of the editors of the *Journal d'Histoire Naturelle* which published Cuvier's first three papers in its second volume.

27. Nussac, 1906, p. 10.

28. I. Geoffroy St Hilaire, 1847, p. 69 n. Cuvier's 'Mémoire sur le larynx' of 1794 was sent to the Muséum on 3 January 1795 for a report by Mertrud, and read to the Assembly of the Professors on 23 January.

29. BIF MS Flourens 2598/3, f. 26–7, 32, even though written thirty years after these events, is still full of hostility to Haüy in particular. The hostility of Haüy and Daubenton may well have been increased by their own conflict with Fourcroy over Geoffroy's earlier appointment.

30. Faujas de St Fond, 1803–9.

31. BIF MS Flourens 2598/3 f. 32.

32. Previously discussed in Chapter III.

33. The following is based on Nussac, 1912 and 1936. Cuvier's wisdom in refusing subordinate positions such as pupilship at the

Ecole normale (see Chapter III) is emphasised by such comparisons as with the career of Latreille.

34. See Lee, 1833, reprinting a letter from Cuvier to Hermann of 1800 (p. 27): 'If we envy the elephants, it is not because they are better paid than we are, but because, while living on credit, as we do, they are not aware of it, and consequently are insensible to the pain it gives'. Things had been little better before. Geoffroy, writing to Cuvier to inform him of the *coup* of *fructidor*, 1797, thought it worthwhile to include the news 'on paye ici un peu'. (Dehérain, 1923, pp. 78–9).

35. Deleuze, 1823, pp. 102, 107–10.

36. Nussac, 1934, p. 3.

37. Haüy and Daubenton supported Geoffroy and Latreille, for example.

38. Deleuze, 1823, p. 133.

39. De Jussieu, 1808, p. 4.

40. Larévellière-Lépeaux, 1895, II, p. 93–94; I, p. 199. Their son seems to have used the spelling Leclerc and Leclerq indifferently, and was known to Audouin as Leclerc-Thouin; see Théodoridès, 1958–9.

41. Larévellière-Lépeaux, 1895, II, pp. 93–4; BIF MS Flourens 2598/3, f. 20.

42. *Ibid.*, I, p. 163.

43. Sarjeant & Delair (in press). It is worth noting that the term 'laboratory' as used by Cuvier denoted the preparation, dissection and mounting of specimens, rather than a place for the investigation by experimental means of natural laws.

44. Duvernoy, 1939; MNHN MS 85 (plates of drawings for the *Histoire naturelle des poissons*).

45. 'I got into Cuvier's *sanctum sanctorum* yesterday, and it is truly characteristic of the man. In every part it displays that extraordinary power of methodising which is the grand secret of the prodigious feats which he performs annually without appearing to give himself the least trouble, but before I introduce you to this study, I should tell you that there is first the Museum of natural history opposite the house, and admirably arranged by himself, then the anatomy Museum connected with his dwelling. In the latter is a library disposed in a suite of rooms, each containing works on one subject. There is one where there are all the works on ornithology, in another room all on ichthyology, in another osteology, in another law books, etc. etc. When he is engaged in such works as require continual reference to a variety of authors, he has a stove shifted into one of these rooms, in which everything on that subject is systematically arranged, so that in the same work, he often takes the round of many apartments, but the ordinary studio contains no bookshelves. It is a largish room, comfortably furnished, lighted from above, and furnished with eleven desks to stand to and two low tables, like a public office for so many clerks, but it is all for the one man, who multiplies himself as author, and admitting no-one into this room,

Notes to Chapter VIII

moves as he finds necessary . . . from one occupation to another. Each desk is furnished with a complete establishment of inkstand, pens etc. pins to pin MSS together the works immediately in reading, and the MS in hand, and on shelves behind all the MSS of the same work . . . The *collaborateurs* are not numerous, but always chosen well. They save him every mechanical labour, find references, etc., are rarely admitted to the study, receive orders and speak not.' Lyell, 1881, I, pp. 249-50, letter of 23 February, 1829.

46. Mathiot & Duvernoy, 1940, p. 8, letter of 12 April, 1817.

47. Lee, 1833, pp. 223-34, prints a letter from Cuvier to Mme Cuvier of 19 May 1811, on the day of his departure for Holland: ' . . . pour Georges il ne pensait encore qu'au malheur de ne plus avoir des bêtes tous les soirs, mais je te prie de lui en promettre, et même de lui en donner quelque fois de ma part en bois, en plomb, ou en toute autre matière solide, car il m'a très-bien fait remarquer ce matin, que des bêtes en gravure ne pouvaient pas se tenir debout. Ce pauvre enfant ne se doute pas combien il pourrait rencontrer chaque jour des bêtes qui se tiendraient debout.'

48. See Chapter V.

49. Of the nineteen *aides-naturalistes* listed in the 1935 commemorative volume of the *Archives du Muséum*, pp. 64 ff., five were related to other members of the Muséum's staff (Adolphe Brongniart, Jean Thouin, Valenciennes, L. P. de Jussieu, Oscar Leclerq); in addition Laurillard was a compatriot of Cuvier, and Rousseau had been 'discovered' by him. Crosland, 1975, uses the *aides-naturalistes* as examples of the professionalisation of scientific careers made possible by the Muséum.

50. One such reception of a provincial man of science is described in Théodoridès, 1967 b, pp. 5-6.

51. Appel, 1980.

52. This is the reason allegiances in the Muséum were, as we have seen in Chapter V, often so ill-defined and shifting: they were personal, not institutional, responding to pressures which did not always originate in the Muséum itself.

53. For this use of the 'institution' of a science I refer above all to Salomon-Bayet, 1975.

54. Daudin, 1926-7, I, p. 31.

55. They therefore cannot be seen as a simple and inevitable consequence of the increase in the number of known species during Cuvier's lifetime, described in Cailleux, 1953.

56. Daudin, 1926-7, I, p. 62; Foucault, 1970, p. 131; Valenciennes, 1833.

57. Flourens, 1856, I, p. 183.

58. Cuvier, 1803.

59. Deleuze, 1823, p. 97.

60. For the Parisian fashion for the diorama, see Benjamin, 1970, 1973; Cuvier's success in predicting the bone structure of the small fossil marsupial the *sarigue* before it had been removed from the

surrounding rock was the high point of this image-making process and is described in Cuvier, 1804 c.

61. Deleuze, 1823, p. 95.
62. 'Plutôt toléré qu'accordée', according to WHM MS 2500, f. 28, the original version of Geoffroy, 1838.
63. Daudin, 1926–7, I, pp. 62, 85, n. 1; Cuvier, 1795 b, pp. 394–6.
64. A fact carefully noted in even popular guide books to the collections: e.g. Anon (James de St Hilaire), an IX (1801), pp. 154, 169, 193.
65. Geoffroy, 1838; I. Geoffroy St Hilaire, 1847, pp. 40–44.
66. Forbes (ed.), van Marum, 1969, II, p. 367.
67. *Ibid.*, p. 368.
68. Fischer, 1802, I, p. 445; 'Cuvier erschien, und ein neues Licht gieng [sic] dieser Wissenschaft in Frankreich auf.'
69. *Ibid.*, p. 449.
70. Outram, 1980 a, pp. 3–5, examines this topic in more detail.
71. Examination of the sources cited in the *Recherches sur les ossemens fossiles*, for example, reveals the extent of the network of contacts with provincial *savants* on which Cuvier relied, and explain his eagerness to join the provincial scientific societies. Such relations are discussed in Outram 1980 a, pp. 2–3, and his correspondence with the *savant* Traullé of Amiens is possibly the prime example. More exalted contacts which Cuvier used to obtain specimens included the councillor of state and governor of Corsica, Miot de Mélito, Lacroix's brother-in-law: BIF MS Flourens 2598/3, f. 36.
72. For Cuvier's census see Théodoridès, 1969.
73. Fischer, 1802, I, p. 445: 'Seine Vorlesungen, welche im Ampitheater gehatten werden, sind immer so gefüllt, das selbst die Seitengange voll stehen'.
74. Deleuze, 1823, pp. 116–7, 126.
75. Flourens, 1856, I, p. 185.
76. Deleuze, 1823, pp. 116–17.
77. Bourdon, 1844, pp. 116–17; Moreau de la Sarthe, 1824, p. 356 and note; Moreau also points out that Cuvier owed his initial success to Fourcroy's enthusiastic recommendation of his lectures. They were often noted down by his pupils in the Muséum. Besides his own BIFC 3102, 'Cours de l'an XIII à l'an XIV', there exist notes taken by Brongniart in 1796–7 (MNHN, MS 2323), by Hyacinthe Bonnet in 1803–4 (WHM, MS 1317), and by Duméril, 1797, MNHN, MS 344. The complete series of lectures were, of course, printed as the *Leçons d'anatomie comparée*.
78. Laurent, 1977.
79. Cuvier, 1795 c.
80. Daudin, 1926–7, I, p. 91.
81. Letter of Frédéric Cuvier to Victor Cousin, 8 August 1830, Bibliothèque Victor Cousin, Sorbonne, Paris, condemning Cuvier's concentration on the dead animal, a view confirmed by Cuvier 1819–27, I, p. 91, '... ce n'est qu'en vivant parmi les cadavres qu'on

peut les [les animaux] reconnoître'.
82. *Décade philosophique*, 1794, an II, pp. 519-21, 'Notice succincte sur le Muséum d'Histoire naturelle'.
83. E.g. Anon, 1801 a, Anon, 1801 b.
84. Benjamin, 1973, p. 159: 'In the dream in which every epoch sees in images the epoch which is to succeed it, the latter appears coupled with elements of pre-history, that is to say of a classless society ... to give birth to the utopias which leave their traces in a thousand configurations of life, from permanent buildings to ephemeral fashions.' This 'utopic' ideal of the Muséum was endorsed by the professors themselves: at Daubenton's burial in its gardens in 1800, Fourcroy stated 'Ces jardins seront un Elisée dont l'ami de la Nature n'approchera qu'avec respect': Fourcroy, an VIII, p. 9; Cuvier, 1819-27, III, p. 436, calls the Muséum 'Le temple le plus grand et le plus beau qui ait été consacré à la nature'.
85. Cahn, 1962, pp. 186-93; Haug, 1932; Salvandy, 1827.
86. Cuvier and Lacepède, 1802; Cuvier, 1808.
87. Bastin, 1973.
88. Lefebvre, 1821.
89. Candolle, 1822, p. 174, 'Ce qui fait la base d'un jardin d'enseignement, c'est la publicité'; Deleuze, 1823, p. 128.
90. *Ibid.*, p. 3.
91. Hatin, 1866, p. 573.
92. De Jussieu, 1802-08; Deleuze, 1804, articles on Dombey and Michaux.
93. Cuvier, 1832; Dupuis, 1974, p. 6.
94. Confirmed by Hamy, 1908.

Notes to Chapter IX

1. This argument is developed at more length in Outram, 1980 b.
2. E.g. Jardin & Tudesq, 1973.
3. Boltanski, 1973, XIV, pp. 3-26.
4. E.g. Boissevain and Mitchell, 1973. More helpful is Boissevain, 1977.
5. Outram, 1980 a.
6. Daubenton's remark to Geoffroy, 'J'ai sur vous l'autorité d'un père', is the 'moment' of his acceptance as a client by the older man; Frankel, 1978, related the 'moments' in the relations of Biot and Laplace. I. Geoffroy St Hilaire, p. 47.
7. Letter of 1 February 1799, cited in Outram 1980 a, and printed in Viénot, 1932, pp. 114-15. Later letters between Cuvier and the muncipal authorities of Montbéliard also in Outram, 1980 a, and Goguel, 1864, p. 117.

Manuscript sources

History of the archive

Cuvier's papers passed to his family on his death. As his closest male relative, Frédéric Cuvier passed them to his son, also Frédéric, who on his own death in 1890 willed the papers for the most part to the Institut de France. A smaller portion passed to the Library of the Muséum. Comparison of Brianchon, 1876–7, with the catalogues cited below, makes it clear that some material, including the complete text of Cuvier's autobiography, truncated successively by Mme Cuvier and by Pierre Flourens, was forever lost in the intervening sixty years.

Major collections

Cuvier's papers are grouped in two main collections:
 1. Institut de France, Fonds Cuvier. A detailed inventory exists: H. Dehérain, *Catalogue des manuscrits du fonds Cuvier conservés à la Bibliothèque de l'Institut de France*, 2 fascs., Paris and Hendaye, 1908–22.
 2. Bibliothèque centrale du Muséum national d'histoire naturelle, Paris. There is no catalogue devoted specifically to the Cuvier papers, which are, however, mentioned in detail in A. Boinet, *Catalogue générale des manuscrits des Bibliothèques publiques de France: Paris, II: Muséum national d'histoire naturelle*, Paris, 1914; pp. 1–357; Y. Laissus, *Catalogue générale des manuscrits des bibliothèques publiques de France, LV: Paris: Bibliothèque centrale du Muséum national d'histoire naturelle: supplément*, Paris, 1964.

Other collections

 1. Archives de l'Académie des sciences, Paris: Dossier Cuvier – contains no documentary manuscript material.
 2. Archives nationales, Paris: contains documents relating to Cuvier's career in the history of education. Partially listed in Outram, 1974, and in Negrin, 1977.
 3. Archives de la Légion d'honneur, Paris: contains no manuscript material on Cuvier.

4. Bibliothèque de l'histoire du Protestantisme français, Paris: there is no printed catalogue to this library. A card index exists on the spot. Contains documents relating to Cuvier's career in the administration of the non-Catholic religions, mainly letters to Cuvier, but little material emanating from him. See Robert, 1961.

5. Wellcome Historical Medical Library, London: MS no. 1998, 'Papiers relatifs aux académies de l'Italie' (48 fols.). Autograph collection, nos. 68159, 69102: miscellaneous correspondence and papers.

6. Library of the Société d'emulation de Montbéliard and Bibliothèque municipale: now contain no manuscript material relating to Cuvier.

Single documents, including lecture notes on Cuvier's courses

1. Drawings of crabs,? 1790,? 1788: Bibliothèque muncipale, Le Havre. Noted in Petit & Théodoridès, 1961.

2. Diarium zoologicum I, 1786-7: Bibliothèque municipale, Hyères. MS 27. Noted in Petit & Théodoridès, 1961.

3. 'Instructions anthropologiques ... pour le voyage du *Géographie* et du *Naturaliste* aux terres Australes',? 1799: WHM, MS autograph 68159. Hervé, 1910, pp. 389-6.

4. Lecture notes on Cuvier's lectures on comparative anatomy, 7 messidor-7 fructidor an XI, by G. Poirier: Bibliothèque municipale, Rennes, MS 175, fols. 125-95.

5. MS of his treatise on the mistletoe (?), 26 vendémiaire IX (18 October 1799): Sotheby sale catalogue, 3-4 March 1969, pp. 74-5.

6. Fragments of *Leçons d'anatomie comparée*, fifteenth lesson: 'les organes de l'odorat et du goût', II, p. 628, 1800, 4 pp. Landesbibliothek Stuttgart, Cod. hist. 4.° 333. b. 41.

7. 'Abrégé des leçons de géologie faites au Collège de France en l'an XIII', 1805, 24 pp: Institut de France, MS 2378/6.

8. 'Projet d'un journal littéraire et scientifique digne de la nation française', 14 pp, 1807: with additions by Champagny, Minister of the Interior. *Maison Charavay, Bulletin d'autographes*, 126 è. année, no. 764, January 1979, no. 37812.

9. 'Questions de combustion'. 22 July 1809, 1 p: New York Historical Society, B. V. Vail collection, I, p. 33.

10. 'Cours de M. Cuvier sur la génération comparée dans les animaux, 1817': Bibliothèque centrale de la Faculté de médicine de Paris, MS 5160.

11. Notes for the *Histoire naturelle des poissons:* Bergerbliothek, Berne, MS hist. helv. xxiii. 463.

12. 'Proclamation des prix remportés et des sujets de prix proposés', 16 June 1828 (the competition of the Parisian *Lycées*): Fitzwilliam Museum, Cambridge, Perceval Collection, MS R. 4.

13. 'Rapport à l'Académie royale des sciences sur les collections rapportés récemment de la mer des Indes par M. Dussumier de

Bordeaux': Bibliothèque municipale, Bordeaux. Annales des sciences naturelles, XXI, 1830, pp. 458–70.

14. 'Extrait de deux lettres de Scarpa à Weber sur les nerfs etc., mai et juin aoust [sic] et septembre, 1831, des *Annales universelles de médicine, Milan*; British Museum (Natural History), London, Owen papers, 4 pp.

15. Autograph MS describing the essential attributes of a would-be scholar, 1 p., n.d. John Wilson Autograph Catalogue, 28, p. 5.

16. Plan by Cuvier of a dissection room for large animals in the Muséum, WHM, Autograph Collection.

17. Notes on Scheuzer, Bergerbiliothek Berne, MS hist. helv. xxiii. 463.

18. Sheet beginning 'La plante a son hymen, la plante a son amour', 1 p: B. Gagnebin, *MSS et autographes français: fondation M. Bodmer*, Coligny & Geneva, 1973, Catalogue I, p. 17 (Collection Stefan Zweig).

Cuvier's correspondence

Letters to Cuvier form the major part of Dehérain, 1908–22, and are also listed in Boinet, 1914, and Laissus, 1965. Letters from Cuvier are listed in Outram, 1980 a. Twenty further letters from Cuvier were recently discovered in an unlisted collection in the Dibner Library of the Smithsonian Institute, Washington DC and I am grateful to Toby Appel for informing me of this discovery.

Cuvier's library

Cuvier's books were sold on his death. Half of them passed to the Ecole Normale and half to the Muséum. The Ecole Normale possesses a manuscript copy of the original inventory of the books sold to it in 1832, of which the courtesy of M. J. Petitmengin, its librarian, permitted me to consult a microfilm copy. Those volumes which passed to the Muséum were absorbed into its general collections of the Bibliothèque Centrale and can now only be traced by systematic interrogation of its card index. All Cuvier's books are marked with a distinctive bookplate.

Bibliography

Note: Works in French were published in Paris, and those in English in London, unless otherwise indicated.

Publications by Cuvier

(Publications with Geoffroy as the major author are cited in the general bibliography.)

'Mémoire sur les cloportes terrestres', *Journal d'histoire naturelle*, II, 1792, pp. 18–31.

'Anatomie de la patelle commune *(Patella vulgata, Linn.)*', *Journal d'histoire naturelle*, II, 1792, pp. 81–95.

'Observations sur quelques Diptères', *Journal d'histoire naturelle* II, 1792, 253–8.

'Mémoire sur le larynx inférieur des oiseaux lu à la Société d'histoire naturelle', *Magasin Encyclopédique*, première année, II, 1795 a, pp. 350–58.

'Mémoire sur la structure interne et externe et sur les affinités des animaux auxquels on a donné le nom de vers: lu à la Société d'histoire naturelle le 21 floréal de l'an 3', *La décade philosophique* V, 1795 b, pp. 385–96.

'Discours prononcé par le Citoyen Cuvier à l'ouverture du cours d'anatomie comparée qu'il fait au Muséum d'histoire naturelle pour le citoyen Mertrud', *Magasin Encyclopédique*, première année, V, 1795, pp. 145–55.

(with Geoffroy St Hilaire), 'Lettre du Citoyen Geoffroy, professeur au Muséum d'histoire naturelle, et du Citoyen Cuvier, aux rédacteurs du Magasin Encyclopédique, sur le rhinocéros bicorne', *Magasin Encyclopédique*, I, 1795 a, pp. 326–28.

(with Geoffroy St Hilaire), 'Mémoire sur les rapports naturels du Tarsier, *(Didelphus macrotarsus*, Gm), lu à la Société d'histoire naturelle le 21 messidor, an 3', *Magasin Encyclopédique*, première année, III, 1795, pp. 147–54.

'Mémoire sur les espèces d'éléphants tant vivantes que fossiles, lu à la séance publique de l'Institut national le 15 germinal an IV', *Magasin Encyclopédique*, II, 1796, pp. 440–45. A first version of Cuvier, 1799 (see below).

Tableau élémentaire de l'histoire naturelle des animaux par Georges Cuvier de l'Institut national de France, professeur d'histoire naturelle à l'Ecole centrale du Panthéon, adjoint à la chaire d'anatomie comparée du Muséum d'histoire naturelle... membre de la Société des naturalistes de Paris, de la Société philomatique; de celles de médecine, des pharmaciens, de la Société d'Emulation de Rouen, etc., an VI.

'Mémoires sur les ossemens fossiles des quadrupèdes: extrait', *Journal de physique*, XLVII, an VI (1798), pp. 315–18; *Bulletin de la Société philomatique*, I, 1798, pp. 137–9.

'Mémoire sur les espèces d'éléphants vivantes et fossiles, lu le 1 pluviôse an IV', *Mémoires de l'Institut national des sciences et arts: sciences mathématiques et physiques*, II, fructidor an VII, pp. 1–22 (p. 22 puts the reading date as 'an V'.)

Leçons d'anatomie comparée de Georges Cuvier, recueillis et publiées sous ses yeux par C. Duméril. Tome I, contenant les organes du mouvement; Tome II, contenant les organes des sensations, 1800.

Rapport fait... au nom d'une commission de l'Institut national pour examiner s'il n'y auroit point quelque amélioration à faire au règlement qui concerne les séances publiques', 5 nivôse IX (1801 a).

'Extrait d'un ouvrage sur les espèces de quadrupèdes dont on a trouvé les ossemens dans l'intérieur de la terre, adressé aux savans et aux amateurs des sciences, par Georges Cuvier, membre de l'Institut, professeur au Collège de France, et à l'Ecole Centrale du Panthéon, etc., imprimé par ordre de la Classe des sciences mathématiques et physiques de l'Institut national du 26 brumaire an IX', *Magasin Encyclopédique*, VII, 1801 b, pp. 60–82; *Journal de physique*, LII, 1801, pp. 253–67.

Review of Lamarck, *Nouvelle système des animaux sans vertèbres*, *Magasin Encyclopédique*, VI, 1801 c, pp. 387–8.

(With Lacepède) *La ménagerie du Muséum d'histoire naturelle ou les animaux vivants peints d'après nature... avec une note descriptive et historique pour chaque animal*, 1801 d.

'Rapport sur le Galvanisme, fait à l'Institut national par le Citoyen Georges Cuvier', *Journal de physique*, LII, 1801 e, 318–21.

Cuvier, G. et al., *La ménagerie du Muséum national d'histoire naturelle, ou description et histoire des animaux qui y vivent ou qui y ont vécu*, an X (1801 f.).

'Sur l'établissement de la collection d'anatomie comparée du Muséum', *Annales du Muséum d'histoire naturelle*, II, 1803, 409–14.

'Description ostéologique du rhinocéros unicorne', *Annales du Muséum d'histoire naturelle*, III, 1804, pp. 32–52.

'Mémoire sur l'ibis des anciens égyptiens', *Annales du Muséum d'histoire naturelle*, IV, 1804, pp. 116–35.

'Mémoire sur le squelette presque entier d'un petit quadrupède du genre des sarigues, trouvé dans la pierre à plâtre des environs de Paris', *Annales du Muséum d'histoire naturelle*, V, 1804, pp. 277–92; *Journal de physique*, LXI, 1804, pp. 39–45; *Recherches sur*

les ossemens fossiles, III, 1812, tenth *mémoire*.
'Sur le mégalonix: animal de la famille des paresseux, mais de la taille de boeuf, dont les ossemens ont été découverts en Virginie en 1796', *Annales du Muséum d'histoire naturelle*, V, 1804, pp. 358–75; *Recherches sur les ossemens fossiles*, IV, 1812, seventh *mémoire*.
'Sur le mégatherium: autre animal de la famille des paresseux, mais de la taille du rhinocéros, dont un squelette fossile presque complet est conservé au cabinet royale d'histoire naturelle de Madrid', *Annales du Muséum d'histoire naturelle*, V, 1804, pp. 376–87: *Recherches sur les ossemens fossiles*, IV, 1812, eighth *mémoire*.
'Sur les ossemens fossiles trouvés en divers endroits de France et plus ou moins semblables à ceux du Paleothérium', *Annales du Muséum d'histoire naturelle*, VI, 1804, pp. 346–55.
Leçons d'anatomie comparée de Georges Cuvier, recueillies et publiées sous ses yeux par G. L. Duvernoy, etc., tome III, contenant la première partie des organes de la digestion; tome 4, contenant la suite des organes de la digestion, et ceux de la circulation, de la respiration et de la voix; tome V, contenant les organes de la génération, et ceux des sécrétions excrémentielles ou des excrétions, 1805.
(With Langlès, Delambre, Lamarck & Olivier), *Recherches asiatiques ou mémoires de la Société asiatique de Bengale*, an XIV (1805).
'Mémoire sur les éléphans vivans et fossiles', *Annales du Muséum d'histoire naturelle*, VIII, 1806, pp. 1–58, 93–155, 249–69; *Recherches sur les ossemens fossiles*, II, 1812, ninth *mémoire*.
'Sur le grand mastodonte, animal très voisin à l'éléphant, mais à mâchelières hérissées de gros tubercules, dont on trouvé les os en divers endroits des deux continents, et surtout près des bords de l'Ohio dans l'Amérique septentrionale, improprement nommé mammoth par les anglais et par les habitans des Etats-Unis', *Annales du Muséum d'histoire naturelle*, VIII, 1806, pp. 270–312; *Recherches sur les ossemens fossiles*, II, 1812, tenth *mémoire*.
'Eloge de F. Péron, lu à la classe des sciences physiques et mathématiques le 9 juillet, 1806', in F. Péron & L. Freycinet, *Voyage de découverte aux terres Australes*, second ed., 1824, 4 vols, L, pp. 1–18.
Review of C. Duméril, *Traîte élémentaire*, second edition, *Moniteur universelle*, 1806, p. 1408.
(With Haüy & Lelièvre), 'Rapport de l'Institut national (classe des sciences physiques et mathématiques), sur l'ouvrage de M. André, ayant pour titre: Théorie de la surface actuelle de la terre', *Journal des mines*, XXI, 1807, pp. 413–30; *Mémoires de l'Institut*, 1807, pp. 128–45.
'De la part faite aux sciences et aux lettres dans l'instruction publique', *Moniteur universelle*, 3 November 1807, pp. 1186–8; also printed in *Revue internationale de l'enseignement*, X, 1885, pp. 330-35.
Collection des mamifères du Muséum d'histoire naturelle classé

suivant la méthode de M. Cuvier . . . dessinés d'après nature par Huet fils, 1808 a.
(With Alexandre Brongniart), 'Essai sur la géographie minéralogique des environs de Paris', *Journal des mines*, XXIII, 1808 b, pp. 421–58; *Recherches sur les ossemens fossiles*, I, 1812, third paper.
'Rapport fait à l'Institut sur un mémoire de MM Gall et Spurzheim, relatif à l'anatomie du cerveau', *Annales du Muséum d'histoire naturelle*, XI, 1808 c, pp. 329–76; *Mémoires de l'Institut*, 1809 (Hist.), pp. 109–60. See also general bibliography, s.v. Tenon.
(With Jacques Delille), *Les trois règnes de la nature . . . avec des notes de M. Cuvier, de l'Institut, et autres savants*, 2 vols, The Hague, Amsterdam, Rotterdam, 1809.
'Rapport historique sur les progrès des sciences naturelles, depuis 1789 et sur leur état actuel, presenté à Sa Majesté l'Empéreur et Roi, en son Conseil d'Etat le 6 février 1808, par la classe des sciences physiques et mathématiques de l'Institut, conformément à l'arrêté du gouvernement du 13 ventôse an X, redigée par M. Cuvier', 1810, other editions in 1827, 1828.
(With Coiffier & de Balbe) [sic], 'Rapport sur les établissemens d'instruction publique des départemens au delà des Alpes: fait en 1809 et 1810 par une commission extraordinaire composée de MM Cuvier, de Coiffier et de Balbe', 1810.
'Aristote', *Biographie universelle*, ed. Michaud, II, 1811, pp. 456–64; II, 1843, pp. 218–24.
(With Noël), *Rapport sur l'instruction publique dans les nouveaux départments de la Basse Allemagne, fait en exécution du décret impérial du 13 décembre 1810, par MM Cuvier et Noël*, 1811.
'Sur un nouveau rapprochement à établir entre les classes qui composent le règne animal', *Annales du Muséum d'histoire naturelle*, XIX, 1812 a, pp. 73–84.
'Sur la composition de la tête osseuse dans les animaux vertèbrés', *Annales du Muséum d'histoire naturelle*, XIX, 1812 b, pp. 123–8.
Recherches sur les ossemens fossiles des quadrupèdes où l'on rétablit les caractères de plusieurs espèces d'animaux que les révolutions du globe paroissent avoir détruites, 4 vols, 1812 c; 4 vols, 1821–4; 7 vols, 1825.
'Buffon', *Biographie universelle*, ed. Michaud, VI, 1812, pp. 234–42; VI, 1843, pp. 117–21.
(Ed. R. Jameson) *Essay on the theory of the earth translated from the French of M. Cuvier by R. Kerr, F.R.S. . . . with mineralogical notes and an account of Cuvier's geological discoveries by Prof. Jameson*, Edinburgh, 1813.
'Prospectus', for the *Dictionnaire des sciences naturelles*, 61 vols, 1816–45; I, pp. v–xvi, 1816.
'Animal', *Dictionnaire des sciences naturelles*, II, 1816, pp. 158–74.
'Réflexions sur la marche actuelle des sciences et leurs rapports avec la société, lues dans la première séance annuelle des quatre

Académies, le 24 avril, 1816', *Eloges historiques*, I, 1819–27, pp. 1–33.

Le règne animal distribué d'après son organisation pour servir de base à l'histoire naturelle des animaux, et d'introduction à l'anatomie comparée. 4 vols, 1817; tome I, contenant l'introduction, les mammifères et les oiseaux; tome 2, contenant les reptiles, les poissons, les molluscs, et les Annelides; tome 4, contenant les tables et les planches, second edition, 3 vols, 1829–30. Cuvier's own copy of edition I is located in the D. M. S. Watson Library, University College, London.

Mémoire pour servir à l'histoire et l'anatomie des mollusques, 1817.

'Discours de réception à l'Académie française, 27 August, 1818', *Eloges historiques*, II, pp. 443–67.

Recueil des éloges historiques, 3 vols, Paris and Strasbourg, 1819–27.

'Discours relatif à l'allocation de 50,000 fr. pour encouragements à l'instruction primaire de M le Baron Cuvier, commissaire du Roi. Chambre des députés, séance du 12 juin, 1821'. See also Mavidal & Laurent, second series, XXXII, p. 129.

'Extrait d'un rapport sur l'état de l'histoire naturelle et sur ses acroissements depuis le retour de la paix maritime, lu à la séance annuelle des quatre Académies, le 24 avril, 1824', *Eloges historiques* III, pp. 449–78.

'Nature', *Dictionnaire des sciences naturelles*, XXXIV, 1825, pp. 261–9.

'Vicq d'Azyr', *Biographie universelle*, ed. Michaud, XLVIII, 1827, pp. 374–8.

'Wallerius', *Biographie universelle*, ed. Michaud, L, 1827, pp. 127–9.

(With Valenciennes) *Histoire naturelle des poissons*, vols I–X, 1828–33.

Histoire des progrès des sciences naturelles depuis 1789 jusqu'à ce jour par M. le Baron Cuvier, 4 vols, 1828. Volume I is based on the *Rapport sur les progrès des sciences* of 1810 (qv) The rest contain Cuvier's annual reports on the year's work in science presented to the Academy of Sciences, 1809–27. A fifth, posthumous volume published in 1834, brought the reports up to 1831.

'Avertissement du Nouvelles Annales du Muséum d'histoire naturelle', *Nouvelles Annales du Muséum d'histoire naturelle*, I, 1832, pp. i–iv.

Ed. Audouin, Blanchard, Deshayes, Alcide d'Orbigny, Doyère, Dugès, Duvernoy, Laurillard, Milne Edwards, Roulin et Valenciennes, *Règne animal . . . par une réunion des disciples de Cuvier*, 16 vols, 1836–49.

Histoire des sciences naturelles depuis leur origine jusqu'à nos jours, commencé au Collège de France par Georges Cuvier, completée par T. Magdelaine de St Agy, 5 vols, 1841–5.

Bibliography of printed works by Cuvier

Duvernoy, G. L., 1833, pp. 158–72: a chonological listing, with brief interpretative comments attached to some of the papers. Incomplete, but includes all major works.

Royal Society of London, *Catalogue of Scientific Papers, 1800–63*: II, London, 1868, pp. 114–22: contains 212 items, with alternative printings in many cases. The nearest approach to a definitive listing of the papers.

Bibliothèque nationale: *Catalogue générale des livres imprimés de la Bibliothèque nationale: auteurs* XXXIV, Paris, 1908, cols. 983–1000: lacks copies of early editions of many works.

Daudin, H., II, 1926, pp. 285–93: a chronological listing of high accuracy, concentrated on the taxonomic works of Cuvier.

British Museum, London, *General Catalogue of Printed Books: photolithic edition to 1955*, XLVII, London, 1966, cols. 389–401.

The National Union Catalogue: pre-1856 imprints: a cumulative author list presenting Library of Congress printed cards, and titles reported by other American libraries, London and Chicago, 1971, CXXX, pp. 423–31.

Coleman, 1964, pp. 192–6, offers a summary catalogue of the most important articles and books but does not aim to be a complete listing.

Reviews of Cuvier's works: bibliography and sources

Fischer, G. *Das Nationalmuseum der Naturgeschichte zu Paris, von seinen ersten ursprunge bis zu seinem jetzigen Glanze*, 2 vols., Frankfurt-am-Main, 1802, I, pp. 450–54.

Royal Society of London (ed.), *Catalogue of Scientific Papers, 1800–63*, II, London, 1868, pp. 114–22.

Houghton, W. E. (ed.), *The Wellesley Index to Victorian Periodicals 1824–1900*, 3 vols., Toronto, 1966–79.

Iconography

Bultingaire, L., 'L'iconographie de Cuvier', *Archives du Muséum national d'histoire naturelle*, IX, 1932, pp. 1–12.

Lane, W. C. & Brown, N. E. (eds.), *Library of Congress: ALA Portrait Index: index to portraits contained in printed books and periodicals*, Washington, 1906, p. 376.

Burgess, E., (Ed.), *Portraits of Doctors and Scientists in the Wellcome Institute of the History of Medicine: a Catalogue*, London, 1973, pp. 89–90, nos 742.1–742.21.

General bibliography

Abrams, P., 'Rites de passage: the conflict of generations in industrial society', *Journal of Contemporary History*, V, 1970, pp. 175–90.

Abrantès, Duchesse d', (Laure Permon, Maréchale Junot) *Histoire des salons de Paris: tableaux et portraits du grande monde sous Louis XVI, le Directoire, le Consulat et l'Empire, la Restauration et le règne de Louis Philippe* 6 vols, Brussels, 1837–8.

Académie des sciences, *Procès-verbaux des séances de l'Académie des sciences tenues depuis la fondation de l'Institut jusqu'au mois d'août 1835*, 10 vols, Hendaye, 1910–22.

Agulhon, M., *Le cercle dans la France bourgeoise, 1810–1848: étude d'une mutation de sociabilité*, Cahiers des Annales, XXXVI, 1977.
'Vers une histoire des associations', *Esprit*, June 1978, pp. 13–18.

Ahnne, L., 'Notice sur les autographes offerts par Mme Alfred Bovet à la Société d'Emulation', *MSEM*, XXXIII, 1906, pp. 11–26.

Albury, W. R., 'Physiological explanation in Magendie's "Manifesto" of 1809', *Bulletin of the History of Medicine*, XLVIII, 1977, pp. 90–99. 'Experiment and explanation in the physiology of Bichat and Magendie', *Studies in the History of Biology*, I, 1977, pp. 47–132.

Alibert, J. L., 'Quelques réflexions sur la valeur des systèmes dans l'étude des sciences', *Magasin encyclopédique*, XVI, 1797, pp. 460–72.

Alphonse, Baron d', *Aperçu sur la Hollande*, 's Gravenhage, 1900. (First printed 1813.)

Anderson, L., 'Charles Bonnet's taxonomy and the chain of being', *Journal of the History of Ideas*, XXXVII, 1976, pp. 45–58.

André, A., *Mme André-Walther, 1807–1886*, 1896.

Annales des sciences d'observation, 4 vols, 1829–30, ed. F. Raspail & J. Saigey.

Anon., *Tableau des membres de la Société des amis des noirs, année 1789*, 1789.

Anon., *Catalogue des plantes du jardin de l'Académie de Rouen*. Rouen, 1790.

Anon., *Tableau des leçons publiques qui se donneraient à l'Université Caroline de Stouttgard depuis Pâques 1791 jusqu'à Pâques 1792*, Stuttgart, 1791.

Anon., *Précis des causes de L'insurrection du département du Calvados et de la ville de Caen en particulier*, Caen, 1794.

Anon., (Jaume de St Hilaire), *Notice des principaux objets d'histoire naturelle conservés dans les galéries du Muséum du jardin des plantes de Paris, à l'usage des personnes qui les visitent: on y a joint quelques réflexions sur la vie et les ouvrages du Comte de Buffon*, 1801 a.

Anon., *Notice des animaux vivants actuellement à la ménagerie du Muséum d'histoire naturelle, et une description historique sur la manière de vivre et les habitudes de chacun d'eux: avec la portrait de la Lionne allaitant ses lionceaux*, 1801 b.

Anon., review of Cuvier, G., *Leçons d'anatomie comparée*, vols. 1 and 2, *Annals of Medicine*, VI, 1802, pp. 223–53.

Anon., *Dr Galls Darstellung des Gehirns als Organ der Seelenfähigkeiten und Gemuthseigenschaften nebst der Kunst das Innere das Menschen aus dem Aeussern seines Schaedels zu Erkennen. Ein schrieben Villers an Cuvier, uberstezt mit vielen Bemerkungen*, Vienna and Leipzig, 1803.

Anon., 'Réflexions sur l'état présent de la république des lettres', *Archives littéraires de l'Europe*, IX, 1806, pp. 149–59.

Anon., *Description de tout ce qu'on voit de remarquable tant à la ménagerie que dans la vallée suisse et au cabinet d'histoire naturelle, contenant la vie et moeurs des animaux féroces qui y sont renfermés*, 1807.

Anon., 'Review of Géographie minéralogique des environs de Paris', *Edinburgh Review*, XX, 1812, pp. 369–89.

Anon., *Dictionnaire des protées modernes, ou biographie des personnages vivans qui ont figuré dans la révolution français, depuis le 14 juillet 1789, jusques et compris 1815, par leurs actions, leurs écrits ou leur conduite, par un homme retiré du monde*, 1815 a.

Anon., (A. Emory), *Dictionnaire des girouettes*, 1815 b, second edition, 1831.

Anon., 'Egyptian antiquities', *Quarterly Review*, XLIII, May–October 1830, pp. 111–55.

Anon., 'Charles Bracq ou Brack', *Archives historiques et littéraires du Nord de la France et du Midi de la Belgique*, n.s., VI, 1847, pp. 223–6.

Anthony, R., 'A propos de la taxinomie des Pangolins: rectification du *Règne Animal* de Georges Cuvier', *Bulletin du Muséum national d'histoire naturelle*, XXV, 1919, pp. 429–31.

Anthony, R., 'Cuvier et la chaire d'anatomie comparée du Muséum national d'histoire naturelle', *Archives du Muséum national d'histoire naturelle*, IX, 1932, pp. 21–31.

Appel, T. A., *The Cuvier–Geoffroy Debate and the Structure of Nineteenth–century French Zoology*, University of Princeton PhD., thesis, 1975.

— 'Henri de Blainville and the animal series: a nineteenth century chain of being', *Journal of the History of Biology*, XIII, 1980, pp. 291–320.

Archives du Muséum, sixth series, XII, 1935, (volume commemorating the foundation of the Jardin du roi, 1635).

Ardouin, P., *Georges Cuvier, promoteur de l'idée évolutionniste et créateur de la biologie moderne*, 1970.

Arnaud, E., *Répertoire de généalogie français imprimée*, I, 1978.

Arnault, A. V., *Souvenirs d'un sexagénaire*, 4 vols, 1833.

Artz, F., *France under the Bourbon Restoration*, New Haven, 1931.

Aucoc, L., *L'Institut de France: lois, statuts et règlements*, 1889.

Aulard, F. A., *L'éloquence parlementaire pendant la révolution française*, 3 vols, 1882–6.

— 'Les adhésions aux Bourbons en 1814', *La Révolution Française*, XVIII, 1890, pp. 367–75.

— *Napoléon et le monopole universitaire: origines et fonctionnement de l'Université impériale*, 1911.
Autenrieth, J. H. F., *Handbach der Empirischen menschlichen physiologie zum Gebrauche seiner vorlesungen*. 3 vols, Tübingen, 1801–2.
Baer, J. G., 'Un ms inédit de Louis Agassiz sur Cuvier', *Muséum neuchâtelois*, third series, II, 1974, pp. 39–45.
Bailey, R. M., 'The authorship of names proposed in Cuvier and Valenciennes, Histoire naturelle des poissons', *Copeia*, III, 1951, pp. 249–51.
Balan, B., 'Premières recherches sur l'origine et la formation du concept de l'économie animale', *Revue d'histoire des sciences*, XXVIII, 1975, pp. 289–326.
— 'Organisation, organisme, économie et milieu chez Henri Ducrotay de Blainville', *Revue d'histoire des sciences*, XXXII, 1979, pp. 73–96.
Baldenspurger, F., *Le mouvement des idées dans l'émigration française*, 2 vols, 1924.
Bapst, G., 'Histoire d'un cabinet minéralogique: le cabinet d'histoire naturelle des Princes du Condé', *Revue des deux mondes*, II, 1892, pp. 437–49.
Barber, G., 'Treuttel & Würtz: some aspects of the importation of books from France, c. 1825', *The Library*, fifth series, XXIII, 1969, pp. 118–44.
Barthélemy St Hilaire, J., *M. Victor Cousin, sa vie et sa correspondence*, 3 vols, 1895. A letter from Cuvier at I, p. 113.
Bassan, F., *La famille Pastoret d'après leur correspondence, 1788 à 1856*, 1969.
Bastin, J., 'A further note on the origins of the Zoological Society of London', *Journal of the Society for the Bibliography of Natural History*, VI, 1973, pp. 236–41.
Batz, A. F., *Description de l'Académie Caroline de Stouttgard*, Stuttgart, 1784.
Beach, H. W., *Charles X of France: his life and times*, Boulder, Colorado, 1971.
Beaujour, S., *Essai sur l'histoire de l'église reformée de Caen*, Caen, 1877.
Beaurepaire, C. de., 'Georges Cuvier, Secretaire greffier de la commune du Bec-aux-Cauchois', *Précis de l'Académie de Rouen*, LXVIII, 1866, pp. 305–22.
Becker, M., 'Le style de Cuvier', *MSEM* LXVII, 1970, pp. 7–26.
Ben-David, J., *The Scientist's Role in Society: a Comparative Study*, Englewood Cliffs, 1971.
Bénichou, P., *Le sacre de l'écrivain, 1750–1830*, 1973.
Benjamin, W., 'Paris, capital of the nineteenth century', *Dissent*, XXI, pp. 439–47, trans. S. Ruta, 1970, and in *Charles Baudelaire: a Lyric Poet in the Era of High Capitalism*, trans. Q. Hoare, 1973, pp. 155–76.

Bernardy, F. de., *The Princes of Monaco: the Remarkable History of the Grimaldi*, 1961.
Bertaut, B., *La vie à Paris sous le premier Empire*, 1944.
Bertier de Sauvigny, G. de, *La Restauration*, 1955.
Bertrand, A. J. F., *Lettres sur les révolutions du globe*, 1824.
Bichat, X., *Traîté d'anatomie descriptive*, 5 vols, an X–an XII (1801–3).
— *Recherches physiologiques sur la vie et la mort*, fifth edition, ed. F. Magendie, 1829.
Bignan, A., *Epitre à Cuvier: prix de l'Académie français*, 27 août 1835.
Biot, J. B., *Essai sur l'histoire générale des sciences pendant la révolution française*, 1803.
— 'Sur le charlatanisme', *Mélanges scientifiques et littéraires*, 3 vols, 1858, 69–85. First published in 1808.
— 'De l'influence des idées exactes dans les ouvrages littéraires', *ibid.*, II, pp. 1–19. First published in 1809.
— 'Sur l'esprit de système', *ibid*, II, pp. 109–16. First published in 1809.
Blainville, H. M. Ducrotay de, 'Prodrome d'une nouvelle distribution systématique du règne animale', *Journal de physique*, LXXXIII, 1816, pp. 244–67.
— *Considérations générales sur les animaux et leur classification*, 1840.
— *Histoire des sciences de l'organisation et de leurs progrès comme base de la philosphie*, 3 vols, 1845.
— *Cuvier et Geoffroy St Hilaire: biographies scientifiques*, 1890.
Blumenbach, J. F., *Handbuch der Naturgeschichte*, 2 vols, Göttingen, 1779–80.
— *Manuel d'histoire naturelle, traduit de l'Allemand ... par Soulange Artaud*, an XI (1803), Paris and Metz.
— *A short system of comparative anatomy, translated from the German ... by William Lawrence ... with numerous additional notes and an introductory view of the classification of animals by the translator*, 1807. The notes are taken from the *Leçons d'anatomie comparée* of Cuvier.
Boas, G., *The Cult of Childhood*, 1966.
Boinet, A., *Catalogue générale des mss des bibliothèque publiques de France, Paris: II: Muséum national d'histoire naturelle*, 1914.
Boissevain, J., *Friends of Friends: Networks, Manipulators and Coalitions*, 1977.
Boissevain, J. and Mitchell, J. G., *Network Analysis: Studies in Human Interaction*, The Hague, 1973.
Boltanski, L. & Maldidier, P. 'Carrière scientifique, morale scientifique et vulgarisation', *Social Science Information*, IX, 1970, pp. 99–118.
Boltanski, L., 'L'espace positionnelle: multiplicité de positions institutionelles et habitus de classe', *Revue français de sociologie*, XIV, 1973, pp. 3–26.
Bonaparte, C. L. J. L., Principe di Musignano, *Sulla seconda edizione*

del Regno animale del Barone Cuvier: osservazioni, Bologna, 1830.
Bonstetten, J., *Recherches sur la nature et les lois de l'imagination*, 2 vols, Geneva, 1807.
Boudard, R., *L'organisation de l'Université et de l'enseignement secondaire dans l'Académie impériale de Gênes entre 1805 et 1815*, Paris and The Hague, 1962.
Boule, G. M., 'Georges Cuvier, fondateur de la paléontologie', *Archives du Muséum*, sixth series, VII–IX, 1931-2, pp. 33–46.
Bourdier, F., 'Geoffroy St Hilaire vs Cuvier: the campaign for paleontological evolution, 1825–1838', in C. J. Schneer (ed.) *Towards a History of Geology*, Cambridge, Mass., 1969, pp. 36–61.
— 'Cuvier, Georges', *Dictionary of scientific biography*, ed. C. C. Gillispie, III, New York, 1971, pp. 521–8.
Bourdieu, P., 'Le marché des biens symboliques', *L'année sociologique*, third series, XXII, 1972, pp. 49–126.
Bourdon, Isidore, *Illustres médecins et naturalistes*, 1844, Cuvier, pp. 1–146.
Bourgeaud, C., *L'Académie de Calvin dans l'Université de Napoléon*, Geneva, 1909.
Bouteiller, M., 'La Société des Observateurs de l'homme, ancêtre de la Société d'Anthropologie de Paris', *Bulletins de la Société d'anthropologie de Paris*, tenth series, 7 (1956), 448–65.
Bowler, P. J., *Fossils and Progress: Paleontology and the Idea of Progressive Evolution in the Nineteenth Century*, New York, 1976.
Boyer, F., 'Les conquêtes scientifiques de la Convention', *Revue d'histoire moderne et contemporaine*, XVIII, 1971, pp. 354–74.
— 'Le Muséum d'histoire naturelle à Paris et l'Europe des sciences sous la Convention', *Revue d'histoire des sciences*, XXVI, 1973, pp. 251–7.
Brancas–Lauraguais, Duc de, *Lettres aux Citoyens Lebreton et Cuvier de l'Institut National à l'occasion de l'éloge du Citoyen Darcet*, an X (1800).
Brandt, A., 'Le docteur Curie et le St Simonisme à Mulhouse', *Bulletin de la Société industrielle de Mulhouse*, CIV, 1938, pp. 398–421.
Bravard, A., ... l'Abbé Croiset et Jobert aîné, *Recherches sur les ossemens fossiles du départment du Pûy de Dome ... ouvrage dédié à M. le Baron Cuvier*, 1826.
Brianchon, M., 'La jeunesse de Cuvier', *Société nationale havraise d'études diverses* XLIII–XLIV, 1876-7, pp. 225–64. The promised further studies on Ficquainville and Stuttgart did not appear.
Brifaut, C., *Souvenirs d'un académicien sur la révolution, le premier empire et la Restauration*, 2 vols, n.d. (1921).
Brongersma, L. D., 'Some notes on Bravard, Croiset and Jobert, *Recherches sur les ossemens fossiles de Département du Pûy de Dome*', *Journal of the Society for the Bibliography of Natural History*, I, 1936–43, pp. 123–8.
Brongniart, Adolphe, 'Notice historique sur Antoine-Laurent de Jussieu', *Annales des sciences naturelles*, second series, Botanique,

VII, 1837, pp. 5–24.

Brown, A. W., Chinard, G, et al., *Jacquemont*, 1959.

Brown, A. W., 'Some political and scientific attitudes to literature and the arts in the years following the French Revolution', *Forum for Modern Language Studies*, II, 1966, pp. 230–52.

Brown, P. R. L., 'The rise and function of the holy man'., *Journal of Roman Studies*, LXI, 1971, pp. 80–101.

Brunschwig, H., *Société et romantisme en Prusse au dix-huitième siècle: la crise de l'état prussien ... et la genèse de la mentalité romantique*, 1973.

Bryant, D., 'Revolution and introspection: the appearance of the private diary in France', *European Studies Review*, VIII, 1978, pp. 259–72.

Buckland, W., *Vindiciae Geologicae: or the connexion of geology with religion explained in an inaugural lecture delivered before the University of Oxford, May 15, 1819*, Oxford, 1820.

Buffon, G. L. L. Comte de, 'De la manière d'étudier et de traîter l'histoire naturelle', *Oeuvres philosophiques de Buffon*, ed. J. Piveteau, 1954, pp. 7–26.

Bugg, W., *Scriptural geology, or geological phenomena consistent only with the literal interpretation of the sacred scriptures, upon the subjects of the creation and deluge, in answer to an Essay upon the theory of the earth, by M. Cuvier ... and to Professor Buckland's theory of the caves, as delineated in his Reliquiae Diluvianae*, 2 vols, 1826–7.

Bultingaire, L., 'L'iconographie de Cuvier', *Archives du Muséum national d'histoire naturelle*, IX, 1932, pp. 1-12.

Burckhardt, R. W. jr., 'Lamarck, evolution and the politics of science', *Journal of the History of Biology*, III, 1970, pp. 275–98.

Burckhardt, R. W., jr., *The Spirit of System: Lamarck and Evolutionary Biology*, Cambridge, Mass., 1977.

Burgess, R., *Portraits of Doctors and Scientists in the Wellcome Institute of the History of Medicine*, 1973.

Butts, R. E., 'Hypothesis and explanation in Kant's philosophy of science', *Archiv für Geschichte der Philosophie*, XLIII, 1961, pp. 153–70.

Bynum, W. F., 'The great chain of being after forty years: an appraisal', *History of Science*, XIII, 1975, pp. 1–28.

Cahn, T., *La vie et l'oeuvre d'Etienne Geoffroy St Hilaire*, 1962.

Cailleux, E., 'Progression du nombre d'espèces de plantes décrites de 1500 à nos jours', *Revue d'histoire des sciences*, V, 1953, pp. 42–9.

Cain, A. J., 'Function and taxonomic importance', in *Function and Taxonomic importance*, Systematics Association Publication 3, 1959, pp. 5–19.

Callot, E., 'Un discours de Dominique Villars sur l'histoire naturelle: 1 frimaire V', *Revue d'histoire des sciences*, XX, 1967, pp. 281–8.

Camper, A., 'Du rhinocéros à deux cornes', *Oeuvres*, 3 vols, Paris & Bordeaux, an XI (1803), I, pp. 197–290.

— *Observations anatomiques sur la structure intérieure et la squelette de plusieurs espèces de cétacés . . . avec des notes de M. G. Cuvier,* 1820.
Canat, R., *Une forme de mal de siècle: du sentiment de la solitude morale chez les Romantiques et les Parnassiens,* 1904.
Candolle, A. P. de, *Théorie élémentaire de la botanique ou exposition des principes de la classification naturelle et de l'art de décrire et d'étudier les végétaux,* second edition, 1819.
— 'Jardin botanique', *Dictionnaire des sciences naturelles,* XXIV, 1822, pp. 165–81.
— 'Mort de Georges Cuvier', *Bibliothèque universelle des sciences, belles-lettres et arts,* CX, 1832, I, pp. 442–8.
— *Mémoires et souvenirs . . . publiées par son fils,* Geneva, 1862.
Cap, P. A., *Le Muséum d'histoire naturelle,* 1854.
Capefigue, J. B. H. R., *Histoire de la Restauration et des causes qui ont amené la chute de la branche aînée des Bourbons,* 2 vols, 1837.
Carozzi, A. V., 'Une nouvelle interprétation du soi-disant catastrophisme de Cuvier', *Archives des sciences,* XXIV, 1971, Geneva, pp. 367–77.
Cartailhac, E., 'Georges Cuvier et l'ancienneté de l'homme: histoire de l'anthropologie préhistorique', *Matériaux pour l'histoire primitive et naturelle de l'homme,* XVIII, 1884, pp. 27–35.
Caumont, M. de, 'Sur M. le Conte d'Héricy', *Annuaire des cinq départements de l'ancienne Normandie,* XV, 1849, pp. 536–8.
Chaine, J., 'La grande époque de l'anatomie comparée', *Scientia,* L, 1931, pp. 365–74.
Chalmers, T., 'Remarks on Cuvier's *Theory of the earth*', *Works,* Glasgow, 1836–42, XII, pp. 347–72.
Charléty, S., *La restauration, 1815–1830,* 1921.
Chateaubriand, F. R. de, *Génie du christianisme ou beautés de la réligion chrétienne,* 5 vols., 1802. References to this work in the text are to chapter and section and not to page, because of the great variety of editions which may be accessible.
Clark, T. N. & Clark, P. D., 'Le patron et son cercle: clé de l'Université français', *Revue française de sociologie,* XIII, 1971, pp. 19–39.
Cobb, R., 'La campagne pour l'envoi de l'armée révolutionnaire dans la Seine-Inférieure, septembre 1793–frimaire an II', *Annales de Normandie,* II, 1952, pp. 243–62.
— *The Police and the People: French Popular Protest, 1789–1820,* 1972.
Cohen, I. B., 'The eighteenth century origins of the concept of scientific revolution', *Journal of the History of Ideas,* XXXVII, 1976, pp. 257–88.
Coleman, W., 'Georges Cuvier, biological variation and the fixity of species', *Archives internationales d'histoire des sciences,* XV, 1962, pp. 315–31.
— 'Abraham Gottlob Werner vu par Alexandre von Humboldt avec

des notes de Georges Cuvier', *Sudhoffs Archiv*, LVII, 1963, pp. 465-78.
— *Georges Cuvier, Zoologist: a Study in the History of Evolution Theory*, Cambridge, Mass., 1964.
— 'Les organismes marins et l'anatomie comparée dite expérimentale: l' oeuvre de Georges Cuvier', *Vie et milieu*, supplementary volume XIX, 1965, pp. 225-38.
— *Biology in the Nineteenth Century: Problems of Form, Function and Transformation*, New York, 1971.
Cormenin, L. M., *Le livre des orateurs*, 1842 (twelfth edition), Cuvier, p. 142 ff.
Corsi, P., 'The importance of French transformist ideas for the second volume of Lyell's *Principles of Geology*', *British Journal for the History of Science*, II, 1978, pp. 221-44.
Cottin, P. (ed.), *Le journal de Mme Moitte*, 1932.
Coulmann, J. J., *Reminiscences*, 3 vols, 1862-9.
Courrier, R., 'Georges Cuvier, 1769-1832': certains aspects de sa carrière', *Notices et discours: Institut de France: Académie des sciences*, V, 1963-72, pp. 641-61.
Courtaux, T., *Histoire généalogique de la maison de Touchet*, 1911.
Courtealt, P., *Les origines du lycée de Bordeaux: le lycée de l'an XI (1802-1809)*, Bordeaux, 1905.
Courtès, G., 'Georges Cuvier ou l'origine de la négation', *Revue d'histoire des sciences*, XXIII, 1970, pp. 8-34.
Cousin, V., trans. Horner, L., *On the State of Education in Holland, as regards Schools for the Working Class and for the Poor*, 1838. Appendix D, p. 257 ff, contains a translation of Cuvier & Noël, 1810, which does not appear in Cousin's *De l'instruction publique en Hollande*, 1837.
Coveney, P. J., *The Image of Childhood*, 1967.
Cowan, C. F., 'Cuvier's *Règne animal*, first edition', *Journal of the Society for the Bibliography of Natural History*, V, 1968-71, p. 219.
— 'Notes on Griffith's *Animal Kingdom of Cuvier*, 1834-5', *ibid.*, V, 1968-71, pp. 137-40.
— 'On Guérin's *Iconographie*: particularly the insects', *ibid*, VI, 1971, pp. 18-29.
Cramer, G. & Hermehnle, H. (eds.), *Register zu den Matrikeln der Universität Tübingen, 1477-1817*, 4 vols, Stuttgart, 1906-53.
Crosland, M. P., *The Society of Arcueil: a View of French Science at the Time of Napoleon I*, 1967.
— 'Development of a professional career in science in France', *Minerva*, XIII, 1975, pp. 38-57.
Cucuel, G., 'Le pays de Montbéliard vu par les voyageurs du dix-huitième siècle', *MSEM*, XLIII, 1914, pp. 139-62.
Cuvier, C., 'Souvenirs relatifs à Georges Cuvier', *MSEM*, XIII, 1881, pp. 142-9.
Daget, J., 'Les poissons dans l'edition allemande de *Règne animal de*

Cuvier', *Bulletin du Muséum national d'histoire naturelle*, second series, XXXIV, 1967–8, pp. 1056–9.

Dagonet, F., *Le catalogue de la vie: étude méthodologique sur le taxinomie*, 1970.

Dalberg, C. T., *De l'influence des sciences et des beaux-arts sur la tranquillité publique*, Parma, 1802.

Darnton, R., *Mesmerism and the End of the Enlightenment in France*, Cambridge, Mass., 1968.

— 'Reading, writing and publishing in the eighteenth century: a case-study in the sociology of literature', *Daedalus*, XXXIV, 1971, pp. 214–56.

Daru, P., *La cléopedie ou la théorie des réputations littéraires*, an VIII (1800).

Daudin, H., *Cuvier et Lamarck: les classes zoologiques et l'idée de série animale, 1790–1830*, 1926.

— *De Linné à Lamarck: méthode de la classification et idée de série en botanique et en zoologie, 1740–1790*, 1927.

Daumard, A. & Furet, F., 'Les archives notariales et la mécanographie' *Annales ESC*, XIII, 1959, pp. 676–93.

Daumard, A., *Les bourgeois de Paris au dix-neuvième siècle*, 1970.

— (ed.), *Les fortunes françaises au dix-neuvième siècle*, 1973.

Debard, J. M., 'Subsistances et prix des grains à Montbéliard de 1571 à 1793', *MSEM* LXXI, 1974–5, pp. 1–276.

Dehérain, H., 'Une autobiographie de Baron Ramond', *Journal des savants*, 1905, pp. 121–9.

— *Catalogue des manuscrits du Fonds Cuvier conservées à la Bibliothèque de l'Institut de France*, 2 vols, Paris & Hendaye, 1908–22.

— 'Lettres à Georges Cuvier sur l'organisation de l'Institut en l'an XI', *Journal des savants*, nouvelle série, XVI, 1916, pp. 368–76.

— 'Les manuscrits de Georges Cuvier conservés à la Bibliothèque de l'Institut', *Journal des savants*, 1923, pp. 72–81.

— 'Georges Cuvier, membres de l'Académie des Inscriptions et Belles-lettres', *Journal des savants*, 1932, pp. 222–8.

Delair, J. B. & Sarjeant, W. A. S., 'The earliest discoveries of dinosaurs', *Isis*, LXVI, 1975, pp. 5–25.

Delaunay, L., *Une grande famille de savants: les Brongniart*, 1940.

Deleuze, J. P. F., *Histoire critique du magnetisme animal*, 2 vols, 1813.

— *Histoire et description du Muséum royal d'histoire naturelle*, 2 vols, 1823. Consulted in the anonymous English translation of the same year, published in Paris, and on stylistic grounds possibly to be assigned to Sarah Lee (q.v.) The copy in the University Library, Cambridge, belonged to her daughter, Tedlie Hutchison Bowdich.

Denise, L., *Bibliographie historique et iconographique du Jardin des Plantes . . . et Muséum d'histoire naturelle*, 1903.

Depping, L., 'Notice sur les premiers temps de la Société philotechnique', *Annuaire de la Société philotechnique*, I, 1840,

pp. 5–32; II, 1981, pp. 1–13.
Destutt de Tracy, *Observations sur le système actuel d'instruction publique*, 1801.
— *Commentaire sur l'esprit des lois de Montesquieu, suivi d'observations inédits de Condorcet sur ... le même ouvrage, et d'un mémoire sur cette question, quels sont les moyens de fonder la morale d'un peuple*, 1819.
D'Harcourt, R., *La jeunesse de Schiller*, 1928.
Dieckmann, H., 'The concept of knowledge in the Encyclopédie', *Essays in Comparative Literature*, St Louis, 1961, pp. 73–107.
Diehl, C., *Americans and German Scholarship, 1770–1870*, New Haven, 1978.
Dollfus, G. F., 'Le séjour de Georges Cuvier en Normandie: ses premiers études d'histoire naturelle', *Bulletin de la Société Linnéenne de Normandie*, seventh series, VIII, 1925, pp. 156–78.
Döllinger, I von, *Ueber den Werth und die Bedeutung der vergleichenden Anatomie: ein Programm*, Würzburg, 1814.
Douen, O., *Histoire de la société biblique protestante de Paris, 1818 à 1868 ... avec des notices bibliographiques par F. Schickler*, 1868.
Douglas, M., *Natural Symbols: Explorations in Cosmology*, 1970.
— *Rules and Meanings: the Anthropology of Everyday Knowledge*, 1973.
Dubois, J., *Le vocabulaire politique et social en France de 1869 à 1872*, 1965.
Duchesne, A. N., 'Sur les rapports entre les êtres naturelles: mémoire lu à la Société d'Histoire naturelle', *Magasin encyclopédique*, VI, 1795, pp. 289–94.
Dujarric de la Rivière, R., *Cuvier, sa vie, son oeuvre: pages choisis*, 1969.
Dulieu, L. 'Antoine Gouan', *Revue d'histoire des sciences*, XX, 1967, pp. 33–48.
Duméril, A. M. C., *Zoologie analytique ou méthode naturelle de classification des animaux rendue plus facile à aide de tablaux synoptiques*, 1806.
— *Traîté élémentaire d'histoire naturelle, ouvrage composé par ordre du gouvernment pour servir à l'enseignement dans les lycées nationaux*, an XII (1804).
Dupin, C., 'Eloge de Mme de Prony', *Mercure du dix-neuvième siècle*, II, 1823, pp. 203–15.
Dupont, P., 'Notice biographique sur le contre-/amiral Ducrest de Villeneuve', 1852.
Dupuis, P., 'Pierre Antoine Latreille, 1762–1833: the foremost entomologist of his time', *Annual Review of Entomology*, XIX, 1974, pp. 1–13.
Dupuy, P., *L'école normale en l'an III*, 1895.
Durand, Y., *Les fermiers-généraux au dix-huitième siècle*, 1971.
Dureau, A., *Notes bibliographiques pour servir à l'histoire du magnétisme animal: analyse de tous les livres, brochures, articles*

de journaux publiées sur le magnétisme animal en France et à l'étranger à partir de 1766 jusqu'au 31 Décembre, 1868, 1869.

Duroselle, J. B., *Les débuts du Catholicisme social en France, 1822–1870,* 1951.

Duvaucel, A., 'Lettres familières sur l'Inde', *Revue des deux mondes,* II, 1833, pp. 601–31; III, pp. 59–80.

Duvernoy, C., 'Montbéliard au dix-huitième siècle', *MSEM*, XXII, 1891, pp. 1–493.

Duvernoy, C. L., ed. M. Menot, 'Nouvelles ephémerides du pays de Montbéliard', *MSEM*, LX, 1955–9, pp. 1–303.

Duvernoy, G. L., 'Review of X. Bichat, *Recherches physiologiques sur la vie et la mort', Magasin Encyclopédique* VI, 1800, pp. 306–31.

— *Notice historique sur les ouvrages et la vie de M. le baron Cuvier,* Strasbourg and Paris, 1833.

Duvernoy, M., 'Sophie Duvaucel d'après des correspondences inédits', *MSEM*, LIV, 1939, pp. 49–86.

Ellis, D., *Memoirs of the Life and Writings of John Gordon, M.D., FRSE,* Edinburgh and London, 1823.

Emonot, A., 'Les lettres de privilèges, maîtrises, jurandes, brévets, offices, institutions etc. déposées à la municipalité de Montbéliard les 24 et 25 nivôse an 2 (13–14 Janvier, 1794)', *MSEM*, XXXVI, 1897, pp. 429–59.

Estaintot, C. H. R. Langlois d', 'Un procès entre deux seigneurs haut-justiciers: Valmont et Cany-Caniel au dix-huitième siècle', *Précis de l'Académie de Rouen,* 1888–9, pp. 321–73.

Falconer, H., 'On Professor Huxley's attempted refutation of Cuvier's laws of correlation in the reconstruction of extinct vertebrate forms', *Annals and Magazine of Natural history,* second series, XVII, 1856, pp. 476–93.

Fallot, E., *Un voyage à la Cour de Prusse en 1775 par D. C. E. Berdot . . . physician adjoint de la principauté de Montbéliard, d'après un manuscrit de l'auteur,* Montbéliard, 1903.

Falls, W., 'Buffon et l'agrandissement du Jardin du roi à Paris', *Archives du Muséum national d'histoire naturelle,* sixth series, X, 1934, pp. 131–98.

Fallue, L., *Histoire de la ville et de l'Abbaye de Fécamp,* Rouen, 1841.

Farber, P. L., 'The type concept in zoology during the first half of the nineteenth century', *Journal of the History of biology,* IX, 1976, pp. 93–119.

Farin, *Catalogue des plantes du jardin de bontanique de Caen,* Caen, 1781.

Faujas de St Fond, B., *Essai de géologie ou mémoires pour servir à l'histoire naturelle du globe.* 3 vols, Paris, 1803–09.

Favre, R., 'Author du bicentenaire de la naissance de Georges Cuvier: la réponse de Cuvier au discours de réception de Lamartine à l'Académie française', *Annales de l'Académie de Mâcon,* third series, L, 1970, pp. 69–76.

Febvre, L., 'De Linné à Lamarck et à Georges Cuvier', *Combats pour l'histoire*, 1953, pp. 318–36.

Figlio, K. M., 'Theories of perception and the physiology of mind in the late eighteenth century', *History of Science*, XIII, 1975, pp. 177–212.

— 'The metaphor of organisation: an historigraphical perspective on the bio-medical sciences of the early nineteenth century', *History of Science*, XIV, 1976, pp. 17–53.

(Fitton, W.), Review of Cuvier and Brongniart, Géographie minéralogique des environs de Paris', *Edinburgh Review*, XX, 1812, pp. 369–89.

— Review of Cuvier, *Discours préliminaire*, ed. R. Jameson, *Edinburgh Review*, XXII, 1814, p. 22.

Fischer, G., *Das Nationalmuseum der Naturgeschichte zu Paris, von seinem ersten ursprunge bis zu seinem jetzigen Glanze*, 2 vols, Frankfurt-am-Main, 1802.

Fleming, J., 'The geological deluge as interpreted by Baron Cuvier and Professor Buckland inconsistent with the testimony of Moses and the phenomena of nature', *Edinburgh Philosophical Journal*, XIV, 1826, pp. 205–39.

Flourens, M. J. P., *Recherches expérimentales sur les propriétés et les fonctions du système nerveux dans les animaux vertébrés*, second edition, 1842. Cuvier's report at pp. 60–84.

— *Analyse raisonée des travaux de George Cuvier, précédée de son éloge historique*, 1845.

— *Cuvier: histoire de ses travaux*, 1845, 1858.

— 'De l'opinion de Cuvier sur la partie philosophique de la physiologie de Bichat', *Journal des savants*, novembre 1856, 665–75.

— *Recueil des éloges historiques lus dans les sciences publiques de l'Académie des sciences*, 3 vols, 1856–7. Cuvier's 'autobiography' is at I, pp. 167–93.

— *De l'unité de composition et du débat entre Cuvier et Geoffroy St Hilaire*, Paris, 1865.

Fontvieille, L., *Evolution et croissance de l'état français: 1815–1969*, 1976.

Forbes, R. J., *Martinus van Marum: Life and Work*, Haarlem, 1969 (in progress).

Fossati, J. A. L., *Questions philosophiques, sociales et politiques traîtés d'après les principes de la physiologie du cerveau*, 1869.

Foucault, M., *Naissance de la clinique*, 1963. Translated as *The Birth of the Clinic: an Archaeology of Medical Perception*, 1973.

— *Les mots et les choses*, 1966. Translated as *The Order of Things*, 1970.

— 'Cuvier's position in the history of biology', *Critique of Anthropology*, IV, 1979, pp. 125–31.

Fourcroy, A. & Thouin, A., *Extrait des registres du Muséum d'histoire naturelle sur la fête funéraire relative à l'inhumation du corps du*

Citoyen Daubenton, dans le Jardin de cet établissement, an VIII (1800).
Fox, R., 'The rise and fall of Laplacian physics', *Historical Studies in the Physical Sciences*, IV, 1974, pp. 89–136.
Frankel, E., *Jean Baptiste Biot: the career of a physicist in nineteenth century France*, University of Princeton PhD thesis, 1972.
— 'Career-making in post-revolutionary France: the case of J. B. Biot', *British Journal for the History of Science*, XI, 1978, pp. 36–48.
Fraysinnous, D., *Défence du Christianisme ou conférences sur la réligion*. 3 vols, 1825–6.
Fregnac, C., *Merveilles des châteaux de Normandie*, 1966.
Frey, M., *Les transformations du vocubulaire français à l'époque de la révolution, 1789–1800*, 1925.
Gall, F. J., *Recherches sur le système nerveux en général et sur celui du cerveau en particulier: mémoire présenté à l'Institut de France le 14 mars 1808: suivi d'observations sur le rapport qui en a été fait à cette compagnie par ses commissaires . . .*, 1809.
— *Sur les fonctions du cerveau et sur celles de chacune de ses parties*, 6 vols, 1825.
Gall, F. J. & Spurzheim, G., 1809, *Recherches sur le système nerveux en général et sur celui du cerveau en particulier, mémoire présenté à l'Institut de France le 14 mars 1808, suivi d'observations sur le rapport qui a été fait à cette compagnie par ses commissaires*.
Galland, A., *Essai sur l'histoire du Protestantisme à Caen et en Basse Normandie, de l'Edit de Nantes à la Révolution*, 1891.
Garnier, A., *Fraysinnous: son rôle dans l'Université sous la Restauration, 1822–1828*, Paris & Rodez, 1925.
Gaudin, M. M. C., duc de Gaëte, *Mémoirs, souvenirs, opinions et écrits*, 2 vols., 1826.
Genevray, P., 'Professeurs protestants dans l'enseignement supérieur pendant la Restauration', *Bull. Soc. Hist. Prot. Fr.*, LXXXIV, 1940, pp. 22–39, pp. 163–81, 288–304.
Geoffroy St Hilaire, E. & Cuvier, G., 'Mémoire sur une nouvelle division des mammifères et sur les principes qui doivent servir de base dans cette sorte de travail, lu à Société d'histoire naturelle le 1 floréal de l'an 3', *Magasin encyclopédique*, première année, II, 1795, pp. 164–90.
Geoffroy St Hilaire, E. & Cuvier G., 'Histoire naturelle des orang-outangs', *ibid.*, première année, III, 1795, p. 451.
Geoffroy St Hilaire, E., review of Cuvier, G., *Tableau élémentaire*, *ibid.*, troisième année, V, 1797, pp. 507–22.
— 'Première mémoire sur les poissons, où l'on compare les pièces osseuses de leurs nageoires pectorales avec les os de l'extrémité antérieure des autres animaux vertébrés . . .', *Annales du Muséum* IX, 1807, pp. 357–72.
— 'Second mémoire sur les poissons: considérations sur l'os furculaire une des pièces de la nageoire pectorale', *Ibid.*, IX, 1807, pp. 413–27.
— 'Troisième mémoire sur les poissons, où l'on traîte de leur sternum

sous le point de vue de sa détermination et de ses formes générales', *ibid.*, X, 1807, pp. 87–104.
— 'Considérations sur les pièces de la tête osseuse des animaux vertébrés, et particulièrement sur celles du crâne des oiseaux', *Annales du Muséum d'histoire naturelle*, X, 1807, pp. 342–65.
— 'Tableau des quadrumanes ou des animaux composant le premier ordre de la classe des mammifères', *Ibid.*, XIX, 1812, pp. 85–122, 156–70.
— 'Du squelette des poissons, ramenés dans toutes ses parties à la chapente osseuse des autres animaux', *Bull. Soc. philom.*, 1817, p. 125, 185.
Geoffroy St Hilaire, E., *Philosophie anatomique: des organes respiratoires sous le rapport de la détermination et de l'identité de leurs pièces osseuses*, 1818.
— *Principes de philosophie zoologique, discutés en mars 1830 au sein de l'Académie royale des sciences*, 1830.
— 'Discours sur le tombe de Cuvier', *Annales des sciences naturelles*, XVVI, 1832, p. 403.
— 'Fondation de la ménagerie du Muséum d'histoire naturelle', *Fragments biographiques*, 1838, pp. 143–85.
Geoffroy St Hilaire, E & Cuvier F., *Histoire des mammifères de la ménagerie*, 1826.
Geoffroy St Hilaire, I., *Essais de zoologie générale ou mémoires et notices sur la zoologie générale, l'anthropologie et l'histoire de la science*, 1841.
— *Vie, travaux et doctrine scientifique d'Etienne Geoffroy St Hilaire*, 1847.
Gérando, G. de, *Lettres inédits et souvenirs biographiques de Mme Récamier et Mme de Staël*, Paris & Metz, 1868.
Gérando, J. M. de, *Des signes et de l'art de penser, considérées dans leurs rapports mutuels*, an VIII (1800), 4 vols.
— *Histoire comparée des systèmes de philosophie considérées relativement aux principes des connaissances humaines*, second edition, 8 vols, 1822–47.
Gerbod, P., *La condition universitaire en France au dix-neuvième siècle*, 1965.
— 'Les inspecteurs-généraux et l'inspection générale de l'instruction publique de 1802 à 1882', *Revue historique*, CCXXXVI, 1966, pp. 79–106.
— (ed.) *Les épurations administratives: dix-huitième et vingtième siècles*, Geneva, 1977.
Gerstner, P. A., 'Vertebrate paleontology: an early nineteenth century transatlantic science', *Journal of the History of Biology*, III, 1970, pp. 137–48.
Gillispie, C. C., *Science and Polity in France at the End of the Old Regime*, Princeton, 1980.
Godard, C., 'Essai sur le gymnase de Monbéliard', *MSEM*, XXIII, 1893, pp. 1–248.

Gode von Aesch, A., *Natural Science in German Romanticism*, New York, 1941.
Goethe, W. von, 'Reflexions sur les débats scientifiques de mars 1830 dans le sein de l'Académie des sciences', *Annales des sciences naturelles*, XXII, 1831, pp. 179–93.
Goguel, G., *Hommes connus dans le monde savant en France et à l'étranger nés ou élevés à Montbéliard: études, analyses, appréciations d'après leurs ouvrages, leurs notes, des documents authéntiques, des pièces inédites, des renseignements intimes*, 1864.
Gohau, G., 'Plaidoyer pour Georges Cuvier', *Cahiers rationalistes*, CCLXXIX, 1971, pp. 1–32.
Gontard, M., *L'enseignement primaire en France de la révolution à la loi Guizot, 1789–1833*, 1959.
Gosselin, L., 'Le baron Cachin, Inspecteur-général des Ponts-et-Chausées à Caen, et Marie-Judith Rivière, son épouse', *Mémoires de l'Académie de Caen*, XV, 1963, pp. 61–9.
Gouhier, H. (ed.), *Maine de Biran, Journals*, 3 vols., Neuchâtel, 1954–7.
Gower, B., 'Speculation in physics: the history and practice of Naturphilosophie', *Studies in the History and Philosophy of Science*, III, 1973, pp. 301–56.
Graña, C., *Bohemian vs Bourgeois: French Society and the French Man of Letters in the Nineteenth Century*, New York, 1964.
Gravier, C., 'Les vers et les arthropodes dans le *Règne animal*', *Archives du Muséum national d'histoire naturelle*, IX, 1932, pp. 63–7.
Gross, M., *Structure and Function in Nineteenth Century French Physiology*, University of Princeton PhD thesis, 1974.
— 'The lessened focus of feeling: a transformation in French physiology in the early nineteenth century', *Journal of the History of Biology*, XII, 1979, pp. 231–71.
Grouvel, Vicomte, 'Le régiment suisse de Waldner au service de la France', *Vert et rouge*, I, 1945, pp. 28–38.
Gudger, E. W., 'Pliny's *Historia naturalis*: the most popular natural history ever published', *Isis*, VI, 1924–5, pp. 269–81.
Guedès, M., 'La méthode taxonomique d'Adanson', *Revue d'histoire des sciences*, XX, 1967, pp. 361–86.
Guillaumin, A., 'André Thouin et l'enrichissement des collections de plantes vivantes au Muséum aux dépens des Jardins de la liste civile, des émigrés et condamnés d'après des notes inédites', *Bull. du Muséum de Paris*, second series, XVI, 1944, pp. 483–9.
Guitton, E., *Jacques Delille et le poème de la nature en France de 1750 à 1820*, 1974.
Guizot, F., *Du gouvernment représentatiff et de l'état actuel de la France*, 1816.
Gunnell, D., *Sutton Sharpe en ses amis français, avec des lettres inédits*, 1925.

Haag, E., *La France protestante ou vies des protestants français qui se sont fait un nom dans l'histoire depuis les premiers temps de la réformation jusqu'à la reconnaissance du principe de la liberté des cultes par l'Assemblée Nationale*, 9 vols, Paris & Geneva, 1859–68.

Haber, F., *The Age of the World: Moses to Darwin*, Baltimore, 1959.

Hahn, R., 'Fourcroy, advocate of Lavoisier?', *Archives internationales d'histoire des sciences*, XII, 1959, pp. 285–8.

— 'Elite scientifique et démocratic politique dans la France révolutionnaire', *Dix-huitième siècle*, I, 1961, pp. 229–35.

— *The Anatomy of a Scientific Institution: the Paris Academy of Sciences, 1666–1803*, Berkeley, 1971.

— 'Scientific careers in eighteenth century France', in M. Crosland (ed.), *The Emergence of Science in Western Europe*, 1975 a, pp. 127–38.

— 'L'autobiographie de Lacepède retrouvée', *Dix-huitième siècle*, VII, 1975 b, pp. 49–85.

Hallé, J. N., Review of Cuvier, G., *Leçons d'anatomie comparée*, *Magasin encyclopédique*, sixième année, II, an VIII (1800), pp. 145–203.

Hamel, E., *Histoire de la Restauration faisant suite à l'histoire du premier Empire*, 2 vols, second edition, 1897.

Hamy, E. T., *Les origines du musée d'ethnographie: histoire et documents*, 1890.

— 'Les anciens ménageries royales et la ménagerie nationale, fondée le 14 brumaire an II (4 novembre 1793)', *Nouvelles archives du Muséum*, fourth series, I, 1893, pp. 1–22.

— *Les derniers jours du Jardin du roi et la fondation du Muséum d'histoire naturelle*, 1893.

— 'Julie Charpentier, sculpteur et préparateur de zoologie, 1770–1845' *Bulletin du Muséum d'histoire naturelle*, VII, 1899, pp. 1–6.

— *Etienne Geoffroy St Hilaire: Lettres écrites d'Egypte à Cuvier, Jussieu, Lacepède, Monge, Desgenettes, Redouté jeune, Norry, etc. aux professeurs du Muséum et à sa famille*, 1901.

— 'Dicquemare jugé par Cuvier, 1805', *Bulletin du Muséum d'histoire naturelle*, IV, 1906, p. 181.

— 'Notes intimes sur Georges Cuvier, du Docteur Quoy', in *Les débuts de Lamarck suivis de recherches sur Adanson, Pallas, Jussieu, Geoffroy St Hilaire, Georges Cuvier, etc*, 1908, pp. 306–45.

— 'La mission d'Etienne Geoffroy St Hilaire en Espagne et en Portugal, 1808: histoire et documents', *Nouvelles archives du Muséum*, fourth series, X, 1908, pp. 1–82.

Hannaway, O., Review of Crosland, M. P., 1961, *Isis*, LX 1969, pp. 578–81.

Harcourt, R. D., *La jeunesse de Schiller*, 1928.

Harpaz, E., *L'école libérale sous la Restauration: le 'Mercure' et la 'Minerve', 1817–20*, Geneva, 1968.

Hartman, M. S., 'The sacrilege law of 1825 in France: a study in anticlericalism and myth-making', *Journal of Modern History*, XLIV,

1972, pp. 21–37.
Hatin, E., *Bibliographie historique et critique de la presse périodique française*, 1866.
Haug, H., 'Le giraffe de Charles X', in *L'art populaire en France*, IV, 1932.
Hervé, G., 'A la recherche d'un ms: les instructions anthropologiques de Georges Cuvier pour le voyage du *Géographe* et du *Naturaliste* aux terres australes', *Revue de l'école d'anthropologie de Paris*, XX, 1910, pp. 289–306.
Hoefer, E. (ed.), *Biographie universelle depuis les temps les plus reculés jusqu'à nos jours*, nouvelle édition, 46 vols, 1852–66.
Holler, F. H., (ed.), *C. F. von Kielmeyer, Gesammelte Schriften*, Berlin, 1938.
'Homo', *Remarks on Jameson's preface to Cuvier's theory of the earth*, 1815.
Houghton, W. E. (ed.) *The Wellesley Index to Victorian Periodicals, 1824–1900*, 3 vols, Toronto, 1966–79.
Houtin, A., *La question biblique chez les catholiques de France au dix-neuvième siècle*, 1902.
Huard, P. and Montagné, M., 'Georges Cuvier et son temps', *L'extrême-orient médical*, I, 1949, pp. 179–259.
(Imbert) *L'art d'obtenir des places, où la clef des ministères: ouvrage dédié aux gens sans emploi et aux soliciteurs de toutes les classes*, second edition, 1816.
Institut de France, *Index biographique des membres et correspondants de l'Académie des Sciences de 1666 à 1939*, 1939.
Isler, M., *Briefe an Ch. de Villers von Benjamin Constant ... und vielen anderen. Auswahl aus dem handschriftlichen Nachlasse des Ch. de Villars.* second edition, Hamburg, 1883. A letter from Cuvier, pp. 60–61.
Jacob, F., *The Logic of Living Systems*, 1974.
Jameson, L., 'Biographical memoir of the late Professor Jameson', *Edinburgh New Philosophical Journal*, LVII, 1854, pp. 1–49.
Jameson, R., *Essay on the Theory of the Earth Translated from the French of M. Cuvier ... with Mineralogical Notes and an Account of Cuvier's Geological Discoveries*, Edinburgh, 1813, 1815, 1817, 1822, 1827.
Jardin, A. & Tudesq, A. J., *La France des notables, 1815–1848*, 2 vols, 1973.
Jeannin, P., 'Une lettre d'Augustin Perier, sur la suppression de l'Ecole Normale (1822)', *Revue d'histoire moderne et contemporaine*, XV, 1968, pp. 466–70.
Johnson, D., *Guizot: Aspects of French History, 1787–1874*, 1963.
Jolyclerc, N., *Phytologie universelle ou histoire naturelle et méthode des plantes*, 6 vols, an VIII (1800).
Jordanova, L. J., *The Natural Philosophy of Lamarck in its Historical Context*, University of Cambridge, PhD thesis, 1976.
Joubin, M., 'Etudes de Cuvier sur les molluscs', *Archives du Muséum*

d'histoire naturelle sixth series, VII–IX, 1931–3, pp. 55–61.

Jussieu, A. L. de, *Genera Plantarum secundrum ordines naturales disposita, juxta methodum in horto regio parisiensi exaratum*, 1789.

— 'Notice historique sur le Muséum d'histoire naturelle', *Annales du Muséum d'histoire naturelle*, I, 1802, pp. 1–14; II, 1803, pp. 1–16; III, 1804, pp. 1–17; IV, 1804, pp. 1–19; VI, 1805, pp. 1–20· XI, 1808, pp. 1–41.

— *Principes de la méthode naturelle des végétaux*, Paris & Strasbourg 1824.

Kennedy, E., 'Destutt de Tracy and the unity of the sciences', *Studies in Voltaire and the Eighteenth Century*, CLXXI, 1977, pp. 223–39.

Kerner, J. S., *Flora Stuttgardiensis oder Verzeichnis der um Stuttgart Wildwachsenden Pflanzen*, Stuttgart, 1786.

Kersaint, G., 'Antoine-François Fourcroy, (1742–1804,): sa vie et son oeuvre', *Mémoires du Muséum national d'histoire naturelle*, série D, sciences physico-chimiques, II, 1966, pp. 1–296.

Kidd, J., *On the Adaptation of External Nature to the Physical Condition of Man: Principally with Reference to the Supply of his Wants and the Exercise of his Intellectual Faculties*, 1834 (Cuvier and Aristotle compared), pp. 299–347.

Kielmeyer, K. F., 'Einige Notizen über die Lebensumstände und Verhältnisse Georg Cuviers, während seines Aufenhaltes in der Karlsakademie und einige Jahre nach diesem', *Württembergische Jahrbücher*, II, 1843, pp. 177–82.

— 'Über Kant und die deutsche Naturphilosophie: ein schreiben an Cuvier', in *Gesammelte Schriften*, ed. F. H. Holler, Berlin, 1938, pp. 239–40.

Kitchin, J., *Un journal philosphique: La décade, 1794–1807*, 1965.

Kohlbrugge, J. H. F., 'Georg Cuvier und K. F. Kielmeyer', *Biologisches Centralblatt*, XXXII, 1912, pp. 291–5.

Kohn, D., 'Theories to work by: rejected theories, reproduction and Darwin's path to natural selection', *Studies in History of Biology*, IV, 1980, pp. 67–170.

Lacepède, Cuvier & Lamarck, 'Rapport des professeurs du Muséum sur les collections d'histoire naturelle rapportés d'Egypte', *Annales du Muséum d'histoire naturelle*, I, 1802, pp. 234–41.

Lacombe, C. de, *Le comte de Serre, sa vie et son temps*, 2 vols, 1881.

Lacroix, A., 'Georges Cuvier et la minéralogie', *Archives du Muséum d'histoire naturelle*, IX, 1932, pp. 69–75.

— 'Une famille de bons serviteurs de l'Académie des sciences et du Jardin des Plantes: les Lucas', *Bulletin du Muséum national d'histoire naturelle*, X, 1938, pp. 440–71.

Laissus, Y., *Catalogue générale des MSS des bibliothèque publiques de France: Paris: Bibliothèque centrale du Muséum nationale d'histoire naturelle*, supplément. LV, 1965.

Lamarck, J. B., 'Mémoire sur les cabinets d'histoire naturelle et particulièrement celui du Jardin des Plantes', 1790.

— ed. A. Giard, 'Discours d'ouverture des cours de zoologie donnés dans le Muséum d'histoire naturelle, an 8, an 10, an 11, et 1806', *Bulletin scientifique de la France et de la Belgique*, XL, 1906, fifth series, IX, pp. 443–595.

— 'Mémoirs sur les fossiles des environs de Paris, comprenant la détermination des espèces qui appartiennent aux animaux marins sans vertèbres', *Annales du Muséum d'histoire naturelle*, I, 1802, pp. 299–312.

Lamarck, J. B., *Philosphie zoologique, ou exposition des considérations relatives à l'histoire naturelle des animaux, à la diversité de leur organisation et des facultés qu'ils en obtiennent, aux causes physiques qui maintiennent en eux la vie et donnent lieu aux mouvements qu'ils exécutent; enfin à celles qui produisent . . . le sentiment . . . et l'intelligence*, 2 vols, 1809.

— *Histoire naturelle des animaux sans vertèbres, présentent les caractères généraux et particuliers de ces animaux, leur distribution, leurs classes, leurs familles, leurs genres, et la citation des principales espèces qui s'y rapportent: précédée d'une introduction offrant la détermination des caractères essentielles de l'animal, son distinction du végétal et des autres corps naturels, enfin l'exposition des principes fondamentaux de la zoologie*, 6 vols, 1815–22.

Lamartine, A. de, *History of the Restoration of the Monarchy in France*, 4 vols, New York, 1853.

Landrieu, M., *Lamarck, le fondateur du transformisme: sa vie, son oeuvre*, 1909.

Lane, W. C. and Brown, N. E. (eds.), *Library of Congress: ALA Portrait Index: Index to Portraits Contained in Printed Books and Periodicals*, Washington, 1906.

Lantéri-Laura, G., *Histoire de la phrénologie: l'homme et son cerveau selon F. J. Gall*, 1970.

Lanzac de Laborde, L. de, 'La haute administration de l'enseignement sous le Consulat et l'Empire', *Revue des études napoléoniennes*, X, 1916, pp. 186–219.

Larévellière-Lépeaux, A., *Mémoires*, 3 vols, 1895.

Larrond, N., 'Cuvier et la géographie', *La géographie*, LVI, 1932, pp. 301–8.

Latreille, P. A., *Considérations générales sur l'ordre naturel des animaux composant les classes de crustacés, des arachnides et des insects*, 1810.

— *Familles naturelles du Règne animal, exposés succinctement et dans un ordre analytique, avec l'indication de leurs genres*, 1825.

Latreille, P. A., *Cours d'entomologie ou de l'histoire naturelle des crustacés, des archnides, des myriapodes et des insectes; à l'usage des élèves de l'école du Muséum d'histoire naturelle*, 1831.

Laurent, G., 'Lamarck: de la philosophie du continu à la science du discontinu', *Revue d'histoire des sciences*, XXVIII, 1975, pp. 327–60.

- 'Le cheminement d'Etienne Geoffroy St Hilaire vers un transformisme scientifique', *Revue d'histoire des sciences*, XXX, 1977, pp. 43–70.
Laurillard, C. L., 'Eloge de M. le baron Cuvier', *Recherches sur les ossemens fossiles*, fourth edition, 10 vols, 1834–6, I, pp. 1–78.
- 'Cuvier', *Nouvelle biographie universelle*, ed. Hoefer, IX, 1852, pp. 590–600.
Leblanc, P., *Catalogue des livres, dessins et estampes de la bibliothèque du feu M. Huzard*, 3 vols, 1842.
Leclerc, J., 'Potestantisme et libre examen: les étapes et le vocabulaire d'une controverse', *Recherches des sciences réligieuses*, LIX, 1969, pp. 321–74.
Lee, S., *Memoirs of Baron Cuvier*, 1833.
Lefebvre, L. H., *Réflexions importantes sur le vice radical de l'enseignement mutuel adopté pour le botanique au Jardin du Roi*, 1821.
Lefranc, A., *Histoire du Collège de France depuis ses origines jusqu'à la fin du Premier Empire*, 1893.
Legée, G., 'Cuvier et la réorganisation de l'enseignement sous le Consulat et l'Empire', *Congrès des Sociétés savantes*, 1970, pp. 197–214.
- 'Le Muséum sous la Révolution, l'Empire et la Restauration', *ibid.*, 1970, pp. 747–60.
Leonardi, C., *Le conseil d'Etat sous la Restauration*, 1909.
Lenoir, T., 'Kant, Blumenbach, and vital materialism in German Biology', *Isis*, LXXI, 1980, pp. 77–108.
Lerond, M., 'Note à propos d'un herbier de Georges Cuvier déposé au Muséum de Rouen', *Histoire et nature*, VII, 1975, pp. 75–6.
Leuilliot, P., 'Ferdinand Curie, un propagandiste montbéliardais de l'enseignement mutuel et populaire à Colmar et dans le Haut-Rhin', *Annuaire de la Société historique et littéraire de Colmar*, XXIV, 1955, pp. 93–103.
Leuilliot, P., *L'Alsace au début du dix-neuvième siècle: essais d'histoire politique, économique et religieuse*, 3 vols, 1959–61.
- 'Le fonds Cuvier à la Bibliothèque de l'Institut et l'Alsace', *Revue d'Alsace*, CIII, 1965, pp. 101–8.
Liard, L., *L'enseignement superieur en France 1789–1889*, 2 vols, second ed, 1894.
Lignier, O., 'Essai su l'histoire du Jardin des Plantes de Caen', *Bulletin de la société Linnéenne de Normandie*, series 5, XIII, 1904, pp. 27–175.
Limoges, C., 'L'économie naturelle et le principe de corrélation chez Cuvier et chez Darwin', *Revue d'histoire des sciences*, XXIII, 1978, pp. 35–62.
- 'L'économie politique d'une percée en histoire naturelle: le Cuvierisme en France au dix-neuvième siécle', unpublished typescript.
Littré, E., *Dictionnaire de la langue française*, 7 vols, Paris, 1863–77.

Longin, 'Souvenirs d'un pensionnaire de l'Académie Caroline de Stuttgart, 1781–83', *MSEM*, XLIII, 1914, pp. 209–37.
Lovejoy, A. O., *The Great Chain of Being: a Study in the History of an Idea*, Cambridge, Mass., 1936.
Lubosch, W., 'Die Akademiestreit zwischen Geoffroy St Hilaire und Cuvier, im Jahre 1830, und seine leitenden Gedanken', *Biologische Centralblatt*, XXXVIII, 1918, pp. 357–84, pp. 397–456.
Luce de Lancival, J. C. J., *Epithalame composé pour le marriage de Georges Cuvier*, ed. E. T. Hamy, 1907.
Lyell, K. M., *Life and Letters . . . of Sir Charles Lyell*, 2 vols, 1881.
Lyon, J., 'The search for fossil man: cinq personnages à la recherche du temps perdu', *Isis*, LXI, 1970, pp. 68–84.
McFarland, J. D., *Kant's Concept of Teleology*, Edinburgh, 1970.
McKillop, I. D., 'Local attachment and cosmopolitanism: the eighteenth-century pattern', in *From Sensibility to Romaticism: Essays Presented to F. A. Pottle*, 1965, pp. 191–218.
Mack Walker, J., 'Rights and functions: the social categories of eighteenth-century jurists and cameralists', *Journal of Modern History*, L, 1978, pp. 234–51.
Macler, P., 'Cuvier et la Société biblique Protestante de Paris', *Bull. Soc. hist. Prot. fr.*, LXXXI, 1932, pp. 253–7.
Magny, E. de, *Nobiliaire de Normandie*, 2 vols, 1863–4.
Maindron, E., *L'Académie des sciences*, 1888.
Maine de Biran, F. P. G. 'Examen du système du Dr Gall', in *Oeuvres*, ed. P. Tisserand, 14 vols, V, 1924, pp. 69–129.
Mandelbaum, J., *La Société philomatique de Paris. Thèse du troisième cycle préparé sous la direction de René Taton*, 1982.
Maneville, J., 'Essai sur l'histoire du Collège Cuvier, collège universitaire de Montbéliard, 1811–1911', *MSEM*, XL, 1910, pp. 231–73.
Marchant, L., *Lettres de Georges Cuvier à C. H. Pfaff sur l'histoire naturelle, la politique et la littérature*, 1858. Translated from *Georg Cuviers Briefe an C. H. Pfaff aus den Jahren 1788 bis 1792*, Kiel, 1845.
Marquiset, A., *Napoleon sténographié au Conseil d'etat, 1804–1805*, 1913.
Martineau, H., *Petit dictionnaire stendhalien*, 1948.
Mathiot, C., *Les origines familiales du grand Cuvier*, Besançon, 1932.
— 'La bibliothèque de Jehan Cuvier, chirurgien et prévôt, arrière-grand-père de Georges Cuvier, décédé le 9 avril 1675', *Bull. Soc. hist. Prot. fr.*, LXXXI, 1932, pp. 258–64.
Mathiot, C. & Duvernoy, D. (eds.), 'Lettres inédites de Charles Laurillard à Georges Louis Duvernoy', *MSEM*, LV, 1940, pp. 1–48.
Matoré, G. and Griemas, A. J., 'La naissance du génie au dix-huitième siécle', *Le français moderne*, XXV, 1957, pp. 256–72.
Maurin, A, *Histoire de la chute des Bourbons*, 6 vols, 1850.
Mauveaux, J., 'Armorial du Comté de Montbéliard et des seigneuries qui en dépendent', *MSEM*, XLII, 1913, pp. 97–424. Cuvier's family, pp. 265–6.

Mavidal, J. and Laurent, E. (eds.), *Archives parlementaires de 1787 à 1860, recueil complet des débats législatifs et politiques des chambres françaises, imprimé par ordre du Sénat et de la Chambre des Députes*, second series, 127 vols, 1862–1913.
Mazoyer, L., 'Catégories d'âge et groupes sociaux: les jeunes générations françaises de 1830', *Annales d'histoire économique et sociale*, X, 1938, pp. 385–423.
Menault, E., *Biographies des hommes remarquables d'Angerville la Gâté: Cassegrain, Blanchet, Tessier*, 1859.
Merton, R., 'Bureaucratic structure and personality', in *A Reader in Bureaucracy*, second edition, Glencoe, Illinois, 1960, pp. 361–71.
Merz, J. T., *A History of European Thought in the Nineteenth Century*, 4 vols, Edinburgh and London, 1896–1904.
Michaud, F. (ed.), *Biographie universelle ancienne et moderne, nouvelle édition*, 45 vols, 1843.
Michel, F., *Fichier Stendhalien*, 2 vols, Boston, Mass., 1964.
Millin de Grandmaison, A. L., 'Discours sur l'origine et les progrès de l'histoire naturelle en France', *Actes de la Société d'histoire naturelle de Paris*, I, 1792, pp. i–xvi.
La Minerve française, 9 vols, February 1818–March 1820.
Molé, M. L., *Life and memoirs 1781–1855*, ed. Marquis de Noailles, 2 vols, 1923–5.
Mollien, Count, *Mémoires d'un ministre du Trésor publique, 1780–1815*, 3 vols, 1898.
Monglond, A., *La France révolutionnaire et impériale: annales de bibliographie méthodique et description des livres illustrés*, 9 vols, 1939–63.
Monin, H. and Lazard, L., *Sommier des biens nationaux de la ville de Paris conservés aux Archives de la Seine*, 2 vols, 1920.
Monod, T., 'Achille Valenciennes et L'Histoire naturelle des poissons' *Mémoires de l'Institut français de l'Afrique noire*, LXVIII, 1965, pp. 9–45.
Montbel, G. de, *Souvenirs du Comte de Montbel*, 1913.
Montigny, L. G., *Le provincial à Paris*, 1825.
Moore, F. C. T. (ed.), De Gérando, J. M., *The Observation of Savage Peoples*, 1969.
Moravia, S., *Il pensiero degli idéologues: scienza e filosofia in Francia, 1780–1815*, Florence, 1974.
Moreau, F., 'Histoire des serres du Jardin des Plantes de Caen', *Mémoires de l'Acádemie des sciences et belles-lettres de Caen*, new series, XIV, 1962, pp. 76–82.
Moreau de la Sarthe, J. L., 'Exposition critique du système de Gall', *Moniteur universelle*, 1805, pp. 707-8, 740–42, 763–4.
— *Encyclopédie méthodique ou par ordre de matières . . . section médecine*, II, 1824; Cuvier at p. 356 and note.
Mornet, D., *Le sentiment de la nature en France, de J. J. Rousseau à Bernadin de St Pierre: essai sur les rapports de la littérature et des moeurs*, 1907.

Mortier, R., 'Les *Archives littéraires de L'Europe*, 1804–1808, et le cosmopolitisme littéraire sous le premier Empire', *Mémoires de l'Académie royale de Belgique*, LI, 1956, fasc. 4, p. 1–252.
Moulard, J., *Le comte Camille de Tournon, préfet de la Gironde, 1815–22*, 1914.
— *Lettres inédites du Comte Camille de Tournon*, 1914.
Mourlot, F., *Le cahier d'observations et doléances du tiers état de la ville de Caen en 1789*, 1912.
Nadault de Buffon, H., *Buffon, sa famille, ses collaborateurs, et ses familiers*, 1863.
Negrin, H. E., *Georges Cuvier: Administrator and Educator*, New York University PhD thesis, 1977. This work came to the author's attention too late to be utilised in this book.
Neppi Modona, L., 'Il diario delle persecuzioni di Ferdinando Fossi', *Rassegna storica toscana*, XV, 1969, pp. 151–201.
Nettement, A., *Histoire de la Restauration*, 6 vols, Paris, 1868.
Newman, E. L., 'The blouse and the frock-coat: the alliance of the common people of Paris with the liberal leadership and the middle class during the last years of the Bourbon Restoration', *Journal of Modern History*, XLVI, 1974, pp. 26–59.
Newth, D. R., 'Lamarck in 1800: a lecture on the invertebrate animals and a note on fossils taken from the *Système des animaux sans vertèbres*', *Annals of Science*, VIII, 1952, pp. 229–54.
Newton, W. R. & Uttée, J. M., 'The minutier centrale: a research note', *French historical studies*, VIII, 1974, pp. 489–93.
Nicholson, M. H., *Mountain Gloom and Mountain Glory: the Development of the Aesthetics of the Infinite*, Ithaca, New York, 1959.
Nock, A. D., 'Conversion and adolescence', in *Essays on Religion and the Ancient World*, 2 vols, 1972, I, pp. 469–80.
Nussac, L. de, 'Les premiers rapports de Latreille avec le Muséum, d'après une lettre de Lamarck', *Bulletin du Muséum d'histoire naturelle*, XII, 1906, pp. 7–11.
— 'Le centénaire de P. A. Latreille', *Archives du Muséum national d'histoire naturelle*, sixth series, XI, 1934, pp. 1–12.
Oberkirch, baronne d', *Mémoires*, 2 vols, n.d.
O'Boyle, L., 'The problem of an excess of educated men in Western Europe, 1800–1850', *Journal of modern history*, XLII, 1970, pp. 471–95.
Olivier–Martin, B., *Le Conseil d'Etat de la Restauration*, 1941.
Outram, D., *Education and the State in the Italian Departments Annexed to France 1802–1814*, University of Cambridge PhD thesis, 1974
— 'Education and politics in Piedmont, 1796–1814', *Historical Journal*, XIX, 1976 a, pp. 611–33.
— 'Scientific biography and the case of Georges Cuvier: with a critical bibliography', *History of Science*, XIV, 1976 b, pp. 101–37.

— 'The language of natural power: the funeral *éloges* of Georges Cuvier', *History of Science*, XVI, 1978, pp. 153–78.
— *The Letters of Georges Cuvier: a Summary Calendar of Manuscript and Printed Materials Preserved in Europe, the United States of America, and Australasia*, Chalfont St Giles, 1980 a, British Society for the History of Science, monograph series, II.
— 'Politics and vocation: French science, 1793–1830', *British Journal for the History of Science*, XIII, 1980 b, pp. 27–43.
— 'Politics, publicisation and natural history: the correspondence between Georges Cuvier and Giovanni Fabbroni', *Ricerche storiche*, XIII, 1982, pp. 412–40.
Ozouf, M., 'La fête révolutionnaire et le renouvellement de l'imaginaire collectif', *Annales historiques de la révolution française*, LXXVII, 1975, pp. 385–405.
Page, L. E., 'Diluvianism and its critics in Great Britain in the early nineteenth century', in C. J. Schneer (ed.), *Towards a History of Geology*, Cambridge, Mass., 1969, p. 257–71.
Pailhès, G., *Du nouveau sur Joubert, Chateaubriand, Fontanes et sa fille*, 1900.
Paillet, A., 'Les cours prévôtales, 1816–1818, *Revue des deux mondes*, IV, 1911, pp. 123–49.
Paradisi, I., *Osservazioni sopra il discorso del. sig. Barone Cuvier, sulle rivoluzioni del globo*, second edition, Rome, 1827.
Pariset, E., *Histoire des membres de l'Académie royale de médecine, ou recueil des éloges lus dans les séances publiques*, 2 vols, 1850.
Parodi, A., *Le Conseil d'etat, ... 1799–1974*, 1974.
Parturier, A., 'Lettres à Sophie Duvaucel: précisions sur Mérimée', *Revue de Paris*, XXXIX, 1932, pp. 63–98, 360–76.
Pasquier, E., *Eloge de M. le baron Cuvier*, 1832.
— *Mémoires*, 6 vols, 1894–5.
Perrot, J. C., *Genèse d'une ville moderne: Caen au dix-huitième siècle*, 1975.
Perroud, C., 'La société française des amis des noirs', *La révolution française*, LXIX, 1916, pp. 122–47.
Petit, G. and Théodoridès, J., 'Les cahiers de notes zoologiques de Georges Cuvier: Diaria zoologica', *Biologie médicale*, numéro hors-série, 1961, pp. iv–xx.
Pfaff, C. M., *Lettres de Georges Cuvier à C. M. Pfaff, sur l'histoire naturelle, la Politique et la littérature, 1788–1792, traduits de l'allemand par Louis Marchant*, 1858.
Picavet, F., *La philosophie de Kant en France de 1773 à 1814*, 1888.
— *Les idéologues: Essai sur l'histoire des idées et des théories scientifiques, philosphiques, religieuses etc. en France depuis 1789*, 1891.
Pillon, F., 'La méthode en biologie: Cuvier, Blainville, Comte', *La critique philosophique*, VII, 1878, p. 129–38.
Pilon, E., 'Le salon de Cuvier au Jardin des Plantes', *Revue des deux mondes*, CII, 1932, pp. 382–94.

Pinel, P., 'Recherches sur une nouvelle méthode de classification des quadrupèdes, fondée sur la structure méchanique des parties osseuses qui servent à l'articulation de la mâchoire inférieure', *Actes de la Société d'histoire naturelle de Paris*, I, 1792, pp. 55–75.
Pinkney, D., *The French Revolution of 1830*, Princeton, 1972.
Piveteau, J., 'Le débat entre Cuvier et Geoffroy St Hilaire, sur l'unité de plan et de composition', *Revue d'histoire des sciences*, III, 1950, pp. 343–63.
Plan, D., *Un génévois d'autrefois: H. A. Gosse, 1753–1816*, Paris and Geneva, 1909.
Playfair, L., 'Review of Jameson (ed.), *Cuvier: Discourse on the Revolutions of the Globe*', *Edinburgh Review*, XXII, 1814, pp. 454–75.
Pliny the younger, *Histoire naturelle de Pline, traduction nouvelle par M. Ajasson de Grandsagne, annotée par MM. Beudant, Brongniart, Georges Cuvier*... 20 vols, 1829.
Poirier, J., 'L'université provisoire, 1814–21', *Revue d'histoire moderne* I, 1926, pp. 241–79; II, 1927, pp. 3–35, 261–306.
— 'Georges Cuvier, second fondateur de l'Université', *Revue de Paris*, XXXIX, 1932, pp. 85–115.
Porter, D., 'Politics, happiness and the arts: a commentary on Stendhal's *Rome, Naples et Florence en 1817*', *French Studies*, XXIV, 1970, pp. 254–61.
Pouthas, C., 'Les projets de réforme administrative sous la Restauration', *Revue d'histoire moderne*, I, 1926, pp. 321–67.
— *La jeunesse de Guizot*, 1936.
— 'La réorganisation du ministère de l'Intérieur et la reconstitution de l'administration préfectorale par Guizot en 1830', *Revue d'histoire moderne et contemporaine*, IX, 1962, pp. 241–64.
Powell, J., *The history and influence of the Athenée de Paris*, University of Aberystwyth MA thesis, 1978.
Pratt, V., 'Foucault and the history of classification theory', *Studies in the History and Philosophy of Science*, VIII, 1977, pp. 163–71.
Prévost, C., 'De la formation des terreins des environs de Paris', *Bull. Soc. philom.*, third series, XII, 1825, pp. 74–77, 88–90.
— *Documents pour l'histoire des terreins tertiaires*, 1842.
Puget, H., 'Cuvier au Conseil d'Etat', *Revue politique et parlementaire*, LII–LIII, 1932, p. 300–19.
Raeff, M., 'The well-ordered police-state and the development of modernity in seventeenth- and eighteenth-century Europe', *American Historical Review*, LXXX, 1975, pp. 1221–43.
Rappaport, R., 'Geology and orthodoxy: the case of Noah's flood in eighteenth-century thought', *British Journal for the History of Science*, XI, 1978, pp. 1–18.
Raspail, F., 'Coteries scientifiques', *Annales de sciences de l'observation* III, 1830, pp. 151–9.
Reardon, B., *Liberalism and Tradition: Aspects of Catholic Thought in Nineteenth-century France*, 1975.

Renard, L., 'L'étrange destin de deux Romanoff-Montbéliard', *MSEM*, LXVI, 1967, pp. 69–75.
Reynal, P. de, *Les correspondante de Joubert*, 1883.
Rice, H. C., jr., 'Jefferson's gift of fossils to the Museum of natural history in Paris', *Proceedings of the American Philosophical Society*, XCV, 1951, pp. 597–627.
Richardson, Dr, *Letter to the Countess of Gosford . . . on his Returning to her Ladyship Cuvier's Geological Essay*, Published by Dr Jameson, Newry, 1816.
Riese, W., 'The 150th Anniversary of S. T. Soemmerring's *Organ of the Soul*: the Reaction of his contemporaries and its significance today', *Bulletin of the History of Medicine*, XX, 1946, pp. 310–21.
Robert, D., *Les églises réformées en France, 1800–1830*, 1961.
— 'Documents concernant les origines de la Faculté réformée de Montauban: lettres de Benjamin-Sigismund Frossard', *Bull. soc. hist. prot. fr.*, CVIII, 1962, pp. 139–65.
Roche, K. F., *Rousseau: Stoic and Romantic*, 1974.
Roederer, P. L., *Observations morales et politiques sur les journaux détracteurs du dix-huitième siècle, de la philosophie et de la révolution*, 1804.
Roger, Jacques, *Les sciences de la vie dans la pensée française du dix-huitième siècle*, 1963.
Roland (ed.), *Un naturaliste à Paris sous Louis-Philippe: Journal de voyage inédit*, by A. Moquin-Tandon, 1944.
Rota, E., 'Per la riforma degli studi ecclesiastici nell'Università pavese al tempo di Giuseppe II', *Bollettino della Società pavese di storia patria*, VII, 1907, pp. 402–12.
Rousseau, G. S., 'Science and the discovery of the imagination in enlightened England', *Eighteenth-century Studies*, III, 1969–70, pp. 108–35.
Roy, C., 'Attitude politique des pasteurs du pays de Montbéliard aux premiers temps de la révolution française', *MSEM*, XVIII, 1887, pp. 23–43.
Royal Society of London, *Catalogue of Scientific Papers, 1800–63*, 10 vols, 1868.
Royer, *Stendhal au Jardin du roi: lettres inédites à Sophie Duvaucel*, Grenoble, 1930.
Rudwick, M., 'The inference of function from structure in fossils', *British Journal for the History of Science*, XV, 1964, pp. 27–40.
— *The Meaning of Fossils: Episodes in the History of Paleontology*, second edition, New York, 1976.
Rue, Abbé G. de la, *Essais historiques sur la ville de Caen*, 2 vols, Caen, 1820.
— *Annales de la ville de Caen*, 2 vols, Caen, 1843.
S...n, de, 'Essai sur les causes qui ont contribué à multiplièr le nombre d'auteurs', *Archives litteraires de l'Europe*, XV, 1807, pp. 3–13.
Sahler, L., 'La fin d'un régime: Montbéliard, Belfort et la Haute-Alsace au début de la Révolution française', *MSEM*, XL, 1911, pp. 3–213.

Ste-Beuve, C. A., *Chateaubriand et son groupe littéraire sous le premier Empire*, ed. M. Allem, 2 vols, 1948.
Salomon, A., 'L'acte de marriage de Jean-Léopold-Frédéric-Nicolas Cuvier', *MSEM*, XLIX, 1927, pp. 17–18.
Salomon-Bayet, C., 'L'institution de la science: un exemplaire au dix-huitième siècle', *Annales, ESC*, XXX, 1975, pp. 1028–44.
— *L'institution de la science et l'expérience du vivant*, 1978.
Salvandy, N. A., *Lettre sur la giraffe*, 1827.
— *Clémentine*, 1827.
— *La révolution de 1830 et le parti révolutionnaire, ou vingt mois et leurs résultats*, new edition, 1855.
Sarjeant W. & Delair, J., 'Joseph Pentland: an Irish naturalist in Cuvier's laboratory', in press, British Museum, (Natural History) Historical series.
Sarton, G., 'Cuvier et les belles lettres', *Isis*, IV, 1922, p. 493.
Schama, S., 'Schools and politics in the Netherlands, 1796–1814', *Historical Journal*, XIII, 1970, pp. 589–610.
Schiller, J., 'Physiology's struggle for independence in the first half of the nineteenth century', *History of Science*, VII, 1968, pp. 64–89.
Schmidt, C., *La réforme de l'Université impériale en 1811*, 1905.
Schmidt, C., 'Le roi n'a pas besoin de savants: discours de l'abbé Eliçagaray au Collège de Marseille en 1821', *La révolution française*, LXI, 1911, pp. 216–28.
Schneider, J. P., 'Science et sensibilite' au dix-huitième siècle: essai sur une aesthétique de paysage selon H. B. de Saussure', *Travaux linguistiques et littéraires*, VII, 1969, pp. 107–31.
Schwab, R., *La renaissance orientale*, 1950.
— 'Cuvier, Balzac et le sanscrit', *Mercure de France*, CCCLX, 1950, pp. 676–86.
Séguy, J., 'Une sociologie des sociétés imaginées: monachisme et utopie', *Annales ESC*, XXVI, 1971, pp. 328–54.
Sennett, R., *The Fall of Public Man*, 1977.
Sherborn, C. D., *Index animalium, sive index nominum quae ab A.D. MDCCLVIII generibus et speciebus animalium imposita sunt*, 9 vols, 1902–32.
— 'The dates of publication of Cuvier and Valenciennes, *Histoire naturelle des poissons*,' *Annals and magazine of natural history*, XV, 1925, p. 600.
Silvestre de Sacy, J., *Alexandre-Théodore Brongniart, 1739–1813: sa vie, son oeuvre*, n.d. (1941).
Snelders, H. A. M., 'The influence of the dualistic system of J. J. Winterl, 1732;1809, on the German romantic era', *Isis*, LXI, 1970, pp. 231–40.
Sonntag, O., 'The motivations of the scientist: the self-image of Albrecht von Haller', *Isis*, LXV, 1974, pp. 336–51.
Sortais, G., *La philosophie moderne depuis Bacon jusqu'à Leibniz*, 2 vols, 1920–22.
Spiel, H. *Fanny von Arnstein: ein Frauenleben*, Berlin, 1962.

Spitzer, A. B., 'The historical problem of generations', *American Historical Review*, LXXVIII, 1973, pp. 1353-85.
Staël, Mme de, *De la littérature considérée dans ses rapports avec les institutions sociales*, ed. P. van Tieghem, Geneva & Paris, 1959.
Stafleu, F. A., *Linneaus and the Linnaeans: the Spreading of their Ideas in Systematic Botany, 1735-1789*, Utrecht, 1971.
Stapfer, P. A., *Breifwechsel*, ed. R. Luginbühl, 2 vols, Basle, 1891.
Stendhal (Henri Beyle), *Vie d'Henry Brulard*, ed. B. Didier, 1973.
Stewart, D., *Collected works*, ed. Sir W. Hamilton, 10 vols, Edinburgh 1854.
Stocking, G. W. 'French anthropology in 1800', *Isis*, LV, 1964, pp. 134-50
Stubler, E., *Johann Heinrich Ferdinand von Autenrieth, 1772-1835*, Stuttgart, 1948.
Suratteau, J., 'Les traîtements des professeurs sous le Directoire', *Annales historiques de la révolution française*, XXXIII, 1961, pp. 102-3.
Swainson, W., *A Preliminary Discourse on the Study of Natural History*, 1834.
— *On the Natural History and Classification of Quadrupeds*, 1835.
Szramkiewicz, R., *Les régents et censeurs de la Banque de France nommés sous le Consulat et l'Empire*, Geneva, 1974.
Taton, R. (ed.), *Enseignment et diffusion des sciences en France au dix-huitème siècle*, 1964.
Temkin, O., 'Materialism in French and German physiology in the early nineteenth century', *Bulletin of the History of Medicine*, XX, 1946, pp. 322-7.
— 'German concepts of ontogeny and history around 1800', *Bulletin of the History of Medicine*, XXIV, 1950, pp. 227-46.
Tenon, J. et al, 'Report on a memoir of Drs Gall and Spurzheim, relating to the anatomy of the brain, presented to be adopted by the Class of mathematical and physical science of the National Institut', *Edinburgh Medical and Surgical Journal*, V, 1809, pp. 36-66.
Théodoridès, J., 'Journal d'un étudiant en médecine, J. P. Audoin', *Histoire médicale*, VIII, 1958, pp. 4-63, 5-56; IX, 1959, pp. 5-48.
— 'Jean-Guillaume Brugière et Guillaume-Antoine Olivier, médecins, naturalistes et voyageurs', *86th Congrès des Sociétés savantes*, 1961, pp. 173-83.
— 'Humboldt and Cuvier', *Biologie médicale*, LIX, 1961, pp. 50-71.
— 'Quelques documents inédits ou peu connus relatifs à Georges Cuvier, à sa famille et à son salon', *Stendhal Club*, XXXIII, 1966, pp. 55-64; XXXIV, 1967 a, pp. 179-88.
— 'Quelques documents inédits sur Toussaint Bastard, 1784-1846, médecin et naturaliste', *Histoire des sciences médicales*, I, 1967 b, pp. 1-10.
'Une lettre inédite de Georges Cuvier à la Gesellschaft Naturforschen Freunde zu Berlin', *Histoire et biologie*, II, 1869, pp. 55-60.

Thouin A., 'Description de l'école d'agriculture practique de Muséum d'histoire naturelle', *Annales du Muséum*, XI, 1808, pp. 92–120.
Thuiller, G., 'Stendhal, Cuvier et l'Ecole normale d'administration', in *Témoins de l'administration*, 1967, pp. 96–108.
Tourlet, M., Review of Lamarck, *Recherches sur l'organisation des corps vivans*, Moniteur universelle, XI, 1802, 28 fructidor an X, p. 1462.
Trahard, P., *La sensibilité révolutionnaire, 1789–1794*, 1934.
Trénard, L., 'L'enseignement sous la Monarchie de juillet: les réformes de Salvandy', *Revue d'histoire moderne et contemporaine*, XII, 1958, pp. 81–133.
— *Salvandy en son temps, 1795–1856*, Lille, 1968.
Trouessart, E., *Cuvier et Geoffroy St Hilaire d'après les naturalistes allemands*, 1909.
Tucoo-Chala, S., 'La diffusion des lumières dans le deuxième moîtié du dix-huitième siècle: Charles-Joseph Panckouke, un libraire éclairé, 1760–99', *Dix-huitième siècle*, IV, 1973, pp. 15–24.
Tuefferd, L., 'Essai sur l'administration gouvernmentale du Comté de Montbéliard... jusqu'en 1793', *MSEM*, I, 1862, pp. 1–40.
Tuetey, L., *Procès-verbaux de la Commission temporaire des arts*, 2 vols, 1912–17.
Tulard, J., 'Problèms sociaux de la France impériale', *Revue d'histoire moderne et contemporaine*, XVIII, 1970, pp. 639–63.
— *Bibliographie critique des mémoires sur le Consulat et l'Empire*, Geneva & Paris, 1971.
Turi, G., *Viva Maria: le reazione alle riforme leopoldine*, Florence, 1969.
Uhland, R. & Adam, R. D., *Cuvier und Württemburg*, Stüttgart, 1969, (exhibition catalogue).
Valenciennes, A., 'Catalogue des préparations anatomiques laissées dans le Cabinet d'anatomie comparée par Georges Cuvier', *Nouvelles annales du Muséum*, II, 1833, pp. 417–508.
Vallois, M., *La formation de l'influence Kantienne en France*, n.d.
Van Duzer, C. H., *Contribution of the Idéologues to French Revolutionary Thought*, Baltimore, 1935.
Vanel, G., 'L'émigration en Normandie: le comte et la comtesse de Manneville d'après leur correspondance et des documents inédits, 1791–98', *Mémoires de l'Académie nationale des sciences, arts et belles-lettres de Caen*, 1907, pp. 35–168.
Vaughan, M. & Archer, M. S., *Social Conflict and Educational Change in England and France, 1789–1848*, 1971.
Vaulabelle, A. de, *Histoire des deux restaurations*, 10 vols, 1874.
Vauthier, G., 'Fontanes et les nominations universitaires', *Annales révolutionnaires*, IV, 1911, pp. 638–53.
— *Villemain, 1790–1870: essai sur sa vie, son rôle et ses ouvrages*, 1913.
Viara, M., 'Gli ordinamenti dell'Università di Torino nel secolo XVIII', *Bollettino storico-bibliografico subalpino*, XL, 1942,

pp. 42–54.
Vicq d'Azyr, F., *Système anatomique des quadrupèdes*, 1792.
Vidalenc, J., *La Restauration*, 1966.
— 'Les milieux dirigeants français sous la monarchie constitutionelle' *Revue d'histoire économique et sociale*, XLVII, 1969, pp. 561–70.
Vielcastel, L. de, *Histoire de la restauration*, 20 vols, 1860–78.
Viénot, J., 'Lettres de quelques Princes de Württemburg à P. F. Bernard', *MSEM*, XV, 1885, pp. 273–88.
— *La vie ecclesiastique et réligieuse dans la principauté de Montbéliard au dix-huitième siècle*, 1895.
— *Lettres inédits de Georges Cuvier à Georges Duvernoy*, Dôle, 1905.
— *Georges Cuvier, le Napoléon de l'intelligence, 1769–1832*, 1932.
Villèle, J. B., *Mémoires et correspondence*, 5 vols, 1904.
Villemain, A. F., *Souvenirs contemporains d'histoire et de littérature* 2 vols, 1864.
Villers, C., *Philosophie de Kant ou principes fondamentales de la philosophie transcendentale*, Metz, 1801.
— *Lettre ... à Georges Cuvier de l'Instutut national sur une nouvelle théorie du cerveau; ce viscère étant considéré comme l'organe immédiat des facultés morales*, Metz & Paris, 1802.
Virey, J. J., 'Sur la classe des vers', *Journal de physique*, XLVII, 1798, pp. 409–40.
— 'Addition au mémoire sur les vers', *ibid.*, XLVIII, 1799, pp. 453–4.
— 'Animal', *Nouveau dictionnaire d'histoire naturelle appliquée aux arts ...* I, 1803, pp. 419–66.
— 'Mort', *Dictionnaire des sciences médicales*, 60 vols, XVIII–XXII, XXXIV, 1819.
— 'Vie ou force vitale', *ibid.*, LVII, 1821, pp. 434–603.
Vovelle, M., *Réligion et révolution: la déchristianisation de l'an II*, 1976.
Walzer, M., *Regicide and revolution: speeches at the trial of Louis XVI*, 1974.
Wetzels, W. D., 'Aspects of natural science in German romanticism', *Studies in Romaticism*, X, 1971, pp. 44–59.
Wheeler, W. M. & Barbour T., *The Lamarck MSS at Harvard*, Cambridge, Mass., 1933.
Whewell, W., *History of the Inductive Sciences*, 3 vols, 1837.
— *History of Scientific Ideas*, third edition, 2 vols, 1858.
Whitehead, P. J. P., 'The dating of the first edition of Cuvier's *Règne animal*', *Journal of the Society for the Bibliography of Natural History*, IV, 1962–8, pp. 300–01.
Wilks, M., *The Flower Faded: a Short Memoir of Clémentine Cuvier, 1832*, 1844.
Williams, L. P., 'Science, education and the French revolution', *Isis*, XLIV, 1935, pp. 311–30.
Winsor, M. P., *Starfish, Jellyfish and the Order of Life: Issues in Nineteenth-century Science*, New Haven & London, 1976.
Wittmer, L., 'Quelques mots sur Charles de Villers et quelques

documents inédits', *Bulletin de l'Institut national génévois*, XXXVII–VIII, 1907–9, pp. 355–477.
Wolin, S., *Politics and Vision*, Boston, 1960.
Young, R. M., *Mind, Brain, and Adaptation in the Nineteenth Century: Cerebral Localisation and its Biological Context from Gall to Ferrier*, 1970.
Zimmerman, G., *La solitude considérée relativement à l'esprit et au coeur: ouvrage traduit à l'alleman . . . par J. B. Mercier*, 1788.

Appendix

Positions held by Cuvier, 1795–1832.

Born 23 August 1769
1795 Member, Commission temporaire des Arts
December 1795–1832 Member, First Class of the Institut National (Académie des Sciences after 1815)
1796–1802 *Suppléant* to Mertrud at Muséum national d'histoire naturelle
1796–1800 Chair of natural history, Ecole centrale du pathéon
1799–1803 Temporary Secretary of the First Class of the Institut
1800–32 Chair at the Collège de France
1802–32 Full chair of comparative anatomy, Muséum national d'histoire naturelle
1802–3 Inspecteur-général des études
1803–32 Permanent Secretary of the First Class
1803–32 Member of the Légion d'honneur
1808–14 Inspector-général des études
1809–32 Vice-rector, Faculty of Sciences, Paris
1810–14 Chevalier de l'Empire
1812–16 Maître des requêtes, Conseil d'Etat (his nomination by Napoleon confirmed by Louis XVIII)
1816–32 Conseiller d'Etat
1818–32 Member of the Académie française
September 1819–December 1821 Acting Grand-Master, Université de France
July 1822–June 1823 Acting Grand-Master, Université de France
1821–7 Chancellor of the Université de France
1822–32 Grand-Master of the Protestant faculties of theology
1827–32 Director of the non-Catholic religions
1830–32 Member, Académie des Inscriptions et des Belles-Lettres
1832 Baron
13 May 1832 Died

Index

Académie des sciences, Paris, 51, 54, 93, 94, 112, 113; Cuvier as Perpetual Secretary of, 107, 109, 118, 124–34; *see also* Institut de France
Academy, Stuttgart, 8, 21, 22–7, 28, 39, 71
André, Noël, 147
Annales de Chimie, 61
Annales des Sciences naturelles, 113, 114, 174
Annales des Sciences de l'observation, 110
Annales du Muséum, 67, 125, 174, 176, 186; *Nouvelles annales du Muséum*, 186
Appel, Toby, 113, 254
Arago, François, 112, 113
Arnault, Antoine Vincent, 56, 58, 70
Arnstein, Fanny von, 129
Asiatic Society of Calcutta, 151
Athenée de Paris, 67, 127, 133, 138; *see also* Lycée de Paris
Audouin, Jean-Victor, 113, 174, 180; *see also* Brongniart, Alexandre
Autenrieth, Johann Heinrich, 31
autobiography, Cuvier's, 8, 20–21, 34, 41, 43–5, 49, 56, 63, 71, 80, 99, 124, 132, 176, 190, 209 n. 60
autobiography, genre, 8

Balbo, Prospero, 85, 224 n. 69
Bank of France, 56, 59
Bartholdi, Baron, 58, 145
Beaurepaire, Charles de, 41

Bec-aux-Cauchois, Normandy, 41, 45, 48
Benjamin, Walter, 184
Berry, Duc de, 103
Berthollet, C. L., 61, 137
Bertier, Ferdinand de, 108
Bertrand, Alexandre-Jacques, 98
Beyle, Henri, 50, 56, 108, 185
Biberstein, Friedrich-August Marschall von, 26, 28, 31, 38
Bichat, Xavier, 182
biographical tradition, Cuvier's, 10, 13, 46, 49, 57, 95, 205 n. 47, 208 n. 48
Biot, J. B., 55, 112, 191, 198-9, 253 n. 6
Blainville, Henri Marie Ducrotay de, 112, 174, 180, 187, 191, 194, 197, 201, 218 n. 76
Bloch, M. E., 40
Boigeol, J. J., 24
Boissevain, Jeremy, 5
Bonaparte, Lucien, 16, 49, 55
Bonaparte, Napoleon, 45, 56, 61, 71–2, 75, 127, 198
Bonnet, Charles, 146, 154
Bonsen, Marie-Anne, (Cuvier's aunt) 19
Bosc d'Antic, Louis Augustin, 172
Brack (Bracq), family, 56; Antoine-Fortuné, 99; Charles, 222 n. 60; Laure, 56, 65; *see also* genealogical table
Brongniart, Adolphe, 113, 174; Alexandre, 54, 113, 153, 174, 187, 191, 197–8, 199; Emilie, 65
Brugmans, S. J., 83, 222 n. 57

Brunschwig, Henri, 28
Buckland, William, 149
Buffon, G. L., Comte de, 9, 20, 38, 161–2, 163, 173, 176, 188
Burckhardt, R. W. jr., 120

Cabanis, P. J. G., 71, 73
Caen, Normandy, 30, 32, 34, 35, 48; Académie des belles-lettres of, 33, 35; botanical garden of, 33, University of, 32–3, 36
Campe, Joachim, 81
Camper, Adriaan, 83, 122, 222 n. 49, 222 n. 57
Candolle, A. P. de, 125, 127, 185, 201
Carbonari, 98, 228 n. 52
cerebral anatomy, Cuvier and, 130–31, 133, 134
Champollion, Jean-François, 151
Chaptal, Jean-Antoine, 66, 189
Charles X, King of France, 104
Charles-Eugène, Grand-Duke of Württemburg, 15, 21, 22, 24, 205 n. 39
Chateaubriand, François-René de 77, 79, 149, 156
Chatel, Anne-Clémentine, (Cuvier's mother) 16, 17, 65; *see also* genealogical table
Choiseul, Duc de, 34
classification, 38–9; Cuvier and, 120–23, 175–9
Coleman, William, 113
Collège de France, 9, 51, 55, 67, 115, 138
Commission temporaire des Arts 54
comparative anatomy, 120; Cuvier and, 159, 176–9, 182–3, 208 n. 48
Conseil d'Etat, 5, 58, 99, 100–101, 104, 113; Cuvier and, 90, 189
Consistory of Paris, 58, 145
Constant, Benjamin, 102, 146
controversy, 9; Cuvier and scientific, 119–24, 128, 138, 158; with Lamarck, 126–8, 152–5, 159; *see also* Gall; Geoffroy St Hilaire; *Naturphilosophie*
Corsini, Prince Neri, 88
cosmopolitanism, 27, 37, 39, 69, 73, 77, 82, 86
Coulmann, J.-J., 57, 58
Crosland, M. P., 196
Curie, Ferdinand, 57, 229 n. 59
Cuvier, Jean-Léopold-Frédéric-Nicolas, called Georges (Cuvier's activities are indexed separately under the appropriate headings); birth, 13, 17; childhood, 13–29; marriage, 56-7, 59, 214 n. 36
Cuvier family, 57–9, 65, 104, 173–5, 197; Cuvier, family, illegitimate, 65, 217 n. 69; Anne, *née* Coquet de Trayzaile (wife), 41, 43, 56, 57, 64, 65, 103, 144, 172, 214 n. 36; Charles (nephew), 57, 101, 102, 103, 172, 197; Charles-Nicolas, 204 n. 21, 204 n. 29; Clémentine (daughter), 104 108, 115, 116, 144; Frédéric (brother), 17, 57, 65, 113, 115, 177, 183, 197, 204 n. 20; Frédéric (nephew), 59; Georges (son), 89, 173; Jean (great-grandfather), 16; Jean-Georges (father), 16, 17, 65, 203 n. 17; Jean-Nicolas, 19; Paul-Nicholas (uncle), 19; Rodolphe (cousin), 102; *see also* genealogical table

Dacier, Bon-Joseph, 66
Darwin, Charles, 202
Daubenton, L.-J.-M., 47, 53, 55, 60, 122, 161, 162, 166, 168, 176, 178, 187, 245 n. 6
Daudin, Henri, 183

Index

Décade philosophique, 51, 77
Décazes, Elie, 103
Delambre, J.-B., 56, 112, 115, 125
Delessert, Benjamin, 55, 58
Deleuze, J.-P.-F., 125, 171, 177, 185–6
Deluc, Jean-André, 157
Desfontaines, René Louiche, 125, 171, 181
Diaria zoologica (Cuvier), 31, 38
Discours préliminaire sur les révolutions du globe (Cuvier), 141–3, 147, 148–52, 155, 156–60
Doctrinaires (political group), 98 105
Dolomieu, Déodat, 157, 165
Ducos, Joseph-Basile, 56, 58
Dumas, Jean-Baptiste, 113, 174
Duméril, A. M. C., 125, 218 n. 76
Duparquet, Charles, 104
Dupin, Charles, 108
Duvaucel, Philippe, 56
Duvaucel, Sophie (step-daughter of Cuvier), 50, 57, 172, 188; see also genealogical table
Duvernoy, Georges, 18, 41, 57, 65, 69, 73, 143, 172, 173, 197

écoles centrales, 71–2, 118
Ecole normale, 53, 61, 105, 115, 146
Ecole normale d'Administration, 104
education, Cuvier and, Chapter IV, *passim*; and elementary, 105; and religious, 69–70, 70–71, 106; and state, 69–71; see also *enseignement mutuel*
egoism, ethos of, 74–5, 76, 91, 184
Egypt, Napoleon's expedition to, 61–2
élite, study of, 2; imperial, debates on, 74–6; in Restoration, 97
éloges, 8, 110; Cuvier's, 66–7, 76, 126

embranchement, Cuvier's idea of 113–14
enseignement mutuel, 100, 115; Cuvier and, 106–7
Etupes (Montbéliard), 15, 16, 21, 34
experimental science, Cuvier and 135–7
extinction, Cuvier's theories of, 122, 152–3, 156, 159

Fabbroni, G. V. M., 67, 86–8, 89, 91, 197
Faculty of Medicine, Paris, 105, 134
Faculty of Sciences, Paris, 80, 221 n. 38
family, study of, 7; in Muséum national d'histoire naturelle, Paris, 171–4; in patronage, 197–9
Fécamp, Normandy, 42, 43, 44
Fiquainville, Normandy, 37, 41, 44, 45
Fischer, Gotthelf, 179–80
Flauhaut de la Billarderie, 162
Flourens, Marie Jean Pierre, 43, 130, 133–4, 138, 189, 202, 218 n. 76
Fontanes, Louis de, 55, 70, 73, 76, 77, 78, 79, 81, 88, 89, 90, 219 n. 22, 219 n. 24
Fossati, J. A. L., 134
Foucault, Michel, 91, 156
Fouché, Joseph, 75
Fourcroy, Antoine, 56, 61, 66, 72, 73, 87, 161, 165, 166, 172, 174, 186
Fraysinnous, Abbé, 102
French revolution, 36, 37, 44, 50, 52
friendship, cult of, 27, 195

Gall, Franz-Joseph, 124, 129–34, 139
Garat, J. D., 42, 43, 45, 71–2, 209 n. 74
Gauthier, Mme, 55, 58

Gay-Lussac, Joseph-Louis, 125, 191, 199
Geoffroy St Hilaire, Etienne, 9, 43, 44, 45, 47, 53, 55, 60–62, 63–5, 67, 75, 87, 93, 95, 107, 109–12, 113, 125–34, 154, 164, 165–7, 174, 179, 181, 182, 186–7, 194, 199, 200, 202; collaboration with Cuvier, 121–2, 216 n. 52; controversy with Cuvier, 113–15, 116, 119, 120, 121, 125–6, 140, 216 n. 52
Geoffroy St Hilaire, Isidore, 45, 53
geology, Cuvier and, 141–3, 145–50, 158; scriptural, 142–3, 147–49, 156–7, 158
Gérando, Joseph-Marie de, 55, 73, 74, 75, 85, 88, 89, 106, 199, 222 n. 62
Gesner, C., 40
Gilbert, Hilaire-François, 76
Ginguéné, P. L., 42, 43, 45, 71–2, 209 n. 74
giraffe, in Muséum national d'histoire naturelle, 184
Grandmaison, Louis Aubin Millin de, 44, 46, 53
Grimaldi, family, 34, 46
Guizot, François, 79, 98, 101, 105–6, 146

Haber, Francis, 157, 158
Hartmann, J. G. A., 31
Haüy, René-Just, 43, 47, 55, 87, 122, 137, 165, 166, 167, 168, 169, 187
Héricy d', family, 31, 32, 33, 34, 36–8, 41, 46, 206 n. 16; Achille, 33, 42, 45, 46, 48, 206 n. 16; Marquis, 36–8, 42; Marquise, 36–8, 73, 206 n. 16
Histoire naturelle des poissons (Cuvier), 114, 173, 201
history, Cuvier and study of, 155–6, 157, 160
historical scholarship, development of, 151–2, 158

Humboldt, Alexander von, 62, 186

Idéologie, 66, 71–2, 74
Imperial University, 69–91, 99, 118; see also education; Université de France
income, Cuvier's, 41, 59, 73, 119, 170, 214 n. 45
Institut d'Egypt, 61
Institut de France, 47, 49, 54, 65–6, 199–200; Cuvier's election to, 54–5; Cuvier as Permanent Secretary of the First Class of, 50, 59, 63, 65, 66, 118, 124–34, 138, 199; First Class of, 50, 54, 65; Third Class of, 72, 74
Italy, Cuvier tours in, 84–8; his patronage in, 88–9; patronage in modern, 192–3; universities of (Genoa, Pisa, Turin, Tuscany), 84–8

Jameson, Robert, 142, 156
Japy, Ingénu, 98
Jones, Sir William, 151
Joubert, Jean, 79
Joseph II, Emperor of Austria, 15, 21, 70
Josephine, Empress, 58
Journal de Paris, 77
Journal de Physique, 138
Journal des Débats, 109
Jussieu, Bernard de, 33
Jussieu, Antoine Laurent de, 43, 44, 45, 55, 56, 125, 186

Karlsakademie, see Academy, Stuttgart
Kerner, Johannes-Simon, 26
Kerr, James, 141
Kielmeyer, Karl Friedrich, 28, 31, 132, 135–6
Koestlin, Charles-Heinrich, 26

Lacepède, Bernard-Germain, 40,

Index

43, 44, 46, 55, 87, 124, 125, 165, 166, 167, 172, 185, 189, 190, 201
Lacroix, Sylvestre-François, 54
Lalande, Joseph-Jérôme le François de, 127
Lamarck, J. B., 6, 75, 87, 109, 110, 119, 120, 121, 122, 123–5, 126–8, 129, 142, 152–3, 154 159, 167, 168, 169, 170, 174, 182, 201–2
Lamétherie, Jean-Claude de, 43, 44, 138, 218 n. 76
Laplace, Pierre-Simon, 54, 55, 64, 66, 87, 108, 112, 149, 150, 195, 196, 201
Larévellière-Lépeaux, Louis Marie, 46, 171–2
Latreille, Pierre André, 165, 167, 168–70, 174, 191, 199
Laurencet, G. P., 114, 115
Laurillard, Charles-Louis, 57, 99, 172–3, 197
Lavoisier, Antoine-Laurent, 52, 55, 137, 165
Leclerc, J. B., 171
Leçons d'anatomie comparée (Cuvier), 57, 122, 135, 176, 178
lectures, Cuvier's, 51, 60, 119, 127, 168, 177, 180–82, 184, 250 n. 77
Lee, Sarah, 41, 43–4
Lefebvre, Louis, 185
Libre examen, 146–7
Linnaeus, Carl von, 26, 33, 38, 40, 120, 123
Louis XVI, King of France, 36
lycées, Cuvier and, 72–3
Lycée des arts, 50
Lycée de Paris, 9, 118; *see also* Athenée de Paris
Lyell, Charles, 116, 156, 173

Mafia, 192
Magasin Encyclopédique, 51
Magendie, François, 133
Maine de Biran, F. P. G., 106, 131, 132

Marat, Oliver, 166
Marum, Martinus van, 179, 221 n. 49
materialism, Cuvier and, 129–30
Merimée, Prosper, 108
Mertrud, A. L., 45, 167, 168, 176, 178
mesmerism, 125
Meyranx, P. S., 114, 115
Ministry of the Interior, 103
Mirbel, C. F. B. de, 103
Moniteur universelle, 127
Moreau de la Sarthe, J. L., 129
Montbéliard, 13, 14, 31, 58, 98, 199, 251 n. 7
Moysant, François, 33
Muséum national d'histoire naturelle, 6, 7, 9, 40, 45, 50, 54, 55, 57, 60, 113, 122, 125, 161–88; collections of, 176–9, 182, 188; Cuvier's election to, 54–5, 166–7, 187, 199; guides to, 179–80, 183–4; menagerie of, 51, 57, 161, 164, 177, 179, 182, 184, 185; Cuvier's work within, 161–88
Mussy, Guéneau de, 78
Mussy, Philibert de, 78

Napoleon I, Emperor of the French, *see* Bonaparte
natural history, Cuvier and, 37, 53, 62–3, 151, 182–3, 186, 200; image of, 62–3, 184
Naturphilosophie, 39, 115, 124, 135–7, 147
network analysis, 195–6

observation, in science, 75, 135–6
Oken, Lorenz, 136–7
Olivier, Guillaume Antoine, 43, 44
oratory, Cuvier's, 50, 51

palaeontology, 120, 142, 147–50, 151–2, 154, 158–9, 180
Paley, William, 156

Paris, 43–5, 46, 47, 48, 49–53
Parmentier A. A., 44
Parrot, Georg-Friedrich, 29, 203 n. 4
Pastoret family, 55, 223 n. 69
patronage, 5, 6, 7, 54, 110, 163, 174, 189–99; Cuvier's use of, 47, 53–4, 70–73, 80, 86–9, 102, 108, 169, 179–80, 189–99; international, 35; provincial, 58, 197; under Restoration, 97–8, 163; *see also* family
Paul, Grand-Duke (Russia), 15, 24
Pentland, J. B., 172, 188
Peter Leopold, Grand-Duke of Tuscany, 85, 86
Petit, Antoine, 165
Pfaff, Christian, 13, 20, 24, 25, 26, 27, 30, 31, 32, 35, 37, 38, 39, 41, 60, 76, 187
phrenology, 119; Cuvier and, 119, 124, 129–34, 185
physiology, 120, 159, 178, 181–2
Piveteau, Jean, 113
pluralism, 104; Cuvier's, 104–8
Portal, A., 86
press, 109, 110, 211 n. 8; Cuvier and, 109, 119, 133, 210 n. 8; *see also* titles of journals
Priestley, Joseph, 147
Principes de philosophie zoologique (Geoffroy St Hilaire), 115
professionalisation, 51; of science, thesis of, 51, 132, 188, 189, 190, 249 n. 49
Protestantism, 58, 59, 101, 146; Cuvier's, 32, 85, 101, 102, 103, 116, 142–7; Cuvier and administration of, 101, 145–6; Cuvier and Protestant education, 80, 101, 145; and science, 146; *see also* Consistory of Paris; *libre examen*
public, and revolution, 50; for science, 50–53, 118–19, 129–33, 135, 138–40, 177, 180–82, 183–5, 188, 200

Raspail, François, 97, 98, 109–12
Réamur, A., 33
Recherches sur les ossemens fossiles des quadrupèdes (Cuvier), 141, 159, 223 n. 70
Restoration, Bourbon, 93; politics in, 93–4, 95, 98, 100–101, 189–90
Richard, L. C. M., 45, 54, 55, 167
Richelieu, Duc de, 101, 103
Ritter, J. W., 135, 137
Roederer, P. L., 66, 71, 75, 77
Roland, Mme, 172
Rousseau, Jean Jacques, 1
Royer-Collard, Hippolyte, 98, 105, 106, 228 n. 52
Rudwick, Martin, 157
Rue, Abbé Gervais de la, 33, 36, 37

St Fond, Barthélemy Faujas de, 55, 125, 152, 153, 164, 168, 187
St Pierre, Jacques Henri Bernadin de, 119, 162
salons, 55, 213 n. 27, 213 n. 28; Cuvier's, 108–9, 112, 198
Saussure, Horace-Bénédict de, 27–8, 146
savant, image of the, 52, 62–3
Schelling, F. W., 135–6
Schiller, F., 23, 24, 27, 205 n. 42
science, 1; as cultural commodity, 52, 67, 118, 177, 184–5; debates on definition of, 52, 129–31, 201; ethos of, 79, 81, 94–5, 99, 107, 109–11, 115, 117, 200; institutions of, 52, 67, 171, 175, 189; language of, 109–11; societies, 54, 55, 59, 60, 211 n. 21; specialisation in, 67; *see also éloges*; professionalisation; *savant*; titles of scientific societies

Index

sociability, Cuvier and, 55–6, 60, 68, 108, 196–7, 215 n. 46
Société des observateurs de l'homme, 74–5
Société d'histoire naturelle, Paris, 45, 211 n. 21
Société pour l'instruction élémentaire, 106–7
Société philomatique, 45, 67, 122 211 n. 21
Société philotechnique, 56, 60, 67
solitude, ethos of, 37, 48, 55
Spaendonck, Gerard van, 181
species, 120; fixity of 95, 124, 154; mutability of 120–21, 122, 124, 154–5; problem of definition of, 120, 154
Stadtholder of Holland, collection of, 164, 175
Staël, Mme de, 76, 79
Stendhal, see Beyle, Henri
Stuttgart, 31, 32, 33, 40

Talleyrand, Charles Maurice de, 46, 56, 75
Talma, F. J., 51, 181
Terror, French revolutionary, 10, 34, 40, 41, 45, 47, 52, 54, 164, 165–6, 172, 175, 233 n. 101
Tessier, Abbé Henri, 42–6, 47, 53
Thouin, André, 162, 164, 171
Tournon, Camille de, 89
Tracy, Antoine Louis Claude Destutt de, 71–2, 74
transformism, 111, 127, 182, 202
Treuttel and Würtz (publishers), 58
Tübingen, university of, 20

Uccelli, Paolo, 88
United Provinces, Cuvier's tour in, 81–3; education in, 71, 81, 83, 89; universities of, 83
Université de France, 99; Cuvier and, 99–100, 107, 115, 134, 145, 189; see also Imperial University

Valmont, Normandy, 34, 42, 44
Ventenat, E. P., 146
Verfeu, Henri Coiffier de, 79, 220 n. 34
Vien, Jean-Marie, 66
Viénot, John, 66
Villers, Charles de, 129
Vincent, Samuel, 146
Viviani, Domenico, 223 n. 75
vocation, scientific, 7–8

Waldner, Count Christian-Frédéric-Dagobert, 16, 21
Walther, General, 57, 58, 145; see also genealogical table
Werner, A. G., 153
Wetzel, J. P., 18, 26
Wild Boy of Aveyron, 75
Wilks, Mark, Pastor, 143–4
Winterl, Jacob Joseph, 137
Württemburg, 14

Zoological Society of London, 185